This publication is one of three which
form the printed version of the
Theatre Engineering and Architecture Conference 2002
held in London on 16, 17 and 18 June 2002.

First published 2004

Publisher:
Theatrical Events Ltd
55 Farringdon Road
London, EC1M 3JB

Transcriptions of papers provided by *The Wordsmith.*
www.the-wordsmith.co.uk

Key references
Theatre, Engineering, Architecture

ISBN   0-9547666-1-X   Casebound
ISBN   0-9547666-0-1   Paperback

Printed by Pims Print, Yeovil, Somerset
Layout in Microsoft Publisher ® by the Editor
Typefaces: Arial, Tahoma, Century Gothic

Editing a book with ninety-six authors was never going to be an easy task, but becoming the first person who had effectively attended every session at the Theatre Engineering and Architecture Conference soon showed the value of the material presented. This is what has made the editing task so acceptable: while the Conference was a great success, the content of each of the papers, and of the discussions, has also created a very valuable resource for those involved in the planning, design or operating of a performing arts building. The extent of this material in the three books is indicated clearly on the following Contents pages.

The transcriptions of the Conference have been edited for clarity and remove many of the repetitions and colloquialisms. The texts have also been related to the large amount of visual material that was offered. Each of the speakers received a copy of their paper in its draft form and most of them have offered comments, additions and corrections. I would like to take this opportunity to thank them all again for their great effort in presenting their papers to Conference in the first place, and for then putting up with my pressure to get the published version as right as we can!

In order to satisfy a worldwide market, additional explanations, and indeed some pictures, have been provided where the location or a reason might not be clear to a reader without the benefit of attendance at the event itself.

Spelling and references are generally in UK English, but American spelling has been retained for speakers from that continent. Attempts have been made to provide as much information as practicable on pictures or graphics where these have not been fully described in the paper. Most measurements are given both metric and Imperial values, and costs have been converted at a mid-2003 rate for comparison between US Dollars, Pounds Sterling, Euros and, in one paper, from Australian Dollars.

The Conference was sponsored by a number of theatre equipment contractors, theatre architects, consultants and other theatrical organisations. These are listed at the back of the book and their help is gratefully acknowledged. In order to finance the printing of this publication, a number of firms and organisations have again come forward with funding. Each of these firms or organisations has a page in one or more of the volumes describing their contribution to the theatre industry. It is important to note the importance of the support such firms provide to the performing arts industry worldwide.

The financial result of the Conference was that a surplus was able to be passed to the Association of British Theatre Technicians (ABTT), which is a registered charity working for the benefit of the performing arts in the United Kingdom. Any surplus arising from the publication of these Books will be similarly made available to the ABTT.

There are plans for a further Conference in 2006, by which time I believe that the industry will be ready to examine, explain and release even more ideas about the business of building and equipping successful performing arts buildings of all sizes. I know that these books will assist many people and hope that the next Conference will further extend the communication between theatre and construction professionals and technicians everywhere.

Richard Brett B.Sc C.Eng FIEE
Conference Director and Editor
April 2004

My grateful thanks for their help and understanding go to my wife, Jenny, my administration assistant, Neville Ware, and to my theatre consulting colleagues who have coped so well while I undertook this additional task.

The record of engineering and technology papers in this book is an important resource for anyone who is involved with backstage working and performance equipment. This volume gives remarkably practical and down to earth explanations of many of the backstage mechanical and electrical mysteries of theatre. As such it provides a record for people who may not have been able to attend the Conference or every technical session, and also for anyone who is planning, designing or studying theatre engineering and technology.

This volume certainly covers the ground. Starting with the basics of the current technology used for both stage elevators and stage wagons (ET1 and ET2), it goes on to describe the many types of suspension and power flying hoist equipment available (ET6). This appropriately follows an analysis of the strain caused by loading and unloading counterweights including an amusing piece by Andy Hayles (ET5-1), and details of the restrictions imposed on the use of counterweights in The Netherlands from Louis Janssen (ET5-9). The British Standard applicable to overhead suspensions is reviewed (ET3) and Ted Fregon and Dave Ludlam present a treatise on the various international standards that affect the theatre industry with a particular slant towards IEC 61508 and its safety lifecycle (ET4). A number of speakers from the larger firms in the stage equipment control field give their ideas on current and future systems (ET6). Other essential reading includes an explanation of the background to the recent Technical Standards for Places of Public Entertainment (ET3) by David Adams and other members of the ABTT.

As light relief Jason Barnes contributes a full history of the development of the adaptability employed in the Cottesloe Theatre which, being largely manual, contrasts with the advanced mechanised systems now available as described by Robert Heimbach and Professor Julian Herrey (ET8). For those who have had power supply problems there is a very readable description of the characteristics and causes of electrical power harmonics from Adam Bennette (ET9-3) together with some facts about lighting dimmer installations not understood by all electrical engineers. The book is rounded off by a fascinating study of working at height (ET10) chaired by Paul Edwards who also provides details of an approach to Risk Assessments. There are serious warnings here about working at height.

There is no other publication, to my knowledge, which gives such a broad and yet detailed coverage of these important aspects of performing arts venues. The topics and solutions are international and generally have application in most situations. I have been working as a theatre consultant for more than 30 years and have always focused on stage engineering – even so there are a number of explanations and facts here which I find useful. The information is presented in such a way as to be understandable by professional and newcomer alike. I sincerely believe that this volume provides a valuable resource to all involved in the engineering and technology of performing arts buildings.

Richard Brett　　　　　　　　*April 2004*

Contents

Contents

Overstage

Fly tower grids and galleries, structural steelwork, stairs and ladders, portal bridges and towers, lighting bridges and frames, multi-line and point hoist flying systems, drum and shaft hoists, personnel flying, curtain tracks and systems for flying, drawing and swagging, cyclorama systems.

Safety equipment

Safety curtains, smoke ventilation systems, sound and fire doors and shutters.

Understage

Stage elevator systems of all types and sizes, for orchestra pits, for instruments, for prompt-boxes, for stage traps; lifting and equalising platforms, load-in and truck elevators, turntables and revolving stages, drum revolves, stage wagon systems, cloth and scenery storage equipment.

> ## Stage equipment
> "as you like it"

Background

When Antonin Dvořák staged his original performance of *From the New World* in 1893, one of the founding firms of Waagner Biro, "Imperial and Royal Court Building Fitters" had already erected the stage systems for the Vienna State Opera and for the Burgtheater in Vienna. Today the new world of modern stage technology is designed, manufactured and installed by Waagner-Biro Stage Systems, not only in the new world, but on every continent.

With design and fabrication based in six countries and agencies all around the globe, Waagner-Biro has achieved a reputation for innovation, quality and reliability as well as for providing practical and economic systems and engineering. Waagner-Biro can bring together, within its own organisation, the state-of-the-art mechanical, electrical, electronic and computer systems that need to be closely integrated in a modern theatre installation.

Opera

As well as providing the stage technology for its parent house, the Vienna State Opera, since 1869, Waagner-Biro has developed and installed stage systems for a large number of major opera houses around the world. Opera houses often require the more sophisticated stage systems to cope with repertoire working and larger settings, and new developments on these projects can form the basis for many practical solutions for other works.

As well as providing the special installations in the famous Sydney Opera House, Waagner-Biro developed equipment for the Teatro Real in Madrid and for the Gran Teatre del Liceu in Barcelona, for the Royal Opera House in London, for the Zurich Opera House and for the Filial Bolshoi Theatre in Moscow. A full list of their installations appears on their web site.

Theatre

One of the early theatres in Rome had revolving scenery on its stage. Some modern theatres still use revolves but many also require a range of other techniques to move, not just scenery, but also parts of the performance space itself. A major requirement of a theatre built for drama, or for a range of other presentations, is that the equipment used during performance is silent. Waagner-Biro have developed a number of techniques for silent flying and stage movements without compromising either loads or the speed of motion.

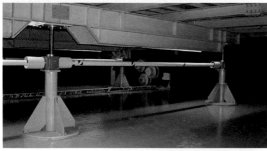

Stages equipped by Waagner-Biro can be found in major cities, including Amsterdam, Athens, Berlin, Copenhagen, Helsinki, Hong Kong, London, Lisbon, Madrid, Moscow, Munich, Prague, Seoul and Sydney, as well as in many other towns and cities world-wide.

Computer controls

The history of computer controls in theatre has been fragmented as a number of small companies all attempted to offer comprehensive systems. In the modern world, safety is a major part of control and Waagner-Biro offer enhanced digital systems for all of their installations developed by their own specialist teams in Luxembourg and Munich. Whilst the systems are standard, the man-machine interfaces can be personalised to suit clients' and consultants' requirements. Ease of use is rated highly and control of lighting, sound and audio-visual systems is also offered.

The size and scale of the available systems is suitable for large opera houses with more than 200 drives, down to small lyric and presentation theatres. Modular design and construction allows extension or upgrading of the more advanced systems at any time and economically.

Special installations

In addition to the more standard theatre installations, Waagner-Biro also majors in custom-made retractable (bleacher or tribune) seating systems, both manually and motor operated, as well as in special stages and mechanisms for congress centres, multi-purpose halls, revolving restaurants and similar unusual applications. Many of these installations are a testimony to their engineers' creativity.

A further significant range of expertise has been developed for the cruise liner industry where highly-sophisticated staging and presentation equipment has been designed to withstand the effects of the vessel's rolling and heavy seas.

With this very extensive world-wide experience, Waagner-Biro work with clients and consultants to ensure they provide stage equipment "as you like it".

Auditoria

Stepped and tilting floors, seating wagons and moving towers, moving ceilings, variable acoustic systems, moveable acoustic reflectors, sound reducing acoustic partitions.

Electrical and control

In addition to providing manual and counterweighted systems, much equipment in a modern theatre requires comprehensive controls to ensure performance with safety. Drives and controls for all the above installations are therefore included.

Handover service

Setting to work, testing, commissioning, documentation, record drawings, operations and maintenance manuals, training, maintenance and stand-by services tailored to the project are all available.

waagner biro

stage systems

www.stagesystems.waagner-biro.com

Unitrack

Chaintrack

Unibeam with Chaintrack

Stagemate

Triple E Ltd sets the standard for precision and performance in the entertainment industry. The company was formed in 1984 and began by manufacturing the award winning purpose made Loose Pin Hinge. We gained a reputation for further innovation with the Unijack™ system. Unitrack was the result of an intense period of R & D starting from the double premise that the running surfaces must always remain parallel and that joining sections should be simple and secure. The unique fabricated I-beam configuration was developed and the Unitrack system has now become the acknowledged market leader. By adding a full range of accessories designed and built to work with the track we are able to offer a product which is superior in reliability, versatility and strength to its competitors.

Unibeam
With its symmetrical I-beam shape, solid cross-section and identical external dimensions to Unitrack, Unibeam is compatible with the extensive range of Unitrack accessories. Unibeam makes an extremely effective fly bar. Most recently specified for Copenhagen Opera and the Stadsteater in Göteburg. The Royal Opera House in London has a total of 2,800 metres of Unibeam fly bars, which are used not just for scenery and borders, but also for lighting and as track systems in their own right. Unibeam will carry a scenery carrier with a safe working load of 440 kg. Uniring is a moulded plastic loop which enables borders and legs to be clipped directly into Unibeam, eliminating the need for repetitive knot tying and reducing turnaround time. Uniring won the 'Widget of the Year' award at LDI 1999.

Unibeam can be fitted with an insert allowing the chain from our Chaintrack system to be used as the driving force for curtains and scenery. This system has been adopted for the main house curtain in Copenhagen where the curtain flies, parts and swags. The system closely replicates the effect achieved with a scissor track but at a more economic price.

Variable Acoustics
Variable acoustics are now a key part of modern performance space design. Opera, symphony and chamber music, and amplified sound require very different environments, yet today many venues are expected to be multi-purpose. In order to provide the different acoustic qualities needed by each type of performance, variable acoustics, in the form of banners, curtains or panels, are being utilised. Acoustic banners are raised and lowered vertically to affect the reflection and absorption of the sound waves. Acoustic curtains which travel horizontally around the auditorium have, in the past, presented the problem of how to store them when they are not in use. Triple E has developed a new system, Chaintrack, which lends itself to this application.

Chaintrack
Chaintrack is based around a duplex roller chain where the top section is driven and the bottom section carries the curtain. The chain can be turned around sprockets with a diameter as small as 55 mm. This enables the curtain to be turned through 90° and 180° curves into storage areas or pockets behind the auditorium walls. The first installation of acoustic banners by Triple E was in 1998 for the City of Birmingham Symphony Orchestra. Since then Triple E has gone on to install acoustic curtains, banners and panels in a range of venues including a Beverley Hills recording studio, The LSO St. Luke's Centre in London, The Maison de la Radio in Brussels, The Sage in Gateshead and the Millennium Centre in Cardiff.

Stagemate
Installed on the flyrail and replacing the existing rope brake, Stagemate enables one person to easily and accurately control several hand lines. With no conversion work, no programming and only simple training necessary, Stagemate is a cost effective way to motorise a counterweight system. Stagemate won the ABTT Product of the Year award in 2003.

We have a policy of constant evaluation of the market and over the last two decades we have been committed to the development and innovation of new products and to the update of our existing product range with new technology. Our key personnel all have experience of working backstage and it is our aim to provide a complete service to the entertainment and presentation industries. Whatever effect you wish to achieve our standard products and ability to produce custom equipment will make it happen.

Triple E Ltd

Equipment Engineered
for Entertainment

Tel +44 (0)1959 570 333
Fax +44 (0)1959 570 888
info@3-eee.com
www.3-eee.com

LSO St Luke's London

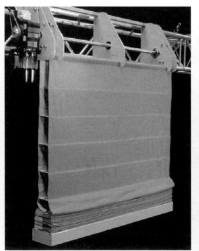
Variable Acoustic Banner

U2 Popmart Tour

Theatreplan LLP offers a range of theatre planning and technical equipment consultancy services to clients, architects and engineers. The team is able to offer these services on drama theatres, music venues, community and school halls as well as on opera houses and major lyric theatres. There are eight partners, each with many years experience in the performing arts covering stage, event and technical management through to auditorium design and technical equipment design and specification. The partners include two qualified architects and two chartered engineers. This team is supplemented by working theatre practitioners with knowledge of current practice in their special areas, such as lighting or sound technology.

Feasibility Studies and Project Development

Theatreplan's approach to each project is to develop the objectives and goals with the client, and to assist with the development of a clear brief and schedules of accommodation. In addition specialist cost information is provided to the project cost consultants. The team can also assist with site assessments.

Auditorium Design

Theatreplan has considerable experience of designing new performance spaces as well as a proven track record in improving existing and historic auditoria. This work is carried out in close collaboration with the client and the architects. Auditoria are designed for the specified uses which may involve the use of computer-generated modelling. Theatreplan has been able to improve sightlines in existing auditoria through re-raking, choice of seat and changed seating layouts. Theatreplan has been at the forefront of the development of flexible auditoria, offering innovative solutions for transitions between formats. Another important task is to ensure the sympathetic integration of technical installations and control positions into the fabric of an auditorium.

Theatre Planning

Theatreplan offers practical planning for the public and backstage areas of any performance building. Some partners have experience as users as well as designers and their practical advice can be particularly valuable. This work is often undertaken in conjunction with the end users so as to achieve their desired solutions, while explaining the possible options and retaining some 'future proofing' of the plans.

Technical Equipment Consultancy

Theatreplan provides planning, design, specification, contractors' drawing review and commissioning services for all types of performance equipment: stage rigging and machinery, stage and work lighting, sound, video communications and audio-visual. Equipment handled ranges from full power flying and mainstage elevators for opera theatres through to suspension systems and moving seating units for smaller venues.

Members of Theatreplan's team have been active as both consultants and practitioners for a total of nearly 200 years: making it one of the world's most widely experienced theatre consultancy organisations. The Partners each have an impressive track record and remain dedicated to maintaining a high standard of excellence by providing imaginative, practical and innovative solutions.

Illustrations from top:
Regent Theatre, Hanley – Levitt Bernstein
Kwai Tsing Theatre – HK Government Architects
Hampstead Theatre – Bennetts Associates
LSO St Luke's – Levitt Bernstein

Theatreplan

T: +44 (0)20 7269 2669
E: info@theatreplan.net
W: www.theatreplan.net

At a glance -
The Unusual
capability

PLANNING

Client Brief

Design

Specification

Purchasing

Planning

PREPARATION

Steel Fabrication

Electrics & Automation

Motors & Winches

Wire Rope Assembly

Warehouse

DELIVERY

Project Rigging

Venue Rigging

Stage Engineering

Production Services

Maintenance & Servicing

Hire & Sales

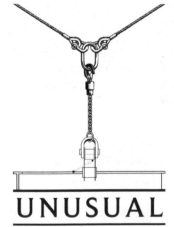

UNUSUAL

Tel: +44/0 870 868 7825
Fax:+44/0 870 744 4464
www.unusual.co.uk

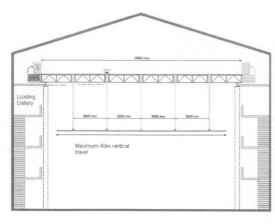

An array of steel-band hoists in the Thalia Theatre in Hamburg and a drawing showing how the aluminium trusses can span the fly tower and form support for an overstage grid.

New Developments

After a management buy out in March, 2003, Hall Stage managed to secure the UK distribution rights for **ASM products**, including the amazing **PR 500 steel band** hoist system. The installation at the Thalia Theatre in Hamburg is shown on the left.

The unique modular construction of the PR truss motor system guarantees the highest flexibility possible for the planning of your theatre and allows total adaptability for any application. The frames of the flying bar system are constructed as an aluminium lattice girder system with integrated deflection pulley sheaves and guides for the steel bands integrated into them. These lattice girders carry the hoist machine frames and integrated control interfaces at each end and can replace the entire grid structure. The horizontal forces are fully within the trusses, so that only the dead loads are passed into the supporting wall structure of the theatre.

Each truss contains all of the necessary diversion pulleys for the steel bands for its separate flying bar. The steel band system is fully patented and gives virtually silent running – less than **30dB(A)** at stage level. In addition the flying bar can travel at up to 1.2m/sec – and stop with precise positioning.

Although it appears difficult the steel bands can be hauled out of line and a diagonal pull is possible in every direction. Also the steel bands, unlike wire-ropes never stretch. Installation is fast and simple using the sets of pre-assembled components.

YOUR STAGE - OUR WORLD

Specialist products

Hall Stage Limited was established in **1898** and designs, manufactures and distributes much of the technical and mechanical equipment used in many UK theatres and live events venues. The business also currently exports to 150 distributors and resellers in 55 countries around the world.

Hall Stage specialist products include **T60 and T70** curtain track systems for all applications – stages, conference rooms, school drama facilities and general presentation environments. **Over 25 Km** of tracking was manufactured by Hall Stage last year alone and the company still services and maintains systems that were installed in the 1930's…!

Other **Hall Stage** specialist rigging products include rolling or flying safety curtains, counterweight sets and hemp rope sets. In addition a range of all-new "**DynaGlide**" powered and manual hoists for powered scenery flying and lighting bar hoist operations and "**DynaLine**" pulleys and motor control systems are available. Hall Stage also have a comprehensive selection of theatrical and scenic hardware fittings and all the associated stage accessories.

Hall Stage are proud to be providing tracks and modern theatre rigging equipment to all sizes of theatre and performance venue and continuing the business which started over a hundred years ago.

Hall Stage Limited
Unit 4, Cosgrove Way
Luton
Bedfordshire LU1 1XL

Tel +44 (0)845 345 4255
Fax +44 (0)845 345 4256

sales@hallstage.com
www.hallstage.com

Current and recent work includes:

WALES MILLENNIUM CENTRE
New home for Welsh National Opera

LONDON COLISEUM
Home of English National Opera

WEXFORD
New Opera House for the Festival

LABAN CENTRE LONDON
SADLER'S WELLS THEATRE
MILTON KEYNES THEATRE

BARBICAN CONCERT HALL
ROYAL FESTIVAL HALL
PERTH 2000

THE OLD VIC LONDON
HACKNEY EMPIRE
HIS MAJESTY'S THEATRE,
ABERDEEN

NEWPORT ARTS CENTRE
HALTON ARTS CENTRE
SALISBURY ARTS CENTRE
TALAWA AT WESTMINSTER

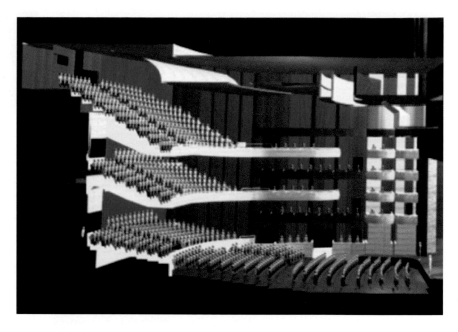

The CARR & ANGIER practice has been operating for thirty years, and has a reputation for the high quality of service provided. Personal attention is given to every job no matter what its size. The highly specialised knowledge offered about theatres and similar arts and entertainment facilities is backed by direct working experience in the business.

The title 'theatre' has been retained in this specialist consultancy but the practice handles all types of buildings which contain an auditorium or a place of public assembly, or the technical facilities to service theatre and the wider fields of entertainment, education and commerce. Our list of completed projects includes Concert Halls, Conference Centres, Cinemas, Arts Centres, Leisure Centres and Educational Facilities as well as theatres.

This experience is used to provide a wide frame of reference for each project, and for the development of imaginative concepts and the preparation of briefing documents.

CARR & ANGIER
THEATRE CONSULTANTS

THE OLD MALTHOUSE
CLARENCE STREET
BATH BA1 5NS

tel: +44/0 1225 446 664
fax: +44/0 1225 446 654
email: info@carrandangier.co.uk
www.carrandangier.co.uk

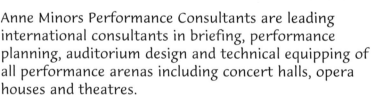
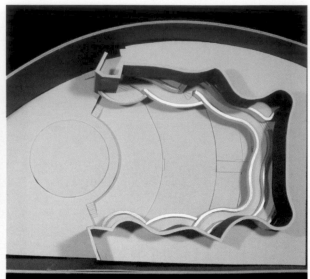

Over the last decade Stage Technologies have engineered some of the most advanced control and mechanical solutions for venues and productions around the world. With a dedicated team of experienced engineers we are on hand to assist our clients throughout the entire production process, from initial brief to detailed design and installation.

It is this level of commitment towards quality and reliability that has gained us ISO 9001:2000 quality assurance certification. Our customers are the primary driver for our product and service development and our clients can expect an accessible, state-of-the-art solution to help them make the most of their performance environment.

Innovation - Constantly striving to push the boundaries of technical innovation, Stage Technologies have engineered solutions for many of the groundbreaking effects seen in today's modern theatre.

Engineering Solutions

Accessibility - Among the first in the industry to develop a standardised product range, this has translated into significant cost savings for our clients and given us the ability to deliver solutions from a simple moving motor to the most complex of 3d performer flying sequences.

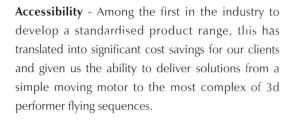

- Nomad & Acrobat multi-user control

- BigTow zero fleet winches

- Bespoke projects

- 24/7 support

STAGE
TECHNOLOGIES

Tel: +44 20 7354 8800
www.stagetech.com
solutions@stagetech.com

THE GREAT PLAYWRIGHTS SAID
LIFE IS THEATRE.

We light life.

Since 1975, ETC (Electronic Theatre Controls, Inc.) has been bringing innovative lighting solutions to entertainment and architectural venues worldwide.

From the revolutionary Source Four™ luminaires to the lighting control wizardry of Smartpack™ portable dimmers, Sensor™ and Unison™ dimming systems, Emphasis™ consoles, and ETCNet2™ networking, ETC technology lights up stages and structures across the globe.

Going far beyond theatre, into the art of illuminating theme parks, conference centers, broadcast-production facilities and more, ETC offers cutting-edge lighting equipment and personalised expertise.

Founded by Fred Foster, with branches worldwide, ETC has built its success on a clear and unwavering service ethic: support the products and support the customer. ETC is also committed to the future of lighting, supporting students of lighting design and theatre through various bursaries and educational programmes.

If 'All the world's a stage,' and that stage needs brilliant lighting, the lighting should be by ETC.

Europe ▪ Unit 5, Victoria Industrial Estate, Victoria Road, London W3 6UU, UK ▪ Tel: +44 (0)20 8896 1000 ▪ Fax: +44 (0)20 8896 2000
Asia ▪ Room 605-606, Tower III Enterprise Square, 9 Sheung Yuet Road, Kowloon Bay, Kowloon, Hong Kong ▪ Tel: +852 2799 1220 ▪ Fax: +852 2799 9325
Americas ▪ 3031 Pleasant View Rd, PO Box 620979, Middleton, WI 53562 USA ▪ Tel: +1 608 831 4116 ▪ Fax: +1 608 836 1736 ▪ Toll free: 800 688 4116 ▪ Toll free fax: 800 555 8912
Web: www.etcconnect.com ▪ **Email:** (US) mail@etcconnect.com ▪ (UK) mail@etceurope.com ▪ (Asia) mail@etcasia.com

Multistage International Ltd is a recently-established stage and studio engineering Company with a great wealth of experience. It originally traded as *JVT Associates* specifically to complete the stage engineering and project management of two prestigious projects in Thessaloniki in Greece. These projects were both completed on time and within budget. The company was formed as Multistage International Ltd in January 2001.

Multistage International Ltd works from new, purpose-designed offices in Bury St Edmunds, in East Anglia and within easy reach of London and a number of airports. The company is currently undertaking design and installation work on projects in Cyprus, Greece and the Middle East as well as in the UK. It has carried out projects to demanding specifications with major international theatre consultants.

Multistage International Ltd has the in-house expertise and facilities to carry out:

- the concept planning, budgeting and project management of theatre, studio, show lounge and conference hall installations.
- co-ordination of theatre and studio services with architects, owners and main contractors.
- site surveys and feasibility studies of refurbishments and new projects.
- full stage machinery designs to required standards, including calculations, general assembly, machine part and layout drawings.
- design and installation of Gala 'Spiralift' elevator drive systems.
- electrical control, lighting, audio and video system designs and schedules.
- the employment and co-ordination of mechanical, electrical, lighting, audio and control system engineering sub-contractors.
- preparation of risk assessments, test schedules, as-built drawings and operation and maintenance manuals.

Multistage International Ltd
Stage & Studio Engineering
59c Eastern Way
Bury St Edmunds
Suffolk IP32 7AB
United Kingdom
Tel: +44/0 1284-750474
Fax: +44/0 1284-750475
info@multistage.co.uk

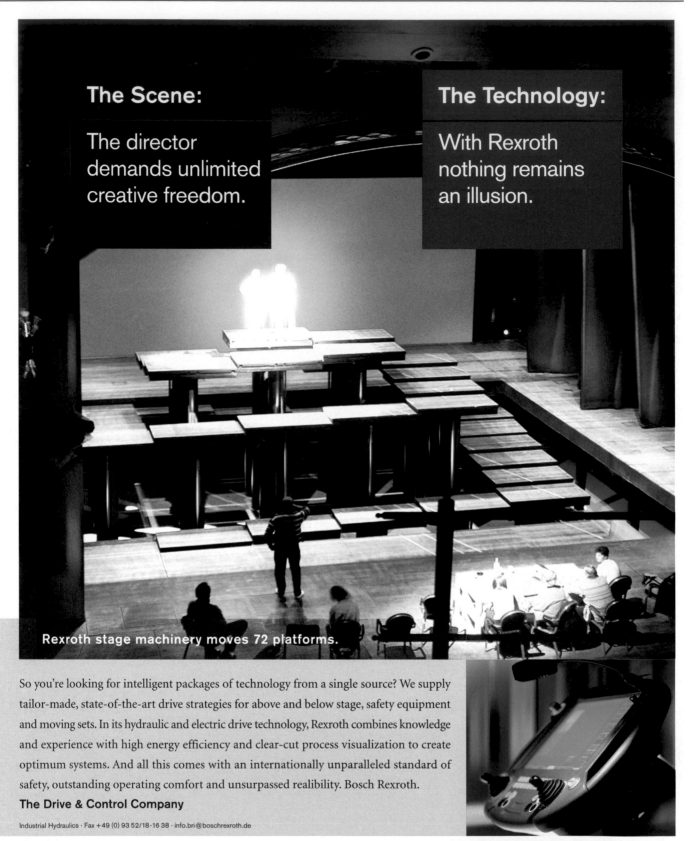

The SPIRALIFT® is the most popular orchestra, stage, scenery and piano lift mechanism in the world.

Pierre-Mercure Concert Hall
Montreal, Quebec, Canada
Two orchestra lifts each driven by three Spiralifts.

Konzerthaus Freiburg
Freiburg, Germany
Architects: Dietrich Bangert, Bangert Scholz. Technical planning and installation: Waagner-Biro. This project incorporates 120 Spiralifts.

The GALA Venue – Transformation in less than 10 minutes!

Mount-Jacob Cultural Center
Jonquière, Quebec, Canada

Theatre Consultants:
Trizart Alliance

Flexibility: to introduce seats, alternate row elevators are raised to create the space to swing the seats up into position.

◄**With full seating**

The seats are swung from under the elevator platform into position on the elevator by an internal mechanism.

◄**Small hall format**

With the seats in position the elevators are lowered to preset levels to form the required raking. Other sets of rows can then be set up. All the actions are mechanised and are carried out remotely.

◄**Flat floor**

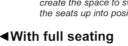

Cosmodôme
Laval, Quebec, Canada

Reliability: these 3 Spiralifts under a turntable have been operated daily on a 20 minute cycle as part of a multi-media show since 1994.

GALA SYSTEMS creates advanced modular lift systems for theatres, concert halls, multi-use auditoria and related venues. GALA SYSTEMS provides ideas, engineering, products and services that help consultants, architects, contractors and owners add value to their facilities.

GALA SYSTEMS' products and services are well-proven, with more than 20 years experience and over 500 successful installations in 45 countries worldwide. Since 1990, we have supplied products such as the Spiralift, including technical support, directly to theatre contractors and other theatre equipment manufacturers, enabling them to use their expertise to install turnkey solutions locally.

GALA SYSTEMS is the new trading name of Gala Theatrical Equipment.

GALA SYSTEMS
CREATIVE SOLUTIONS

3185 First Street
St. Hubert, QC J3Y 8Y6
Canada

Phone +1 450 678-7226
Fax +1 450 678-4060

info@galasystems.com

Our name has changed.

Everything is *Still* Possible.

WHY CHANGE OUR NAME?

Twenty years after its inception, Bytecraft Automation is changing its name to State Automation. This decision is the result of the company's desire to concentrate on its' core activities, products and services, redefine its' image, and focus on what the company knows best: the creation of State-of-the-art, safe and reliable, lighting and automation solutions for entertainment and architecture.

The Bytecraft story started in 1984 when Ted Fregon formed a four-man-band, stage-lighting and automation service company. From there, Bytecraft grew to become one of the most significant players in the Stage Lighting and Automation business and earned a worldwide reputation for innovation and its can-do approach to every undertaking: Everything is Possible.

The company's achievements are spread far and wide; beginning with the development of the first microprocessor based, full fault-reporting dimmer, IDS, in 1984 and followed by the first all-digital dimmer with the now ubiquitous GUI; *BYTESIZE*. The *STATE* automation system, now in its sixth generation followed and has been installed in over forty venues on four continents beginning with the spectacular, but precisely controlled crash of the chandelier in "Phantom of the Opera". Other notable achievements include the world-first, award-winning *VST* theatrical SineWave dimmer, the patented *MEDUSA* automation patch system and *WINCON*$^{V-HSI}$ the first axis-controller built from the ground-up to comply with the rigorous international standard for functional safety, IEC61508.

Over twenty years Bytecraft grew substantially and entered business sectors and markets unrelated to its core business and roots. The Bytecraft group was restructured in 2001 and the lighting and automation unit became known as Bytecraft Automation. Now, in 2004, the company is clearly focussed on the delivery of State-of-the-art engineering solutions for entertainment and architecture and has decided to signal that determination and independent spirit with a change of name to *STATE AUTOMATION*.

WHAT'S NOT CHANGING?

Our people, including a large base of theatre engineering specialists, our commitment to exceeding your expectations, our dedication to quality and innovation, our continuous investment in R&D and our focus on safety – *STATE AUTOMATION* will continue to design, manufacture, install and maintain State-of-the-art lighting and stage automation systems.

STATE Automation
Everything is *still* possible

STATE AUTOMATION

23-27 Fonceca Street
Mordialloc, Victoria 3195
AUSTRALIA

Phone: +61 (0)3 9587 2555
Fax: +61 (0)3 9580 7690
E-mail: info@stateautomation.com
Web: www.stateautomation.com

Annual Theatre Show

Training Seminars

Members' backstage visits

Representation at national and international level

Annual Awards' Dinners

Association of British Theatre Technicians:

- Campaigns on behalf of the theatre industry to ensure that legislation is appropriate to the industry's needs, and that regulations are suitably drafted and enforced.

- Publishes *Sightline*, the quarterly magazine which carries news, reviews, features and *Safety Matters.*

- Provides a telephone enquiry service to help solve safety and technical problems.

- Hosts a website with Green Room Forum for chat and Safety Forum for answers to difficult questions.

- Arranges training courses on technical and managerial skills.

- Publishes Codes of Practice on a variety of subjects specific to the industry's needs.

- Organises the annual Theatre Show of backstage and front-of-house equipment and supplies.

- Arranges periodic conferences and seminars.

- Arranges meetings and visits to theatres and shows of special interest.

- Has a number of highly influential committees, including Safety, Training & Education and Theatre Planning.

- Edits *Technical Standards for Places of Entertainment* and *Model National Conditions.*

- Organises specialist interest groups such as the Production Managers' Forum (in conjunction with the Stage Management Association) and the Archaeology Committee.

- The Society of British Theatre Designers is affiliated to the ABTT.

- Is the UK Centre of OISTAT.

* Peter Ruthven Hall shows the Golden Triga won for the third time by the Society of British Theatre Designers entry to the 2003 Prague Quadrennial.

Association of British Theatre Technicians

55 Farringdon Road London EC1M 3JB

Tel: +44(0) 20 7242 9200 www.abtt.org.uk

Speaker: Richard Pulford

It's a great pleasure to see so many people here – rather surprising, perhaps, for this early on a Sunday morning. And those of you who know me, and some of you do, will know that it's even more of a surprise to find *me* here at this time on a Sunday!

I am Chief Executive of both the Society of London Theatre and of the Theatrical Management Association. I'm not going to say anything very much about them, except that these two organisations between them represent the managing interests of all theatres of any significant size, both producing theatres and receiving venues, throughout the United Kingdom.

I'm here, particularly this morning, as Chairman of the PAID Group; a group which has the purpose of seeking to enhance and facilitate the UK Government's export support for the performing arts in all their variety and in all their aspects. I don't apologise for claiming that Britain has a remarkable reputation for theatre architecture, engineering and technology. Much of this reputation has been enhanced, cemented, over the last 10–15 years, and there has been in this country an astonishing rush of projects of all kinds, including capital projects, designed to develop housing for the arts, projects funded largely out of the National Lottery. Here in London they range from the enormous redevelopment of the Royal Opera House with its ground-breaking technology, to the tiny gem of the Vanbrugh Theatre at the Royal Academy of Dramatic Art. And in between, a project I myself was very closely involved with, the redevelopment – the rebuilding, practically – of the Royal Court Theatre, which was a phenomenally complex logistical and engineering job because of the exceptionally restricted site on which it had to be carried out. Within a couple of years, practically every subsidised theatre in London will have received capital contributions from the lottery and will have completed a major development programme. New venues, too, have been springing up all over the country, from Aberdeen to Cornwall, in Milton Keynes, Salford and so on. The list is almost literally endless, and I cannot name them all here.

Despite this wealth of experience, however we haven't always been very good at exploiting our reputations and our strengths overseas. And now I'm going to revert very briefly to the PAID Group. We're not paid, incidentally; PAID stands for Performing Arts International Development. This is a group which is industry-led and which consists of representatives of the Independent Theatre Council, the Opera and Music Theatre Forum, Dance UK, and the International Artistes' Managers' Association. The purpose of the group is to help this sector to build bridges to Government and perhaps, most importantly, to help explain the performing arts to Government in a language which Government understands and to explain Government to the performing arts! Most people operating within the performing arts have never thought of themselves or of anything that they do as being in any way an export, and they need to be encouraged to understand why this is important, and what the opportunities are.

The PAID group is set up jointly by the Department of Culture, Media and Sport (DCMS) and by Trade Partners UK (TPUK), who are one of the sponsors of this Conference. TPUK offer support services to UK companies trading overseas. They have designated staff in over 200 centres worldwide and throughout the United Kingdom. For British companies, and indeed for sole traders and practices, they offer grants for visits overseas, and they offer grants also for appearances at international trade fairs and exhibitions. For those of you from overseas, your local office of TPUK can help to put you in touch with UK suppliers of goods and services.

I'm pleased to say that the Government is funding a reception at the Department of Culture, Media and Sport as part of the Conference and I hope as many of you as can will attend to learn a bit more about what the United Kingdom can offer to the performing arts world-wide.

I now have the pleasure of introducing our Keynote Speaker, Don MacLean. Don was born in Scotland, and moved as a child to Canada where he began his life as a technician in theatre. He went on to become a technical director and moved into general theatre management. I have to say that in the UK making the break from technical directing into overall management is remarkably unusual, much more unusual than it ought to be.

He has worked more recently and notably in Las Vegas where he was production and technical advisor to *Mystère*, the Cirque du Soleil production. He was then appointed the technical advisor to the construction of the Bellagio Theatre in Las Vegas, and I would recommend very strongly that, should you ever get a chance, you make every effort to visit this and see the show: it is an extraordinary building. After that he become a consultant and worked with Universal Studios in Japan, and with Euro Disney in France. He has now returned to the United States, to Las Vegas, where he is the Theatre Concept Production Manager for Cirque du Soleil. His CV is very impressive; it also has one very disarming quality, which is that it lists his weaknesses! The one that I'm going to draw attention to is that he's a workaholic, which no doubt explains why he too is here at this time on a Sunday morning! Don MacLean. Ω

Theatre Engineering and Architecture

Speaker: Don MacLean, Senior Supervisor, Theatre Projects, Cirque du Soleil, Nevada, Inc.

It's very heartening to see you all here today. Before I get started, I would like to credit the video montage that some of you saw as you entered this plenary session this morning. It was prepared for us by Cirque du Soleil's Las Vegas videographer Gabriel Dupuis, and showed some progress video from the construction of the old theater at the Bellagio Hotel in Las Vegas, and then a rather unique perspective from both backstage and underwater, which the audience never gets to see, of some of the performance itself.

I must say I was a bit surprised when I was originally approached by a contact of Richard Brett's to speak at this Conference. Honestly, I wasn't certain I was the right person for the job. I don't have a very well-known name, unlike many of us here today. I don't have a series of degrees hanging on the wall in my office, and I don't have a lot of partners in a large firm back in the United States. But the more I thought about it I realized there is something I do have which makes me a good candidate, and that's a shared experience but with a unique perspective. Along with OISTAT (Organisation Internationale des Scénographes, Techniciens et Architectes de Theatre), one of the primary supporting bodies for this Conference is the Association of British Theatre Technicians, and I'm happy to say that my first professional job was as an entry-level sound and light technician at the National Arts Center in Ottawa, Canada.

There I was part of a small team transforming an old automobile body repair shop into a 125-seat black-box theater for a company of apprentice actors. I spent a good deal of time learning how to lay floor tiles and do plumbing, which at the time I thought had very little to do with theater – but that was before I understood how important good theater design and construction is for the end users of a facility. At the time I was just so astonished that anyone could have been so foolish as to offer me money to do what I loved, and for the next 21 years I've been fortunate enough to find a string of gullible people to keep up the tradition. I wonder how many of us feel the same way?

However while I started out in the traditional world of ballet, music and the legitimate stage, I've spent most of the last eight years in an environment where the everyday construction of a reality takes on a slightly different color, and that is Las Vegas and the themed entertainment industry of the theme-park. So far I have been lucky enough to be involved in the design phase of three Cirque theaters, and the shows presented in those theaters have been designed as open-ended runs. In addition, I've also worked with Universal Studios and the Walt Disney Company on two major theme parks in Japan and in Europe. Now the processes involved in projects of this size and complexity are certainly a far cry from those used in a black-box theater, but I assure you they do rely on the basic skills learned in that one, and in others along the way.

I've recently rejoined Cirque du Soleil to work on a new project and would like to tell you a little of the history of Cirque du Soleil. I also want to describe the way in which their creative process works in relation to the type of work that we are all familiar with as designers, engineers and consultants.

In much the same way as the Walt Disney Company, Cirque du Soleil was started by, and is still driven by, the creative development team. At the beginning of the 1980s, a group of young street performers – musicians, fire-eaters, jugglers, to name a few – combined their talents and created the *Club des Talons Hauts*, or the High Heels Club, so named because most of the performers involved used stilts. At that time Quebec did not have a circus tradition, unlike most of the countries in Europe, so this merry group decided to start a festival as a way to exchange ideas and to develop their craft and their audience. This is how the *Fete Forraine de Baie St-Paul* began. This festival was the result of bringing all this talent together under one roof, or more specifically, under one tent. With that festival, the seeds for Cirque du Soleil were planted.

Don MacLean After starting his career as a theatre technician in drama, opera and ballet houses, Don was appointed Production Stage Manager/Technical Director and later General manager of a major Festival Theatre Company. He moved to Las Vegas as Production Manager and Technical Director of the Cirque du Soleil production *Mystère* and then became a theatre consultant with architects Scéno-Plus for the Bellagio Theatre in Las Vegas. Taking the independent path, he advised a number of important clients on activities as diverse as scenery construction, box office sales analysis and the live broadcast of an Award Ceremony. Moving to Japan, he successfully delivered four 'show and ride' attractions for Universal Studios, on time and on budget. After managing a facility for EuroDisney, he became Theatre Concept Production Supervisor for Cirque du Soleil. Don brings wide practical international experience of production, technical, construction, management and administrative matters to his global vision of Theatre Engineering and Architecture in 2002.

The original concept combined circus and street arts, theater and outlandish characters, music and fantastic lighting, and it rapidly won the hearts of its audience. The Cirque itself was born in 1984, which was the 450th anniversary of Jacques Cartier's arrival in Canada; the Cirque then presented performances in Quebec city under a yellow and blue 800-seat Big Top tent. The major funding for this tour was provided by the Quebec provincial government. The show then traveled to other cities around the province, and in 1985, after touring Quebec, this tour went to Ontario, and by this time the Big Top had been expanded to 1,500 people. So Cirque du Soleil continued its tour of Canada in 1986 and performed at the opening ceremonies of Expo 86 held in Vancouver. The travel bug had by then bitten the troupe and some of the acts were performed at different circus festivals and competitions around the world. In 1987 Cirque set its sights on the US and began a tour of California. In September, the show *Cirque Réinventé* or *The Circus Reinvented* opened at the Los Angeles Festival. The show was presented in San Diego and Santa Monica, and Californians were enchanted.

Cirque returned to the United States again in 1988, this time visiting both California and New York where the Big Top was installed under the shadow of the World Trade Center. This second trip solidly established Cirque's reputation in the United States – rave reviews were standard throughout the tour. The company ended this tour in Montreal in the midst of a rather cold Canadian winter. By 1990, Cirque's creative team had returned to its idea laboratory and developed a new production entitled *Nouvelle Expérience (New Experience)*. In parallel, the Big Top had once again been expanded, now holding up to 2,500.

The new performances were so popular that Cirque du Soleil set new attendance records, and in July the show left home for a 19-month tour of North America, while at the same time, the original 1987 production of *Cirque Réinventé* left for Paris and London. Cirque du Soleil was now being heard on both sides of the Atlantic. In 1992, Cirque finally forayed into Asia with a series of performances in Japan; *Fascination* was a compilation of the most interesting acts from Cirque's previous

productions, and began a four-month tour in Tokyo, eventually touring to eight Japanese cities. Meanwhile back in North America, Cirque presented *Nouvelle Expérience* in Las Vegas in a Big Top installed behind the Mirage hotel. This was Cirque's first venture into the interesting Las Vegas market.

The creative team made magic once more with *Saltimbanco*, a production in 1992 which moved to Sainte-Foy after its opening in Montreal for an extended tour of pan-American cities. However the creative team was not content to rest on its laurels, and they conjured up a new performance entitled *Mystère*, which many of you may have seen. This show was the replacement for *Nouvelle Expérience*, and its official première was held on January 14th 1994, although the first performance was on Christmas Day 1993, which I have to say was a lovely Christmas present for all of us. This magical production was the first Cirque du Soleil show which was designed to be presented in a permanent venue, the showroom at Treasure Island Hotel Casino in Las Vegas. Now a showroom, which is the Las Vegas dialect for a hotel venue that can present a performance, can range in scale from either an empty ballroom draped with black velour curtains to a fully equipped state of the art theater. In the case of *Mystère*, fortunately it was the latter, and was Cirque's first encounter with the realities faced during the design and fit-up of a hard-walled venue. As you have heard in this little summary history, up until this point in our development the company had always worked in a tent, now it was a big tent to be sure, but it was a tent nonetheless. Earlier productions had always been heavily influenced by the limitations that these structures imposed. By extricating themselves out from under the canvas they were able to envision new ways of presenting both existing and novel acrobatic concepts.

In order to assist the process of developing a new theater for this production, the consulting firm of Scèno Plus from Montreal were engaged by the hotel's owners. In the end, Scèno Plus remained connected with Cirque du Soleil, and their design development process, through three additional theaters, the '*O*' *Theater* at the Bellagio Hotel in Las Vegas, the *Alégría Theater* at the Beau Rivage Hotel in Biloxi Mississippi, that I don't think many of you will have been to, and the *La Nouba* Theater at the Pleasure Island expansion at the Walt Disney World in Florida.

Unfortunately for the theater consultant and the general contractor, the Cirque creative process, while it results in productions of startling beauty and complexity, also produces a very complex client with often contradictory requirements. This client's creative ideas continually drive the development and can be changed at essentially any stage of the project. Now, "What's new?" many of you may be asking. Well, in order to appreciate what this means to the design team of architects, engineers and consultants, I should point out one small part of the process.

The process of developing a new Cirque show is essentially an evolutionary one. It's not a serial progression towards a predetermined goal. Thus it's very hard to develop a snapshot that clearly identifies all the needs of the production early on. Unlike a traditional scripted musical or play, there is only a rough idea of a particular story. The acts that make up these performances are well-defined and clearly understood, but the sequencing of the acts and the way that they will relate to the performance as a whole, is a process of development, ongoing from the very beginning until the day the show opens. Indeed, to paraphrase one of the principal creative members behind the Cirque du Soleil story, he has said that he does not so much have an initial vision but a particular way of seeing things develop. Therefore in order to build the project in a timely manner, the theater consultant must play the role of interpreter, helping to shape the requirements for the theater in a way that respects the needs of the client, budget, schedule, etc, while also partnering with, challenging and validating the assumptions that have been made by the Cirque's creative team.

This is the process of creating a venue custom-made for a specific production, but one which unfortunately may not yet have been fully realized. Now many of you are probably thinking that this sounds like the standard process of designing a performance venue for any other client where the content of the end-user's product is not known. In some ways I would agree with you. The process that the creative team of designers, architects and consultants embark on in creating a new

theater is one which is based on a collective history and mutual understanding of the various skills these partners bring to the project. Hopefully each has their own wealth of experience and talents which when combined are greater than the sum of the parts. I would call this convergence.

'Convergence' is a word which is getting a lot of press these days – convergence in the home electronics market, convergence in the computer software industry, convergence in business communications. However for us, convergence should be a very familiar term; it's an idea that we've already lived with for a long time. For years, we as individuals and collectively as professional groups, have been converging, like we are for this Conference, around the idea of and the needs of a performance, a theater or a building. It is this strength and insight provided by this convergence that allows a facility's creative design team to make educated decisions about how to build a venue without specific knowledge as to its final content.

Basically, design decisions are made which allow the greatest flexibility for the end-user, within historically and empirically defined constraints specific to the particular performance genre. The concert hall has specific needs that are generally well understood by its designers; the same can be said for a dance theater, a lecture hall or a musical theater. Each one needs certain items that may or may not be compatible with other performing genres. But in each case the decisions of the consultants and architects are self-centered in order to prevent making a choice that may eventually have negative consequences for a future use or particular user, and I'm particularly happy to see that there's a session during the Conference where some of these end-users will be here to give feedback about the job we are doing. Sometimes we can get a bit myopic if we lack these opportunities for discussion across the dividing line between theatrical designers and end-users, which is a failing we should guard against.

Creating a new theater custom-built to the needs of a single production places the design team at the edge of a precipice. In this case, particularly when the production is intended to have an open-ended run, some decisions can be made which immediately limit future flexibility. Now this is usually seen as a good thing at the time, done in the interests of creating a tighter fit between venue and production. In engineering terms, it can be equated to specifying a very tight tolerance for a piece of moving equipment. Alignment then becomes critical. To the rest of us that aren't engineers, I would liken it to a Spandex tuxedo; it may look great when you first put it on, but when you gain a little weight … In the case of a truly custom room, the shorthand that is mutually understood by the consultants and designers no longer applies. The process becomes more like a high-stakes game of chess where each decision must also look ahead several moves to ensure that an unforeseen problem will not arise later, like a series of dominoes falling. For Cirque, maintaining a tight fit between the theater and the production is critical, as the theater is seen as becoming as much of a character in the final performance as the artistes are themselves This correctness of fit begins with the artistes and although they have been cast for a particular act or role, the absence of a formal script allows the creative team to transform their final incarnations on stage in order to leverage their abilities while avoiding their weaknesses.

The same then becomes true of the theater once the Cirque's production team has been loaded in. Now this production period in the theater is one that could drive a traditional production manager mad. The entire production team, including the artistes themselves, is seen as a resource that is usually available for the duration of a particular working session. This means that, unlike a traditional production schedule, where each department may be provided a time during the day where they can work undisturbed by the others, the standard Cirque process calls in all crew, all artistes, all support staff, to work full day as a community. In this way the designers and directors of the show can experiment in real time and in full scale. The feedback from these experiments is immediate, and like in genetics or in digital photography, mistakes don't survive long. Part of this experimentation also involves learning about the abilities of the theater. This is where the choices made by the consultants and engineers are validated. The reality is that for a production that develops through evolutionary experimentation even the best-fitting theater will eventually express itself in what happens onstage. If the production is really to be a living thing,

connecting emotionally with the audience, then it must accept the room in which it is to live. If the choices made earlier have all been good ones, there will be no negative surprises. Now of course this is an expensive and time-consuming formula, but it has been used to generate a number of successful shows in the past, and who can argue with success?

In addition to assisting the creative process, the theater consultant plays a vital role in bringing the latest in theater technology to the table when developing a new venue. Now for many years while I was a technical director, I believed that the role of the technical professional was to support the activities of the artiste in a way that was transparent to the audience. A good sound system was a design in which the patrons could only remember the music. A good lighting system design was where the scenery shone. You understand my meaning. With the Cirque technical team, there is in a real sense a similar understanding, as every technician in the production understands that their work, whether it be running the follow spot or mopping the stage floor prior to the performance, has a direct impact on how the artistes perform during the show.

These days, however, the complexity of theater systems has led me to modify my outlook somewhat. Are the systems we engineer supporting the technology of art or are they creating an art of technology? With increasingly complex system designs and the skills required to operate them, where does the line between technician and artiste really fall? In developing ever more complex systems, I think we have also created an intermediate level of creative technical artisans. These individuals function as creative interpreters; they are able to meet the needs of the design team and express these needs in the vocabulary of the technical domain. The sophistication of these new systems allows the creative teams to push the boundaries of what is shown to an audience. But there is a downside, literally, to these ever more complex systems. The old adage *the show must go on* is given the lie when a major technical system or component fails, especially when the premise of the show relies on it. I understand that there was a rather high-profile example of this here in London recently when a major component of the new production of *Chitty Chitty Bang Bang* failed on one of the first nights after opening. Fortunately for the theme park industry, the fare is collected at the main entrance gate, and within limits no refunds are provided for attractions that are closed or not working properly on any given day. That cannot be said for the theatrical performance industry. Even so, the theme park industry goes to extreme lengths to ensure the robustness of their system designs. For a major element in an attraction, it is not uncommon to complete 10 or 20,000 test cycles before the element leaves the factory, with an additional 10 or 20,000 cycles completed after installation in the field. While I was working in Japan, especially as we got close to opening last April, I sometimes wondered to myself why we were paying so much for used equipment!

Yet even with all this testing, elements fail and theme park attractions do run with less than 100% of their designed content in place. How many of you have previously toured a theme park only to find that a key component is out of commission but the rest of the attraction is running fine? If this is the reality that theme parks live with, even after major testing regimes, how then can a theatrical community deal with these issues of reliability?

One suggestion I have to offer is the adoption of standardized industrial components. Now, it's one thing for a small regional theater to cobble together a motion-control system with some switches and wire, but quite another to entrust the same equipment to operating a multi-million-dollar-a-week sales machine. As an example, there are a small number of motion-control hardware vendors who create systems for theatrical use; I'm sure many of you are familiar with them. Of these a number build their own input/output boards. Unfortunately the number of projects that can be carried out by these companies over the course of a year is minuscule compared with industrial production numbers. This means that in many cases their production run for a new hardware revision is limited to a handful of units. The drawback of this situation should be immediately apparent. Sometimes there is little tracking of revision changes within a hardware design. Occasionally, turnover of personnel within a company can remove archival knowledge of past versions of

software or undocumented quirks. I think, incidentally, Microsoft calls these 'features'!

There can only be limited numbers of staff at a particular company and they are likely to be simultaneously trying to build new projects while supporting existing ones, which can result in long lead times for repairs and exorbitant replacement costs. As a personal example, the *Mystère* showroom in Las Vegas was originally provided with an open-loop motion-control system that was built by an American manufacturer. Although he is out of business, he will remain nameless. This system supported 37 controlled axes, and had been custom-made for that particular theater. In addition to the 37 control cards that were installed in the rack, there were an additional 6 units on hand as spares. However the systems customization meant that this total of 43 control cards was all there were, to quote my favorite clause from my confidentiality agreement, 'throughout the universe'. The replacement cost for a new card was approximately US$ 2,500 (£1,1525, €2,125) with greater than an 8-week lead time, and repairs averaged between US$ 400 and US$ 800 (£240-£480, €340-€680) with a one-month turnaround. Two years after opening, a design flaw was discovered which finally explained an intermittently observed problem with the system, namely fluctuating position-reporting at the operator console, and a vibration of the winches when traveling at low velocities. It was discovered that the combination of card and back plane design was such that there was cross-talk across the reference ground between adjacent cards – and that's all the technical stuff I'm going to include!

The solution to this problem necessitated that the entire hardware system be replaced. Over the course of the next 12 months, the in-house technical team designed and built a new motion-control system that was backwardly compatible with the existing drive units. This required no modifications to the building infrastructure, solved the erratic movement problems, and was reasonably priced. In addition to having to construct this system within a specific budget, the choice had previously been made to fabricate the unit in-house, in order to use the knowledge gained during its construction for future operation, repairs and modifications. The programmer who originally wrote the software was engaged to write an upgraded version. Although it had been discussed, the system was not improved to a full closed-loop operation due to the additional costs and necessary infrastructure changes that would have been required. This new system did not use proprietary cards from a single manufacturer. Instead it was based around industry-standard PCs, Pentium class, and used off-the-shelf, industrial-grade input/output cards, back planes, power supplies and other components. In this way the future operability of the system was not tied to the fortunes of one particular manufacturer. Replacement components could be obtained from a number of manufacturers, or from local electronic supply houses, which reduced downtime and minimized expense. The components that were finally selected had had the benefit of significant research and development efforts by their manufacturers, as they were designed to perform a specific function within a myriad of possible systems, not in only one specific system. Thus they were one unit among hundreds of thousands that had been built, not one unit from a handful. The operational results indicate that the initial decisions during that project were well founded. The new motion-control system has been in use for the last six years without incident, although I think now it's getting quite difficult to find replacement Pentium 75 processors and an upgrade may be required soon.

Along with standardization, I believe that the identification of the weakest link (no jokes!) in a system is another key to preventing costly failures. I am certain you are all familiar with what an EP-Rom is, a small erasable, programmable read-only memory chip, and this chip can be custom-programmed by the manufacturer to run software code and carry out a wide variety of different functions. These chips are not tremendously expensive to manufacture, usually costing in the States about $50 (£30, €42). But the important question is not: 'How much does a given EP-Rom cost?' It is: 'How much is it worth?'

Well, like in comedy, that depends on timing. Let me relay a story about the motion-control system used in the O Theater, Cirque's show running at the Bellagio Hotel. If I seem to be reciting a lot of anecdotes about motion-control systems; don't get me wrong, they just make very good examples! In the production of O, the central motion-control processor relies on an EP-Rom to act as a hardware lock, which verifies that the correct licenses have been purchased by the end-user for the different motion-control modules in use in a given system. In effect, it's a kind of electronic security guard.

Unfortunately, one day a series of unrelated failures were repaired which, by creating a current surge, burned out this key EP-Rom. Now as you may have guessed, there was no spare EP-Rom on hand, as it had not been previously identified as a critical spare component. Without a monitoring system to verify the authenticity of the licenses, the show control system would not work. O was – please excuse the pun, Richard – dead in the water. Given that O's theoretical box-office sales for one day are approximately $396,000 (£241,000, €336,000) and the actual daily sales figures have averaged about 99% since opening day, the operations staff was faced with a simple choice: send the audience for that day packing, or call up their controls vendor along with a very friendly charter jet company, and get moving – literally. The cost of having the vendor burn a new EP-Rom on a rush basis was minimal; however the cost for the charter jet to deliver the chip from the factory to Las Vegas from the US east coast that afternoon was over $60,000 (£37,000, €51,000). And yet the decision was ridiculously simple, for at the end of the day the show had minimized its losses and was more than $330,000 (£204,000, €285,000) to the good. I don't mean to imply that $60,000 is small change; even by Las Vegas standards that's still something. However, the real question is how many spare EP-Roms – or, more importantly, how much additional system documentation – could have been obtained for that same $60,000 price tag?

In most projects, there is an overwhelming desire to reduce what are often seen as ancillary costs, especially when the base price of these complex systems keeps rising. This is one example of the frequently observed battle between the capital budget, which is required to build the facility, and the operating budget, which is required to keep it going. As-built drawings, vendor-recommended spare-parts lists, and vendor-recommended preventive maintenance schedules, are all things that are critical to the longevity and maintainability of a system. They are also normally a contractual requirement for a particular system. But the reality is that many times, as the project nears handover, the vendor has either run out of money, interest, time, or all of the above, in order to deliver fully on that contractual requirement. Usually at the same time the owner or their representative is also having to deal with the handover of the building and the systems and with mounting pressures to either start rehearsals or get the show open. They can frequently be focused on other priorities and things do fall through the cracks.

Yet, as this example shows, a better understanding of the key system components, and better long-term planning, would have kept a significant amount of money – probably the better part of a department head's annual salary – in the bank. I can only urge us all to be vigilant when it comes to the handover process. The theme park industry is dogged in completing the documentation process, keeping some employees on for as much as a year following a park's opening to complete the documentation system. Even then, it's not perfect.

Cirque du Soleil has created an international reputation by pushing the boundaries of the theatrical experience. One of their first shows, as I mentioned, was *Le Cirque Réinventé*, or *The Circus Reinvented*. I might go farther and say that Cirque has actually reinvented the notion of opera for the 21st century, which combines music, dance, acrobatics, lighting, sound, scenic design and wardrobe in a way that talks directly to the modern audience's emotions and spirit, bypassing the barrier of language. I wonder if Wagner would have liked it? In the near future, Cirque du Soleil will continue this trend and refine another existing genre, the adult cabaret. This past Thursday, Cirque du Soleil and the MGM Grand Corporation held a joint press conference in Las Vegas in which they announced a new partnership for entertainment. The core announcement was that Cirque du Soleil will create two new shows for MGM Properties in Las Vegas in the years 2003 and 2004. At the New York New York Hotel Casino Michael Flatley's Celtic dance odyssey of *Lord of the Dance* will be closing on July 28th this year. In its place, the Cirque du Soleil will present its own reincarnation of the

cabaret, bringing in a cutting-edge adult-oriented cabaret style performance to the Las Vegas script.

This new show is scheduled to open around July 1st 2003. The Jerry Harris special effects extravaganza *EFX* at the MGM Grand Hotel will close in late 2002. To take its place, Cirque will create a heroic tale which is based on mankind's greatest epic myths. This show will be directed by the internationally renowned Robert Lepage, himself no stranger to the theater community, having acted in, and directed, major performances in North America, Europe and Asia. The new show at MGM is scheduled to open around April 1st 2004.

This announcement comes in the midst of a significant expansion of the theater market in Las Vegas; it has not, just yet, reached saturation. Within the same two-year time frame, two other major shows will be throwing their hats into the Las Vegas ring: Celine Dion's performance at the 4,000-seat Caesar's Palace Colosseum Theater and Steve Wynn's new 1,800-seat Le Rève Theater. Incidentally, both of these new shows will be directed by Franco Dragone who, up until recently, was Cirque's *metteur en scène*. Claude André Roy from Scèno Plus Consultants is with us for the Conference and Scèno Plus is providing the consulting services for these two venues.

Once these four shows have all opened in Las Vegas, excluding arena-style shows and supporting events, the number of seats for sale in Las Vegas production shows each week will approach 180,000. Of that total, Cirque du Soleil will be providing approximately 65,000, or 36%.

I am tasked at the moment with the supervision of the execution of the creative departments' vision for these shows. I like to describe myself as a quality control engineer. I thought you might like to share a quick glimpse at some of the preliminary concepts for the new Cirque cabaret-influenced show at the New York New York Casino. This will give you an idea of some of the planning aspects of Las Vegas theaters. Currently the *Lord of the Dance* theater, the Broadway theater is located adjacent to a food court which is themed to look like the streets of New York city. The existing box office and main entrance are situated along a short alleyway that has

Image of the new box office and theatre entrance.

Theatre and interior design concepts created by Cirque du Soleil ®

architecture for the new entry will look like. As you can see, the box office is being pulled forward into the open area of the food court, allowing the signing and advertising marquee to be seen along two main traffic corridors within the casino proper.

As this is a renovation of an existing building, there are some significant constraints, both physical limitations and contractual obligations regarding the casino's existing tenant base, which cannot be overcome. One of these is the availability of space for retail opportunities. It has often been said that the main reason theme parks are built is in order to sell corporate merchandise. The sales numbers I've heard from the Universal Studios theme park in Osaka, Japan seem to bear this out. Over the first three months of operation, merchandise sales on a *per capita* basis almost equaled the *per capita* ticket price for entrance into the park. Although that particular reference is for a theme park, merchandise sales are becoming more and more important in generating revenue for all manner of performing-arts organizations, including festivals, performing arts centers and individual production companies. As designers of performing-arts venues we must include in the design process a way to account for this important revenue stream.

little competing retail or merchandise outlets thus providing a relatively straightforward access to the theater. However the box office location is hidden within existing themed architecture and so has a relatively low profile. If you don't know where it is, it's hard to find. In addition, the main entrance on the inside of the lobby to the stalls is being relocated, and the existing box office setup would create a very short and congested path into the theater. In order to address these two shortcomings, the main lobby entrance is being moved to the opposite side of the theater envelope.

Now the downside of this choice is that queuing prior to the doors opening will run through the food court area. The existing tenants of the food court may find this an unexpected boon to their sales, with over 12,000 guests passing by each week in a new traffic flow. However, operationally an important issue with queuing will be maintaining the necessary legal clearances for the fire exit which will be adjacent to the new box office. One other consideration with this new location is that one of the hotel tower elevator cores is immediately adjacent to the new theater entrance. However, given the improved visibility of the box office, these difficulties can be overcome with some careful operational planning.

The hallway at the center of the existing theater entrance leads to a retail store which will be removed and renovated into the new main theater entrance. Meanwhile the chicken restaurant on the right hand side will become the new box office area. The artist's rendering shows what the base

The space allocated to retail for the new project is less than ideal, as it will be nestled between the main entrance and box office. This has reduced marketing visibility, but interchanging the locations of box office and retail, which is the retail manager's first choice by the way, would create an unacceptable bottleneck before and between performances. Standard policy in Las Vegas is two performances per night, with an hour and a half window between close of one show and the start of the next – it's all about throughput. Thus placing the retail outlet here is making the best of a bad situation. There is, however, the possibility that in future some satellite retail locations will become available as leases when those of other existing tenants expire. In order to cope with the imposition of this compromised location, one design detail being considered is to provide a direct access into the retail area from the lobby which would only be used after each performance. The retail manager's assessment is that providing this

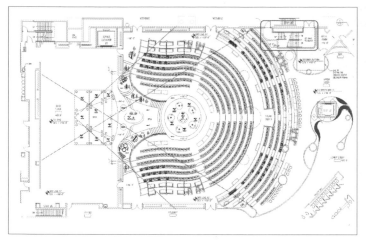 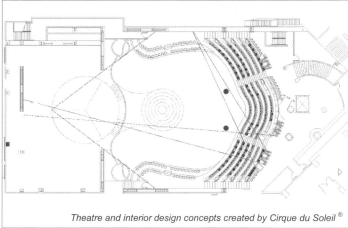

Theatre and interior design concepts created by Cirque du Soleil ®

modification could boost retail sales in the store by 25%. This will also help facilitate clearing the house between performances which, as I mentioned, has a 90-minute window. Unfortunately, there are two potential drawbacks with this solution. The first is that additional ushers will obviously be required to monitor this area and prevent patrons without tickets from coming back into the theater between shows. The second is that Nevada tax law requires an additional 10% tax be levied on all goods sold after the point at which the ushers collect the patron's ticket. By creating a direct link between the theater lobby and the retail area, this could have implications regarding the interpretation of that tax law, and create unwanted additional tax liabilities.

An important facet of previous Cirque performances has been that of audience participation and interaction. Usually this has been in the form of one or more patrons being invited on stage to join the artistes and letting them share the limelight for a few minutes. This concept will be further enhanced in the new show. The interior of the lobby and theater will be designed to create a rich, organic, sensual and inviting environment that encourages the audience to participate from the moment they walk through the main lobby doors. Exploring the environment, making use of all five senses, the architecture will envelop the audience, with straight lines and right angles being minimized wherever possible. These will be replaced with flowing curves and organically inspired shapes. As the design process develops it's going to be very interesting to see how this interface between the interior lobby concept and the external food court, with its New York theme, develops.

As I mentioned earlier, this show will be Cirque's reinvention of the cabaret, designed for an adult audience, which will combine dance, acrobatics and multimedia elements. The show will follow in the footsteps of famous cabarets such as the *Crazy Horse* and *Folies Bergères* in Paris, although with its own unique Cirque style. As such, it will be a new challenge for Cirque, which has up till now been focused on more family-oriented performances, although some people have thought that some of our shows have been relatively dark and adult-oriented in the past. The theater style will be a fusion of Art Nouveau, Parisian Salon, Erté and MC Escher. In addition, in various areas throughout the theater, a series of sensual or erotic images will be integrated into the architecture. Ideas include using oriental-style saké glasses with lenses at the bottom, so you can see an image at the bottom of your drink, or the images might be built into the bar or counter top so that if you set the glass down you can magnify whatever has been printed there; perhaps with different glasses for ladies and men!

The moldings between different surface finishes and the frames around artwork may also have custom-sculpted details. It was even suggested that the toilet paper might be printed with different images from the *Kama Sutra*! If that's the case it will probably make great retail item – but we're worried that it might be hard to get guests out of the toilets. One initial idea in order to reinforce the motion of curves was to install a giant spiral staircase in the lobby to provide access to the elevated rear stalls and balcony. Unfortunately building codes in Las Vegas do not allow this, and a curved escalator was not feasible. So the design team fell back on to a pair of curved grand staircases, each leading to one of the levels

Plans of the stalls and balcony of the new theatre showing the large thrust stage.

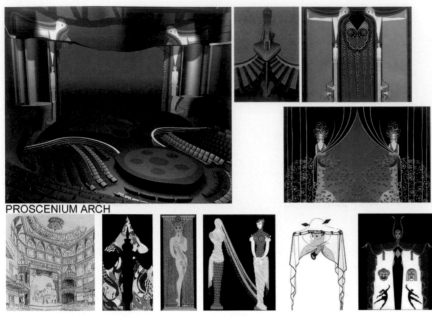

PROSCENIUM ARCH

Above and below: some of the interior design concepts considered for 'New York New York'.

Theatre and interior design concepts created by Cirque du Soleil ®

FLOOR PROJECTIONS AND ANAMORPHOSIS

above. The staircase leading to the rear stalls will arrive at an upper lobby six feet (2 metres) above the main lobby. On this level there will be a small bar at the back of house, and an elevated performance stage for use before or during the show. This is another example of having to accommodate the impositions of an existing building. The performance stage will, in fact, be the roof of the main command center for the hotel's fire prevention and protection systems. As it was totally impossible to move all those systems, we're now making a stage, rather than a silk purse, from a sow's ear!

The second grand staircase in the lobby will lead directly to the balcony, 22 feet (6.7 metres) up. Under this staircase will be hidden a small performance area, or a 'happening stage', which will be a reward for those patrons curious enough to fully explore the lobby environment prior to curtain up. On the balcony level, there will be a second bar area which, like all the bars in the theater, will remain open for service throughout the show. For Cirque, this is a departure to incorporate bars into the performance space, but they are intended to encourage the guests, once again, to interact with the environment during the performance.

Back downstairs in the lobby, the walls themselves will be made of a translucent material, perhaps fiberglass if we can meet Building Code, or resins. These walls will be backlit to allow for shifting, colored lighting patterns that will help create a sense of movement within a relatively small space. The carpet will also have a texture and texture design that echoes the fluid lines of the ceiling suspended above. This ceiling will be created by an undulating sculptural form, using translucent resins which are suspended from the balcony slab above. Its design will be intended to evoke an image of strained muscle tissue, or of flowing water. You can understand that the original concept for this design was to be "under the petticoats". This sculptural form will be used as a projection surface from both above and below. It will have openings and varying capacities to function as a giant gobo when lit from above, creating patterns on the floor which, with moving lights, will also be able to move. The reality is we also need to accommodate the required sprinklers, audio lines and other building mechanical services in that space. The fluctuations in height in the ceiling are also meant to suggest the interior of a body cavity, and to enhance the feeling that the guests are traveling through something organic, not just a theater ante-chamber. Along the right side of the lobby walls, portholes will indicate the locations of interactive sensory displays which will be designed to challenge the guests to take a risk and explore a new and unknown sensory experience, such as "Listen to this sound" or "The oldest thing, look at this". I don't know what 'this' is yet; I'll let you know!

Above the bar, which is situated at the far end of the lobby and across from the main entrance, a sphere – the design team calls it 'the womb' – will float over the guests and be covered with a series of undulating projections, further enhancing the feeling of movement in the space. Mirrors and reflective wall surfaces will play an important role in the design of both the lobby and the performance. Playing with perspective, as in fun-house mirrors outside the bathrooms, and using mirrors to redefine the relationship of audience to stage, placed over and around the audience, plays an important role for this particular director. A rich acoustic soundscape will envelop the guests as they proceed on their voyage of discovery from the main entrance of the theater to their seats. Separate audio zones within the lobby will provide a variety of stimulus meant to evoke an emotional response – body sounds, breathing, whispering, wind, water, are all possibilities that are under discussion. I even heard that the toilet stalls (cubicles) threaten to provide a unique and intriguing experience, all the while respecting the appropriate local health and safety codes, of course. Perhaps the urinals will whisper 'Whee, whee, whee,' when being used, which you could think of as English scatological humor, a French pun, and a Scottish editorial commentary simultaneously.

At various locations in the lobby, 70s-inspired intimate banquette-style seating area will provide opportunities to people-watch both overtly and covertly. Inside the theater, the seating theme will continue with the different styles of seats ranging through traditional theatrical-style seats, theater seats with lip and heart-shaped appliqués spread across four adjacent seats, reclining Lazy-boy chairs in the front row for patrons who want to get up close to the action (sightlines are an issue), special seats at the ends of aisles providing

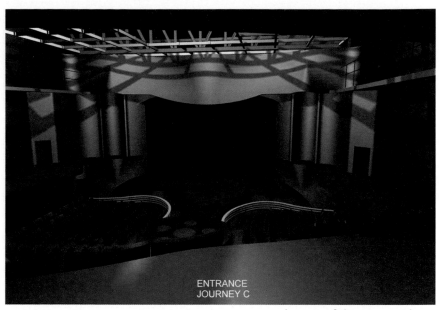

ENTRANCE
JOURNEY C

Image of the proscenium and stalls showing the different seating types.

Theatre and interior design concepts created by Cirque du Soleil ®

greater comfort in overall design, and love seats for couples who don't want an armrest to get in the way of togetherness.

The bar stools which will be used at the back of house and on the transverse balconies, and also seats at the end of aisles, may be designed as hands, if they can be made comfortable enough. Another item that will reinforce the idea of physicality in the theater is the custom-printed fabric that will be used on the various seats. Currently the idea is to use a well-known painting from a Turkish bath scene and imprint sections of that image on individual, or across groups of, seats. Once the fabric is installed, the various patterns will create a general organic feeling across the seating area in the stalls.

The existing theater is a standard proscenium house, seating approximately 1,400 patrons in the stalls area and in a single balcony. I've not heard the reason behind why the original central aisle was placed off-center and while there must have been a good one, it does make getting your bearings in the place kind of difficult. If we kept this we would have to see that the dancers have a good spotting light!

The major design change for the new stage will be the addition of a large thrust downstage of the existing stage apron. This will result in a configuration which, in many ways, is the standard Cirque du Soleil stage. This configuration can be found in two of the other resident shows, *Mystère* in Las Vegas and *La Nouba* at Florida, and five of the touring shows

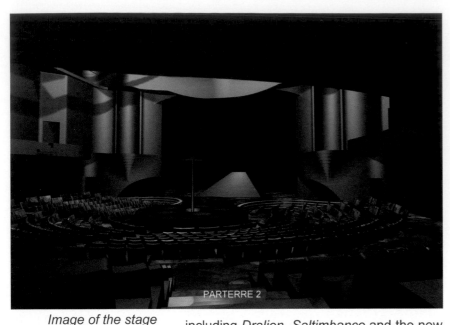

PARTERRE 2

*Image of the stage
from the parterre.*

*Theatre and interior design concepts
created by Cirque du Soleil ®*

this theater cannot be seen from the balcony. The creative team will have to work very hard to ensure that the audience in the balcony are always getting the same level of performance as those in the stalls.

The new balcony seating plan shows new transverse balconies running along the sides of the audience chamber, reminiscent of a traditional lodge box but with bar-stool seating. In order to accommodate the new sightlines to the thrust with a smaller rake, the number of balcony rows has been cut nearly in half, from twelve to seven, and the face of the balcony maintains the flowing curves which are an integral part of the interior architectural design. As you can see in the section of the existing theater, the steeply raked balcony would make any West End theater gods-dweller feel right at home. The control room is currently located on the fourth floor, which works well in this existing configuration, but the desire to have multiple live cameras and projection sources throughout the new showroom makes this location impractical for Cirque. There is currently a single star trap-style lift and a small support area in the basement housing some dressing rooms and wardrobe, but with no trap room at all to speak of.

The new cross section shows the reduction in size, elevation and rake of the new balcony. In addition, a number of technical galleries will be added, running along the sides of the stage and the audience chamber. The control room is being lowered to the third floor, which creates additional working space for the show's administrative and support staff. A trap room is being added to service the stage-lift machinery, and provide performer access from understage. Another significant change is the addition of a technical grid, to be used also by performers, over the entire expanse of the audience chamber. This new level will be a structural grid used to install the front of house rigging equipment, winches and related scenic elements, capable of supporting an anticipated load of approximately 100,000 lbs (44,600 kg). The performer grid will be the primary technical working area for the majority of the cast and crew throughout the show. Flying stages, scenic elements, catwalks and acrobatic equipment that complement and interface with the machinery involved in the stage floor will originate from here.

including *Dralion*, *Saltimbanco* and the new *Varekai* which opened in April. By adopting this basic stage form, the creative team has immediately an innate familiarity with the space, understanding the shorthand which describes what is and is not possible, although one change for this production is that the musicians who are usually sequestered at the rear or the sides of the stage have been moved front and center in a more traditional orchestra-pit style. This will allow them to have greater interaction with the performers onstage and with the audience.

The new seating configuration will hold approximately 1,260 guests, split 70:30 between the orchestra (stalls) and the single balcony. The official plans of the new stalls area shows the different types of seats identified by the different colors in different areas, and shows the hearts and lips on the seats.

The existing balcony has an asymmetrical upper level that makes the acoustic treatment of the room very difficult. The lower balcony sections will be significantly redesigned due to the introduction of the thrust stage. Given the addition of this thrust, the balcony had to be redesigned in order to maintain the minimum operational seating capacity of the room. This is the first time the Cirque will have incorporated a balcony into its theater designs and, in many ways, this will be one of the greatest challenges for Cirque's creative team. This is because one location that has traditionally been a prime staging area for audience interaction is the cross aisle between the two stalls sections, which in

The thrust stage itself will house a main turntable which was initially designed to be a lift also but is now fixed at stage level. The turntable will itself hold an additional six small lift/turntable units which we call 'pods', which allow performers, scenery and props to be loaded from the trap room below. Upstage of this turntable unit will be a small pool, which is really a tongue-in-cheek reference to the show down the street, at the *O Theater*.. We prefer to call it a 'hot tub' because the word 'pool' tends to scare the general contractor.

Unfortunately, as with many renovation projects, the limits of the existing construction have imposed themselves on the design of these lifts and the depths available for the trap room. We recently discovered that there are approximately 75 high-voltage supply and emergency power conduits running directly under the slab in the area of the new thrust stage – thus the importance of as-built drawings! While the New York New York management is very supportive of the project, they're not that keen on inconveniencing their guests for a month while the electrical mains are rerouted. Oh yes, and such a move would be *very* expensive.

The pictures show the preliminary design of the lift mechanics before the problem in the trap room was identified; these designs are currently under revision with the intent of maintaining as much of the original performance criteria as possible. Onstage, a series of three primary lifts will carry embedded stair scenic elements which can assume multiplicity of forms with variable-pitch stairs running down into the trap room or up from the stage in either the up or

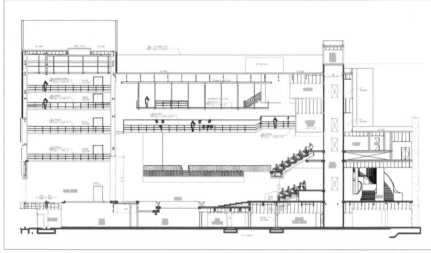

down stage directions. Overhead, the existing 58 counterweight sets will be maintained, with the addition of 25 motorized winches providing power assist, thereby reducing the number of operating crew.

Acoustically, the theater is being treated to create a very dead space, which is a bit of a departure for Cirque. In part this is due to the desire to have a series of interior wall treatments that allow the volume of the audience chamber to be varied by a system of breathing walls. The concepts for this system are in development, but they could be air-filled bladders, mechanical cams or a combination of these and other systems. This idea, in combination with the preponderance of flown elements from the performer grid, virtually precludes the use of standard architectural finishes to achieve the requested RT60 of approximately 1.4 seconds. Oops – sorry; more technical jargon!

Section through 'New York New York' showing the extent of the staging and rigging facilities.

Theatre and interior design concepts created by Cirque du Soleil ®

Views of the stage from the balcony on left and from parterre on right, showing the 'pods' and the retracting stairways.

Theatre and interior design concepts created by Cirque du Soleil ®

In addition, Cirque has had problems developing a feeling of community within the audience, in particular in the Bellagio Theater. The volume of the space and the distance to surfaces capable of supporting an early reflection from the audience are too great. The height of the performer grid over the audience creates a return sound path of greater than 90 ft (27.4 metres), resulting in a smeared reflection of the audience sound and a feeling of isolation for many of the audience. In order to create a feeling of community and participation by early reflections, an electronic processing system for acoustics such as L-RES or VRAS has been proposed. Recently a VRAS system was added to the audio system at the Bellagio Theater and has proven itself to be very beneficial in improving the audience's involvement with the environment. In addition to providing remedial control of the base room acoustics, a system such as this will allow Cirque's sound designer, Jonathan Deans, to adjust the room acoustics on an act by act basis throughout the show, thus either matching or contrasting the intimacy or extravagance of the room, based on the performance onstage. This ability will complement the director's previously stated desire to play with the visual perspective by creating an auditory analogue.

Motion control will be provided by an industry-standard system. I have a feeling that representatives of a number of companies who manufacture such systems are here at the Conference and probably want to talk to me about my earlier anecdotes! Control will be distributed by using standard internet protocols and cabling, which will allow for the use of simultaneous master and local controllers on a single network. The lighting system will be relatively standard, although the requirement for flexibility coupled with a relatively tight budget will have twelve racks of 96 dimmer circuits, that is approximately 1,200 circuits, serviced by only 672 dimmer modules. As patch bays have fallen out of favor, Cirque's approach results in essentially using the dimmer module as a virtual patch cord to select and use a particular circuit. This allows us to reduce the capital expense at the initial acquisition but maintain the flexibility of the system. As the requirements for additional lighting grows, dimmer modules can be added as required.

With that quick "glimpse under the petticoats", as it were, of the upcoming Cirque du Soleil cabaret style production I'd like to thank you all for your great kindness in letting me talk to you today, and to Richard Brett, the Conference Director, for inviting me to this Conference. I wish you all the best and am looking forward to meeting many of you over the next three days, and engaging in further discussions. Ω

Richard Brett introducing the speakers at the Keynote Session in the main Lecture Theatre of the Institution of Electrical Engineers in Savoy Place.

Photo: Jerôme Maeckelbergh

Stage elevator mechanisms

Chairman: Jeff Phillips, Project Manager and Consultant, Royal Opera House
Speakers: Stuart Wilson, Technical Manager, Waagner-Biro Stage Systems (UK)
            Robert Heimbach, President, Gala Theatrical Equipment
            Said Lounis, President, Serapid International

Introduction: Jeff Phillips

Lifts without boreholes: my grown-up daughter asked, "What are they?" I think I managed to explain what they are! But I suppose it is just that, until you need to plan a lift installation, you don't really realise what needs to go underneath the platform. And not only do you need the lift to rise up cleanly, without very much visible support, but also you normally don't want to spend a lot of money drilling big holes down into the ground to put in guides or pistons or whatever, to push and to guide the lift up and down. And guiding, synchronisation and stroke are only some of the challenges that also have to be overcome. The speakers on our panel today all have experience of different ways of achieving elevators which can operate from a flat-floor slab without boreholes or wasting any depth.

Without more ado, I'll introduce Stuart Wilson who is Technical Manager at TeleStage (which is now part of Waagner-Biro) and he's going to explain some tried and tested methods.

First speaker: Stuart Wilson

For many years the cost-effective solution for elevator mechanisms was perceived to be that based upon screw-jacks. In the basic system, the screw is carrying the load and in compression and is driven through a rotating nut in a fixed gearbox which is normally mounted on the floor of the elevator pit. Such schemes usually require boreholes in the base of the elevator pit in which the retracted screw-jacks are stored. Typical arrangements with boreholes or with the screws within a building are indicated in Figures 1 and 2.

The main disadvantage of such schemes is that boreholes would be required, or, in buildings where the base of the pit is not the lowest level in the building, provision has to be made for storage of the lowered (retracted) screws, with a consequent reduction in space utilisation. In older, existing buildings which are being modified to include an elevator for some purpose (often an orchestra pit or forestage elevator), there can be the added problem of maintaining the damp-proof membrane, particularly in areas with a high water table.

Stuart Wilson has an HNC in Mechanical Engineering and is a Grad IE (Aust). He has many years' experience of mechanical engineering for theatres. He re-joined TeleStage Associates plc (now Waagner-Biro Stage Systems (UK)) in 1989 where he is Technical Manager and is involved with the design of structures, hydraulics and transmission systems for projects worldwide.

Diagrams of two screw-jack elevators.

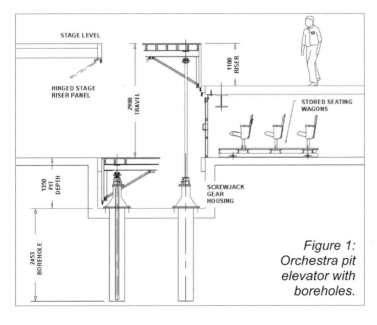

Figure 1: Orchestra pit elevator with boreholes.

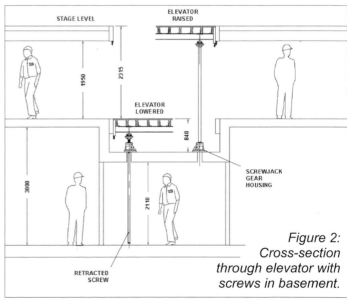

Figure 2: Cross-section through elevator with screws in basement.

Drawings by Waagner-Biro Stage Systems

Screw-jack elevators in the orchestra pit of the Grand Theatre, Swansea in Wales.

Photo: Peter Knowles

Screw-jacks are relatively inefficient, perhaps 25% compared with up to 92% in other systems, with consequently high input power requirements. This low efficiency does ensure that the drives are self-sustaining, which is generally considered a safety feature in that in the event of motor or control failure the lift will either stop in its current position or lower at very slow speed.

Alternatives to basic screw-jacks are available but, in many schemes, these are significantly more expensive. Amongst the most common alternatives are:

(a) Chain and wire-rope lifts
(b) Screw systems, using rotating screws, either top or bottom mounted
(c) Rack and pinion lifts
(d) Scissor lifts
(e) Ramps and wedge mechanisms
(f) Tubular thrust screws (Spiralift)
(g) Rigid chain systems (LinkLift).

The last two alternatives, (f) and (g), are covered in this session by other speakers and so now the principles behind (a) to (e) will be considered in some detail.

To provide a common base reference when reviewing the various alternatives, a platform with a size of 14 metres x 2.5 metres (45'-11" x 8'-3") giving a plan area of 35 m² (377 sq.ft) with static loading of 5 kN/m² (100 lbf/sq.ft) and dynamic (in motion) loading of 2.5 kN/m² (50 lbf/sq.ft) will be considered in each case.

Chain and wire-rope lifts

Figure 3 shows the way in which chains or wire-ropes can be used for a simple arrangement of a platform which moves between, say, a storage level and stage level. The elevator platform is suspended from ropes or chains, which are powered from a drive system in the base of the pit. External guides are required (not shown in the diagrams, for clarity) to ensure accurate travel alignment.

The attachment points of the platform for the ropes/chains have to remain below the top suspension pulley, with an allowance made for over-travel of the mechanism. The minimum pit depth required in this example is, therefore, made up of the depth of floor above the top pulley, the combined diameters of the pulleys, wire-rope and chain tensioning devices, and over-travel and clearances. A pit depth of perhaps 1.2 metres (4 ft) would typically be required.

It is interesting to note how the pit depth increases if the platform is required to travel 1.1 metres (3'-7") above stage level, with protection in the form of fascias fitted on one or more faces. The required pit depth increases by the depth of the fascia, to 2.3 metres (7'-7"). This is shown in Figure 4.

One difficulty sometimes experienced with this type of drive is unequal stretch in the wire-ropes or chains due to unequal loads.

Chain and wire-rope elevator systems.

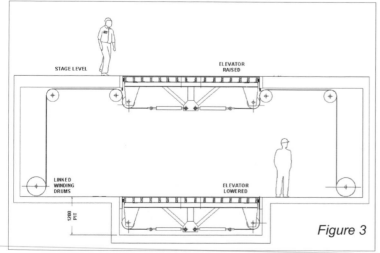

Figure 3

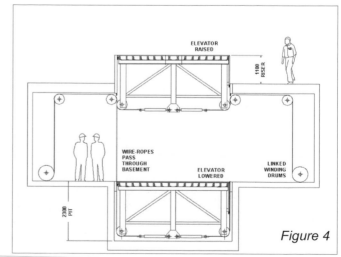

Figure 4

For this reason it is sometimes necessary to install locking pins to hold the platform in its required position if, for example, stage wagons are to run on and off the elevator at a particular level. Without locks the vertical position of the platform will change as load is either removed or added due to elastic strain in the wire ropes or chains.

High operating speeds are possible with this concept, but the drive is non-self-sustaining. Such systems employing wire-ropes or chains, and often with counterweights to balance part of the self-weight of the platforms, are used for major stage elevators by a number of companies.

Rotating screw systems

For platforms with relatively small travels, it is sometimes viable to utilise a rotating screw type of screw-jack shown in Figure 5. In this application the screw gearbox is bolted to the floor of the pit and the screw itself is rotated. The nut is built into the platform structure so that, as the screw rotates, the nut fixed to the moving structure lifts or lowers the platform. With this type of scheme and a travel of about 335 mm (around 12") a pit depth of perhaps 685 mm (2'-3") would be needed. Note that in this application the addition of a fascia does not require any increase in pit depth.

Another form of screw drive is the suspended screw arrangement shown in Figure 6. In this application the screw is in tension and is driven either at the bottom or at the top. Again, the nut is built into the platform structure and screw rotation results in vertical motion. This concept has the advantage that the risk of screw buckling due to compressive loads is eliminated. The screw can therefore often be of a smaller diameter.

Loads on the screw caused by the platform and payload are supported by a thrust bearing located below the stage surface. This in turn may be attached to the building structure at that point or, more usually, to a steel column which transmits the load to the base of the pit. This column often also acts as the platform guide. Minimum depth of pit required would be approximately 850 mm (2'-9"), and is independent of the travel distance.

Screw jacks are available as machine-cut 'square thread' screws, or as ball screws. The latter are more efficient, but less tolerant of a dirty environment. They are also significantly more expensive. For standard screws, operating speeds of up to 2.5 metres/min (8 ft/min) are possible, depending on the application. This is often satisfactory for orchestra pit and forestage lifts and other elevators which can be preset in position and are not moved during the performance.

Rack and pinion drives

For very heavy loads and long travels, rack and pinion systems can offer an economic solution.

In the normal application of this concept, the drive, including the pinions, is mounted within the platform structure, and the pinions engage with racks fixed to the pit shaft walls. The combined platform and drive climbs up the racks in the pit shaft. Obviously electrical power and control wiring has to be fed onto the platform through some flexible cable management system. This type of installation is shown in Figure 7 over the page.

Short travel screw-jack and suspended screw applications.

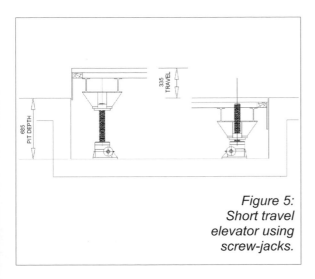

Figure 5: Short travel elevator using screw-jacks.

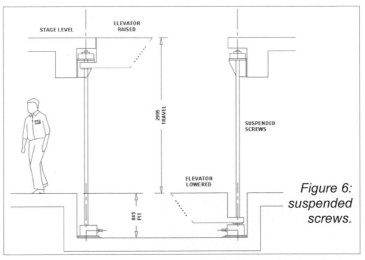

Figure 6: suspended screws.

Drawings by Waagner-Biro Stage Systems

Far right:
Standard scissor lifts at
an exhibition – beware
of the attraction of trying
to use a standard unit in
a theatre application.

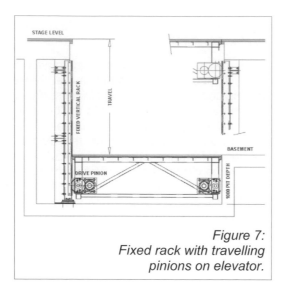

Figure 7:
Fixed rack with travelling
pinions on elevator.

Photo: Techplan

Operating speeds can be high, but, at higher speeds, noise can be significant. Speeds up to about 24 metres/min (80 ft/min) are common. The depth of pit required is influenced by the size of the drive and the overall depth of the moving platform, but minimum pit size would be typically 1 metre (3'-3"). Rack and pinion drives of this sort are often used for scenery or truck elevators as these applications offer the necessary pit walls for the racks.

This type of mechanism can also be used with free-standing rack columns which support the elevator platform. The racks are driven by pinions mounted in a special gearbox with reaction rollers to ensure engagement. The platform requires separate external guidance over its travel.

Scissor lifts

Scissor lifts are a well-established method of providing a lift to operate from a shallow pit, without boreholes, as shown in Figure 8. They may be powered by hydraulic cylinders, or by linear actuators operating between the pairs of scissor arms. Hydraulic schemes are probably the cheapest, but if the system is to be operated only infrequently, there can be reliability problems. Some scissor lifts are operated by screw-jack mechanisms.

The most significant characteristic of this type of elevator mechanism is that in the lowered position the mechanical advantage is very poor. Large forces are therefore required at the start of travel. Also, platform speed varies depending upon the position of the scissors. When the platform is in its lowest position the speed is minimum. When the scissors are at 90° to each other the speed is maximum. There are modified scissor-lift mechanisms available which provide constant speed and demand a constant power input throughout travel, but the added complexity for large lifts usually makes the cost prohibitive.

One distinct advantage of a scissor lift is that it is guided by the scissor-arm mechanism, and so can be used in an array of elevators without the need for external guides. This concept is therefore attractive in multi-platform installations where some platforms are remote from a structural wall.

Major moving-rack and
fixed-pinion drive by
Waagner-Biro on the
mainstage elevators in
the Gran Teatre del
Liceu in Barcelona.

Photo: Techplan

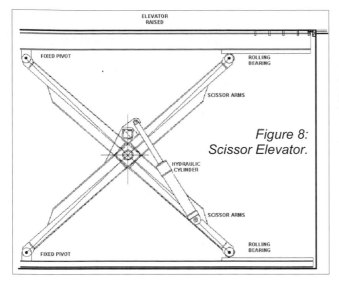

Figure 8:
Scissor Elevator.

Photos: Techplan

Ramps and wedge mechanisms

In some short-travel applications it is possible to use a wedge principle to create vertical travel as shown in Figure 9.

A horizontal force is applied to the wedge by the roller, and the platform rises. The large horizontal force transmitted to the platform must be resisted by the guides. In some applications it is possible to use opposing wedge actions which balance the horizontal forces, reducing the reactions transmitted to the building structure.

Closing comments

These are the most common forms of mechanisms used in theatre elevators, and it is important to note that each application should be considered individually. If you are in the position of specifying an elevator, consider all possibilities, not only the functional design parameters, but also the combined cost of the elevator installation and associated building costs. Ω

Photo: Tony Redmond

Orchestra pit / forestage scissor elevator for the Regent Theatre, Hanley on test outside the factory of Delstar Engineering.

Screw-driven scissor elevators in the Bridgewater Hall in Manchester as installed by TeleStage Associates in 1996.

Wedge mechanism for an equaliser elevator for the Opera Project in Copenhagen in Waagner-Biro's UK test workshop.

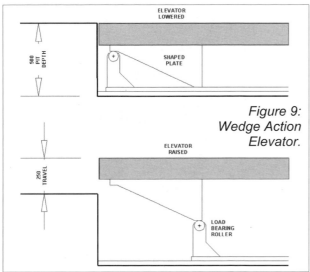

Figure 9:
Wedge Action
Elevator.

Drawing by Waagner-Biro Stage Systems

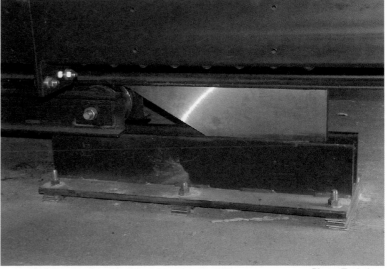

Photo: Techplan

Top: A Spiralift installation in Kwai Tsing Theatre in Hong Kong. Bottom: cut-away view of the 9" or 18" Spiralift.

Second speaker: Robert Heimbach

Gala Theatrical Equipment is the manufacturer of the Spiralift; we started in 1980 manufacturing equipment for theatres. And for theatre installations we've used many different systems – including hydraulic systems and cable systems – and most of our business is still using lifting elements or equipment that is outside the direct use of the Spiralift.

I will talk today about some of the technical parameters of Spiralifts. I won't go through in detail how the Spiralift works, but there is a description at the end of this paper. I will also be explaining some of the applications to which we find Spiralifts are well suited, and describing some of the design and safety features as well.

Photo: Techplan

There are three different sizes of Spiralift; there is a 9" and an 18" Spiralift, which are built on the main principle of 16 rollers and a helix, which can be seen in the cut-away section. As the cam-rollers are rotated through the chain drive, the Spiralift column will rise. There are two bands: a vertical band, stored in the magazine, and the horizontal band stored underneath, which together form the stainless steel column. The 6" Spiralift has its own worm-gear reducer built inside. Rotating the mechanism, through the worm reducer, raises and lowers the column.

Robert Heimbach is President of Gala Theatrical Equipment which is now trading as Gala Systems. Robert began his career as designer of commercial passenger and freight elevator systems for a Canadian Company, APV Inc. He joined Gala in 1992 and was part of the Research and Development team, developing electro-mechanical transformation systems for theatres and multi-use venues. He became Director of Engineering in 1997.

The raising capacity of the 6" (150 mm) unit is about 1.7 tons; that of the 9" (225 mm) unit is 4½ tons, and that of the 18" (460 mm) is 11 tons. The sustained (static) loading is higher – almost twice as much in each case. The travel distances vary from 3.6 metres (11'-10") for the 6" model, to 12.2 metres (40'-0") unguided for the 18". The lifting speed varies between 0.15 and 0.2 metres/sec (up to 8"/sec) and 12 metres/min (nearly 40 ft/min). And Spiralift efficiency goes from 70–80%.

TÜV Certification which was obtained in Berlin in April 2002.

We have just had a test certificate through in from TÜV in Berlin which was given on April 4th 2002; however most of our units that have been installed have each been individually proof-tested through the local regulatory boards.

I now want to talk about some various applications. We have 500 installations, in 40 countries, in which the Spiralift has been used.

Photo: Gala Theatrical Equipment

The use of the orchestra lift for storing audience chairs in the Kimmel Center for the Performing Arts, Philadelphia.

Photos: Gala Theatrical Equipment

A typical application is in Philadelphia, in the Kimmel Center for Performing Arts, and in this case the entire building was designed to rest on acoustic vibration pads, so perforating the elevator pit for screw-jacks or racks was not an option.

This hall has an orchestra lift that also has chair-storage capabilities. The lift lowers the front rows of chairs to chair-storage level, which is beneath the audience. The lift can be raised again to a mid level which would be an orchestra-playing level. Since this is a concert hall, the Philadelphia Opera usually raise it up and extend the stage for their productions.

Another application was the Beau Rivage Theater in Biloxi for Cirque du Soleil. They have a load-in stage lift where there is also a car park underneath a section of the stage, which is actually open to the elements. As this is adjacent to the Gulf of Mexico, every once in a while water comes in here and gets into the elevator pit. One of the specification clauses was that the pit will fill with water two or three times a year, and there is no getting around it. So we inverted the Spiralifts, put stainless steel plates in the bottom, and fitted the drive mechanism on the underneath of the steel construction of the moving platform. All the electrical connections and so on are wired

on an adjacent wall. As the lift comes up, obviously the entire drive system moves up with it. So the only thing, actually, exposed in the pit when it's in this upper configuration is the Spiralift column. So when they see a hurricane coming, they say, "Raise the lift, raise the lift." When the pit fills with water, because the stainless steel columns and the base plates are attached to the pit floor there is no damage. And it's happened several times already!

Drawing of the reverse-mounted Spiralifts for the load-in elevator in Beau Rivage, Biloxi.

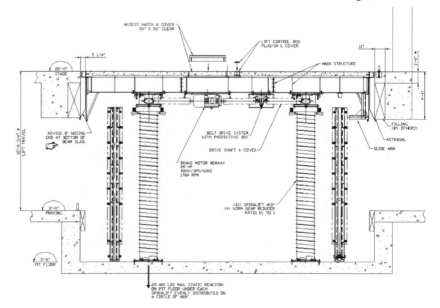

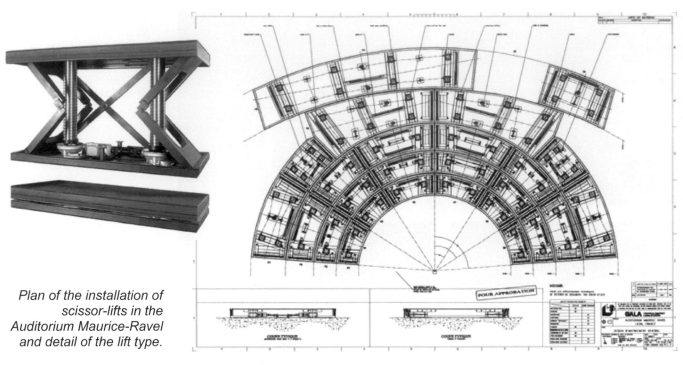

Plan of the installation of scissor-lifts in the Auditorium Maurice-Ravel and detail of the lift type.

The client's requirements in the Auditorium Maurice-Ravel were that within a lowered depth of 300 mm (12") they needed a very sturdy flooring and a static load of 750 kg/m² (150 lbs/sq.ft). Also the users weren't sure what kind of performance they would need the stage for, which required a very high specification. We installed 28 platforms here and they needed to be something compact with enough room to incorporate some strong integral guiding systems. The travel distances vary up to 1½ metres (4'-11") on some of these lifts.

View of the stage of "Mystère" by Cirque du Soleil with the thrust stage elevators lowered.

For *Mystère* by Cirque du Soleil at the Treasure Island Hotel in Las Vegas, there are two reasons that they used Spiralifts, other than the fact that they originally didn't want to drill boreholes. In Las Vegas, there is, believe it or not, a very high water table, and so they couldn't drill boreholes. The other reason was primarily due to the number of cycles it's used – six days a week, two shows a day; the lifts in Las Vegas have now run 200,000 cycles. We actually did remove two units, one about four years ago, and one about two years ago, for inspection, since this is one of our biggest-running lifts, and they both passed. And we're scheduled in the next year to take another one out, to take a look at it, but nothing has been replaced there; they're the original units, installed in 1992.

In the Kennedy Center in Washington, there is duct-work running in the pit, and there was no way of mechanically coupling the lift systems together. So we've put individual motors with encoders on the Spiralifts on the same platform and these are being raised and lowered by separate drive motors that are coupled only electronically. The signal from the motor revolutions can be relied on to maintain synchronization of the motors electrically. This is a very useful method of coping with such problems and in future we will often use this method of synchronizing drives.

Photo Gala Theatrical Equipment: courtesy Cirque du Soleil

Stage elevator mechanisms

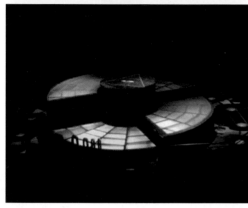

In the Hale Center Theater in West Valley City in Salt Lake City, the lifts have up to a 5-metre (16'-5") travel. These are all independent lifts, all independently guided, within a large sort of drum-revolve system. The centre lift, which is also independently guided, is 2 metres (6'-6") in diameter, and it also has a 5-metre travel. I've stood on top of it and moved from side to side; it's very stable, and the actors use it quite regularly.

The special drum stage in the Hale Center Theater in West Valley City uses many independently guided Spiralifts.

I would like to make the point that it's often impractical to put in many boreholes for some multi-use venues, but in some cases hundreds of lifts or hundreds of Spiralift units have been installed. The installation in Nara is a system that we've adapted and on which I will be giving a presentation in a later session. This raises individual rows of chairs and thus reconfigures a hall completely. In the installation shown on the right in Japan, each row requires as few as four 6" Spiralifts to support and changeover the seating.

Nara, Nara-Shimin Hall which changes its form using individual seating row elevators on Spiralifts.

Photos: Gala Theatrical Equipment

The Spiralift installation in the Kennedy Center in Washington uses electronic synchronisation to overcome services obstructions.

Photos: Gala Theatrical Equipment

Underneath the floor– left: the Nara Nara- Shimin Hall and right: showing the seat row mechanism and how the seats fold away.

Design features: as I have already said, in the Kennedy Center the motors driving the individual Spiralifts are electronically coupled. Another design feature is the ease of handling the 6" Spiralift with the smaller travel. It weighs just 25 kg (55 lbs), can be set in place by hand, and needs to be either grouted to the floor or to be fitted on steel beams; it is more suited for smaller orchestra lifts or smaller platforms. You can also couple motors directly to it. The connection to the drive system is very straightforward; direct motor coupling to the Spiralift or from the end of a drive shaft – and it can have a brake installed directly onto it. The 9" Spiralift, the HD9 unit, also has this integrated worm gear.

Some of the many installation configurations.

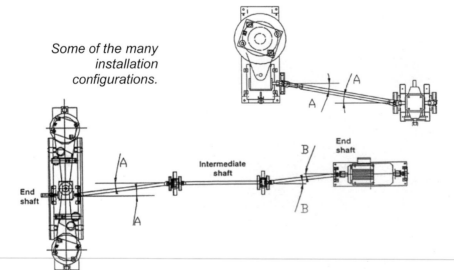

The other models, the 9" and 18" models, are normally installed on a pit floor, but can be fitted to a steel frame of some sort. Most of these units are installed using a low-ratio worm gear with an output shaft. The examples show a double installation base-plate with a chain-drive system to two units. If you had a rectangular lift of, maybe, 3 to 4 metres (9'-10" to 13'-2") in width, two of these units would probably be the most practical way of doing that installation. One of the advantages of Spiralifts is the travel. We can provide up to, again, 12 metres (40 feet) of travel with the 18" model.

To install the Spiralift to the steel platform structure, it is clipped to the top plate; you can move the Spiralift column up manually by putting a rod through the top plate and rotating it to the underside of the top plate. The aluminum die-cast top plate of the 6" Spiralift is attached to the structure, and then the column is mounted and fixed with set screws; when the spring is released the dead load of the structural frame is supported by the Spiralift.

Every drive system that comes out of our factory is pre-tested. We detect any obstruction which is in the way of the platform when it is coming down. We find this is a good design advantage; most lift systems will not do this. As the platform is coming down onto an obstruction, the top-plate safety mechanism circuit will open so that there's no damage to either any equipment underneath or to the drive system itself. If you did this with a screw-jack lift, unless it had similar built-in protective devices it would damage something. There are actually two plates. The top one is connected to the structure. The bottom plate is connected to the top plate of the Spiralift. And there's a spring exerting about 300 kg (660 lbs) of force pushing these plates apart, so that if you do get something obstructing the motion underneath the platform, the drive will shut off. The switch is connected to the safety system which will stop the drive system in the down direction; it is also controlled so that it can only move upwards after that.

The detailed drawings on the right show the switch set in position prior to activation. The cam can go through the first plate; the second plate will move down at a speed of 0.1 metres/sec (4"/sec). You probably have 20–30 mm (approx 1") displacement. Our top-plate design has the possibility of 100 mm (4") displacement before it disengages completely.

Attaching a Spiralift to the top plate and the platform structure.

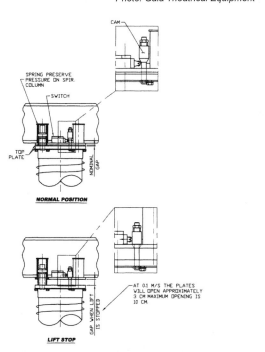

Photo: Gala Theatrical Equipment

No-load detector switch on top of Spiralift: Inset shows it un-operated and in the larger picture the switch has been operated by the downwards motion of the conical actuator.

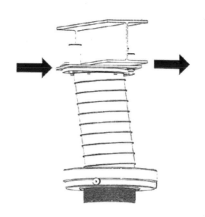

One of the advantages of the Spiralift system is that it has a pin connection between the top and the bottom of the Spiralift columns. When you move the Spiralift column it has 1½° of motion, so it's not a moment connection; it allows a certain amount of misalignment during installation. Obviously you try to get this as perpendicular as possible, but a pin connection, as opposed to any other system, doesn't increase wear.

Illustration of the degree of misalignment permitted during installation procedures.

Stage elevator mechanisms

Photo: Techplan

Underneath the Spiralift installation carrying the seating storage elevator with its marble floor in the Gran Ship Convention Center in Shizuoka, Japan.

Underneath the Spiralift installation in "Mystère" for Cirque du Soleil in Las Vegas.

Right: Spiralifts alongside screw-jack mechanisms in the Vanbrugh Theatre in the Royal Academy of Dramatic Art.

Spiralifts are a high-value product. We have been decreasing our production costs quite substantially. The Spiralift is now cheaper to produce, in actual dollars, than it was 12 years ago. There are about 1,000 units going out of our factories a year, and we are able to increase that with the introduction of the 6" Spiralift, which is an aluminum die-cast model. There is value also in the speed of installation, as well as in the small amount of reduction that's required in the drive system from a 1500-rpm motor to the appropriate input speed for the Spiralift model being used.

There are backstage trips arranged as part of the Conference where you will see Spiralifts. These include orchestra pit lifts in Sadlers Wells Theatre, concert risers in the Barbican Concert Hall, the orchestra-pit lifts in the Royal Opera House, and seating lifts in the Royal Academy of Dramatic Arts and in eight other venues in and around London.

Photo: Techplan

Finally, on the question of the installation of Spiralifts, we have been impressing upon most people that for safety reasons we require to install the entire drive system, or actually to manufacture the entire drive system; again everything is assembled and tested prior to delivery. However, there are now a number of key elevator contractors, to whom we will sell the Spiralift units individually, given certain sales conditions. If you are interested in this possibility I would be very pleased if you would contact me. Thank you. Ω

Photo Gala Theatrical Equipment: courtesy Cirque du Soleil

Third speaker: Said Lounis

Serapid has been in business for about 30 years. Since its inception, Serapid has specialized in transfer technology for heavy loads through the use of the Serapid Rigid Chain, the original product of the company, and its heart and soul. In the beginning, the original founders of the company, some of whom are still with us, practically had to create a whole new market for this innovative technology called the rigid chain, or push chain, or snake chain, or any other name that has been used to described this oxymoron, this contradiction, which allows us to 'push with a rope' so to speak. This spirit of creativity and innovation still lives with us today, and allows Serapid to enjoy a solid reputation as a problem solver in load-transfer technology.

Serapid has a staff of 80 people spread over five countries in two continents, a good 50% being engineers and technicians, working as a team because of a shared passion and enthusiasm for our technology. The stage and theater rigging market is relatively new for us, but it is becoming more and more a major portion of our business. Our other activities are spread out over many industries, mainly automotive and nuclear.

Serapid has centered its activity around Rigid Chain technology. Through product innovation, engineering and manufacturing excellence, Serapid is able to maintain its leadership in load transfer technology. Serapid engineers are known for innovative problem-solving of complex problems in linear transfer.

The three specific application areas that we specialize in are Horizontal Transfer Systems, Lifting Systems and Engineered Systems. For each of these areas, Serapid has developed unique products available either as off the shelf design, or through engineering and product integration.

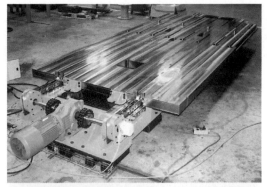

Photos: Serapid

Rigid Chain is magic. If we need a description, I suppose we can describe it like this: "A rigid mechanical telescoping column used to transfer heavy loads. This transfer can be horizontal or vertical."

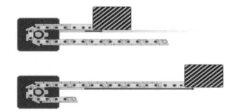

The basic use of a Rigid Chain is as a linear motion transfer device. It is composed of interconnected links with special plates which lock into each other to form a rigid bar or column. When the chain is run through the drive housing, it coils into a compact space for storage.

The three areas of specialisation of Serapid – Horizontal Transfer, Lifting Systems and Engineered Systems.

Said Lounis is the President of Serapid, an international company specializing in the movement of heavy loads using custom-made equipment. He was instrumental in moving the company into stage engineering where it has successfully produced stage and orchestra pit lifts and wagon movement systems. Said has 25 years' engineering experience in various fields and is a Registered Professional Engineer.

"Rigid Chain is magic."

Photos: Serapid

Illustrations of the basic form of LinkLift.

I mentioned earlier how when a load is applied to the chain it turns into a rigid steel bar. For this bar to remain true, each end of it has to be trapped; on one end, by the drive housing, on the other end, when the chain is attached to the load. We have therefore created a column rigid on both ends.

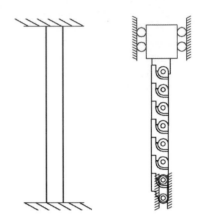

How does it work? It is actually very simple. By applying the load to the chain in a certain way, we create a locking moment.

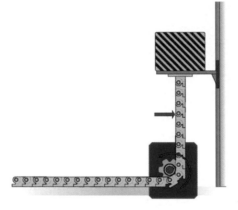

You can see by looking at this diagram that a rigid steel bar is created when the load is applied, yet when the steel bar is run through the drive, it coils like a chain, thus the name rigid chain.

Now before someone asks the question, I will ask it myself: "Can the chain buckle if a load is applied on the chain to open it?"

I was recently at a trade show in the US, where Serapid was exhibiting a lift platform. The first day of the show, probably 50 people asked us this question. So the next day, we brought a baseball bat, and anytime someone asked that question, we invited them to hit the chain as hard as they could, from whichever side they choose. Needless to say, this was a big home run with our visitors, and quite an annoyance with all the other exhibitors around us.

The answer is obvious. The chain does not open, and it will not buckle. Let me explain why.

"Can the chain buckle if a load is applied on the chain to open it?"

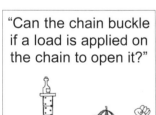

If a load is applied to open the chain, the chain will behave just like a steel column. It will deflect at the spot where the load is applied, and will transmit this deflection to both ends. This diagram shows that for the chain to fail, one of its ends needs to be allowed to rotate, which will not happen because they are rigidly attached. I hope I have now alleviated in your minds any fear of this happening, and that you will, from now on, look at Rigid Chain applications with serene confidence.

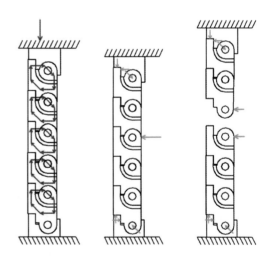

In the next part on the history of the company I will explain how we came about developing the LinkLift, the newest stage and orchestra lift system in the industry.

Stage elevator mechanisms

This scissor lift table is many years old, and has done in excess of 7 million cycles in a very demanding industrial environment. It is not retired yet; it was sent to us for a 7 million cycles overhaul. It is now back in its home, happily lifting and lowering, day in day out, 16 hours a day, in an automotive plant.

So what is so particular about this table? Well, it lifts 2 tonnes (4480 lbs) of weight travels at 200 mm/sec (8"/sec) provides positioning accuracy within ½ mm (0.2"), AND the lifting device is a Rigid Chain.

Serapid has been making Rigid Chain lifting systems for the better part of 20 years. So we are not new to this technology. Our customers include, Renault, Peugeot, Volkswagen, Mercedes Benz, etc, and some handling of very dangerous nuclear material in France and in the UK .

About 10 years ago, I worked with Mr. LinkLift, who was then known as Bob Watson, in the United States, to try and apply the Rigid Chain technology to stage lifting. Try as we might, the product at the time did not have the technical characteristics needed for stage lifting applications, the primary flaw being that it did not have the column strength for higher elevations. We did do some stage lifting over the years, especially in cruise ships, but it was marginal.

Finally, in 1997, Serapid decided to invest heavily in research and development, and the very first project that was given top priority was to develop a mechanical telescoping column that met the criteria for stage lifting.

These criteria were:

Height: Ability to raise loads to at least 6 metres (20 ft).

Load: Ability to lift a minimum of 5 tonnes and hold a minimum of 10 tonnes with industry approved safety margins.

Safety: A column that is safe by design, as safe as a rigid tube.

Quietness: A system that can operate without alerting the audience.

Speed: Fastest speed possible.

Cost: Competitive with existing technology.

One year later, in January 98, the LinkLift was born. It exceeded our objectives of load, speed, noise level. It uses patented technology and has been independently tested and certified by TÜV for personnel elevators. It meets stringent safety standards.

So what is LinkLift and how does it differ from existing Rigid Chain?

Rigid Chain is composed of specially shaped links that mate into each other to form a rigid steel column. When the links run through the drive housing, they coil into a compact magazine.

The differences that make LinkLift are the:

- Load bearing surfaces
- Column effect
- Double pins

There are two different Rigid Chain drive concepts:

1. The conventional drive system for Rigid Chain is driven like any other chain-sprocket assembly, with the chain looping around the sprocket as shown on the right here.

> "What was missing was high loads and high elevations"

Photos: Serapid

LinkLift under test in the Serapid factory in France.

2. The LinkLift drive is a Back Drive.

The Back Drive system is a Serapid innovation, the heart of the LinkLift concept. In this drive the chain does not loop around the sprocket, but is driven in a straight line, the sprocket is located in the back of the chain.

Photos: Serapid

- Driving the chain in a straight line has allowed the development of a special tooth profile. This special profile smoothes out the speed curve, giving a much more **uniform and jerk-free movement**, and **reduces noise and vibration** significantly.

- Locating the sprocket in the back of the chain as shown has allowed the creation of a column effect. As you can see, the chain plates sit flat against each other, holding the chain in one direction. The sprockets, in the back, hold the chain in the other direction, creating a load-bearing surface almost as large as the chain cross-section.

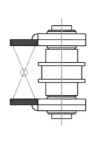 

The Serapid installation by Protech Theatrical Services in the Dorothy Chandler Pavilion, Los Angeles. This project incorporated 24 no. LiftLink 100 units.

The difference between the old Rigid Chain design and the LinkLift is shown in the pictures above. The picture on the left shows a 60 pitch chain and its bearing surface in red. The picture on the right shows a 50 pitch LinkLift with its bearing surface in red.

Stage elevator mechanisms

The noise measurement shown on the right, taken by an independent sound laboratory, attest to the fact that the LinkLift is one of the quietest lifts manufactured. These measurements were taken without a motor, as the motor is often the noisiest component.

In terms of smooth running, the black profile on the lower graph shows a typical cordal effect, while the magenta profile shows a LinkLift speed profile, which is a smooth curve with little amplitude. However, in theory, the amplitude should actually be zero, as the chain is driven in a straight line like a rack and pinion.

To summarise, the benefits of LinkLift Rigid Chain technology are:

- Speed: up to 300 mm/sec
- Quietness: low noise level
- Very low maintenance (static column)
- Totally reliable and stable
- Inherently safe by design: column bolted to floor and to platform.

LinkLift has significantly improved on existing art. I will finish by illustrating below some of the applications of both vertical and horizontal motion in the theatre. Ω

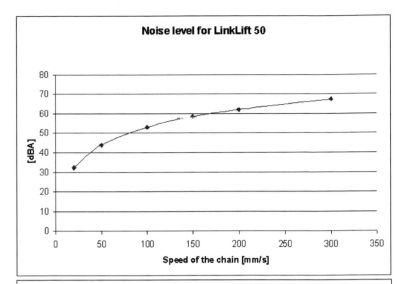

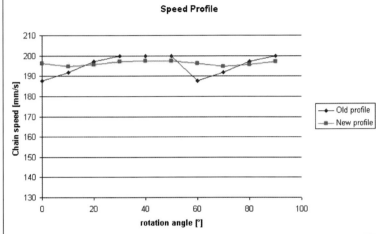

Clockwise from top left: two of the 32 rigid chain-driven scissor lifts in Expo 2000 in Hannover, Germany; the first LinkLift installation in France, the Gaveau Hall in Paris; silent rigid chain drive for stage wagons in Gran Teatre del Liceu, Barcelona; the Rigid Chain Orchestra Pit Elevator in Brighton, Sussex; and a large scissor lift built by Waagner-Biro for the Norwegian Star cruise ship.

*Photos: Serapid,
Waagner Biro, Techplan*

Questions and discussion

Bert Pronk, Het Muziektheater, Amsterdam

We're planning a renovation in summer 2003. The noise made by the lifts was well covered in the third session, but I would like some more information on the guiding of stage lifts because this is very essential to the design of the lift.

Stuart Wilson, Speaker

Generally speaking, all these lifts or elevators require guides – I don't think there's any mechanism which doesn't require some form of guidance system. Most of these things which I outlined would require an external guide fixed to the wall of the pit in some way. One way of overcoming this need is to introduce a scissor mechanism which is non-load-bearing but which provides the guidance required. You could have screw-jacks or compression chain or a Spiralift with a scissor mechanism in there, so you could use it as a central lift platform without external guides. But generally speaking, if you are in an enclosed space with a perimeter that's fixed, the guides would go on that external surface.

There's also another question about noise. Noise, generally, is a function of the speed, and it depends really on the gearbox which is being used to drive the mechanism. A screw-jack is inherently quiet; a rack-and-pinion, if it's aligned correctly, is inherently quiet. Most of the noise will come from the gearbox and the motor that's driving it. And there are commercial gearboxes which will probably give you a noise rating of something like 70–75 dB one metre from the unit. At Waagner-Biro, we have developed a gearbox – for flying, admittedly – which is much quieter than that; it's down to about the 50 dB level. So in very critical applications there are ways of overcoming high noise which is probably not acceptable in a performance lift. If it is critical and you need a special gearbox, another solution is to put an acoustic enclosure around the drive.

Bert Pronk, Het Muziektheater, Amsterdam

Do you have any experience with using acoustic enclosures?

Stuart Wilson, Speaker

Yes, we've done at least one job with an acoustic cover, and it was satisfactory.

Eric Rymer, The Right Solution

I'd just like to ask a question about the LinkLift. You didn't mention in there what depth of pit you need, or what void under the platform. Could you give us some information on that?

Said Lounis, Speaker

It depends on the size of LinkLift that's used, but the drive mechanism for the 100-size LinkLift is 600 mm high. This is the biggest one we have, currently. So basically the minimum height that you need is going to be 600 mm.

Jeff Phillips, Chairman

Well, yes, but I guess it depends on the length you've got to lay the chain out in …

Said Lounis, Speaker

But that's horizontal space, and therefore usually less critical.

Chris Baldwin, ACT Consultant Services

One of the subjects that interests me very much at the moment with all of these lifting devices, particularly the new ones with which I'm becoming familiar, is their ability to deal with the very high dynamic forces that are consistently applied to them by people dancing on the floors. It's very easy to talk about static loading and to see the things moving, but I'm concerned as to what's happening to the self-sustaining issues and the damage to the operation over long-term use with very high dynamic forces on them. Anybody got any ideas on that?

Robert Heimbach, Speaker

I think that in both of the new solutions here you're looking at steel on steel. These mechanisms could both be looked at as a steel column, really, when they are not moving. I know that when we're talking about static platforms the loads on them are live; I think that's what you're talking about – dancers …

Very often we've been asked, "Can your lifts be parked at a certain level for a year?" because they're doing some other performance. And there's really no problem with that. The installation needs to be checked prior to starting it up again, but in terms of movement, or motion, Spiralift can be viewed as a column. And I believe that's true, as well, for other systems.

Said Lounis, Speaker

Yes, that would apply to Rigid Chain. But it depends what you mean by dynamic loading. If it's purely direct vertical dynamic loading then yes, absolutely no problem; I think either system can take that. But if you're talking any side loading, then it's a different issue altogether.

Chris Baldwin, ACT Consultant Services

Well, one of the things that we're doing particularly at the moment is using these sort of platforms in a multi-purpose situation where we might take all the seats out of the auditorium and use it as a flat-floor performance floor for audiences to dance on. And when we consider that situation, if you like, in rock'n'roll terms, then you're looking at forces which are around 2½ times the static forces, and there's constant vibration and energy that is going into the structure.

Robert Heimbach, Speaker

I think any of the vertical loads can be carried without difficulty. Most of the lateral loads that are imposed on the platforms themselves, as Stuart was explaining, will get taken out by the guide systems that are holding these structures in place. But I don't believe that's a concern, even for long-term use. I don't think there's any wear on the columns or anything like that. Stuart, would you agree?

Stuart Wilson, Speaker

Yes. Probably more significant, in designing a platform which is going to be subjected to really live loads, is to ensure that the platform structure is sufficiently rigid that its natural frequency is at a level that it won't self-excite, that you don't get this funny bouncing effect which can arise if the platform structure is too light. And providing that this aspect of the platform design is taken care of, then most lifting mechanisms can withstand the vertical loads which are applied.

Chris Baldwin, ACT Consultant Services

Presumably there must be self-sustaining devices, too, that are holding the lift and stopping it back-feeding (running down).

Said Lounis, Speaker

In Expo 2000 in Germany there were a series of scissor lifts. Like a stage, the complete floor was made of 32 of these scissor lifts. They had all the shows set up during the day for the Hannover Fair, and at night this area became a disco. So the floor was flat and then they had people dancing on it all night, every night. There were no problems.

Jeff Phillips, Chairman

Good test; a very good test.

David Campbell, Victorian Arts Centre

Just following on from that, how does this apply in a live-load situation if you wanted a performance while the elevator was moving? Say you had 20 dancing performers, all moving in unison, obviously, so you've got the magnification effect of the load coming down synchronously while the elevator's actually traveling. Would it sustain that?

Robert Heimbach, Speaker

I think that in general these lifts are all designed for a 250 kg/m^2 (50 lb/sq.ft) live load, and it's always specified as being a live load. With the lateral loads taken out by the guides to the side walls, and even if the elevator is moving, the imposed dynamic loads do not pose a problem. But maybe Stuart has a comment regarding cable systems?

Stuart Wilson, Speaker

The point I was going to make is that certainly in Europe we have problems on the safety aspect of actually operating a lift with personnel performing on it.

David Campbell, Victorian Arts Centre

Well, so do we! But nonetheless it's something that from a performance point of view designers have a desire to do. I think that we should support the necessary infrastructure for that as designers. I'd like to think that we're open to finding solutions to overcome those restrictions.

Stage elevator mechanisms

So I wouldn't like to see the technology going in such a way that we're restricting ourselves to a static platform at whatever height. This requirement is coming from the directors and designers!

Stuart Wilson, Speaker

I suppose it really comes down to how you specify the job. Most commonly, as Robert Heimbach has mentioned, the dynamic load is specified as, perhaps, 2.5 kN/m^2 (50 lbs/sq.ft). But if you foresee an application where you've got a repetitive dynamic load of some other magnitude, if you include that when you are writing your specification, then the elevator designer should take that into account in the selection of the equipment.

Larry Kellerman, Lawrence Kellerman Associates

Staying for the moment with the non-borehole systems and these dynamic weights, if you're on the outside of the LinkLift and/or the Spiralift with a comparatively heavy load, do I have to concern myself with any maximum weights there? If I'm doing, and somebody alluded to this, a rock'n'roll performance, I can wind up with speakers weighing 3,000 lbs (1,350 kg) off to stage right.

Said Lounis, Speaker

As long as your platform is designed to cope with that load and the deflection, the mechanical system, the drive system, is not going to care about that. You're talking about an off-centre load, outside of the box of the LinkLifts, so your platform structure has to be able to carry that deflection, and then the load is going to be transferred over to the Linklift columns. Ω

Readers who were unable to attend the Conference may find this information on how a Spiralift works useful. It is reproduced from information published by Gala Theatrical Equipment.

The Tubular thrust screw is a mechanical device used as a linear Actuator. Linear vertical motion is achieved by using a coiled flat horizontal stainless steel band.

The horizontal stainless steel band A expands and a vertical stainless steel band B is inserted. The heart of the tubular thrust screw is a drum shaped rotor C which rotates on a thrust bearing. The vertical band is stored in a rotating magazine D surrounding the rotor and the horizontal band is stored at the base of the assembly. A slopped set of 16 steel cam roller bearings E attached to the rotor in a helix pattern lifts the horizontal coil and provides a space for the vertical band. Rotating the double chain sprocket F of the tubular thrust screw causes rotation of the rotor with the attached cam rollers mounted in a helix. The cam rollers raise the horizontal band and create an opening so that the vertical band can be inserted without friction between the coils of the horizontal band into the grove located at the center of the horizontal band. This assembly of bands is forced upwards with a continual turning motion of the rotor. The result is a stable fully adjustable column G formed of continuously integrated "I" shaped sections.

The column is continuously formed and can go as high as there is horizontal and vertical band to feed the column assembly. When the rotor is driven in the opposite direction, the process is reversed and the column is lowered.

The vertical band is returned to the rotating magazine surrounding the rotor and the horizontal band is returned to the base of the assembly.

Stage wagon systems

Chairman: Alan Russell, Director, Theatre Projects Consultants
Speakers: Clive Odom, Stage Engineering Consultant, Theatreplan
Dr Peter Lutz, Head of Electrical Engineering, Waagner Biro Stage Systems
Ingemar Carlsson, Owner and Project Manager, NovoScen AB
Eiji Nishimura, Mechanical Design Manager, Mitsubishi Heavy Industries Ltd

Introduction: Alan Russell

Welcome to the second Technical Session in this Conference, to discuss stage wagon systems.

Recently there's been a surge of interest in both of what I reckon are the two major applications for wagons. New technologies are being tried out for production effects, for which I would like to use the traditional word 'truck' rather than 'wagon'. So we have a number of these remotely-controlled truck systems being created and, on the other side, we still have the problem of mechanical handling of major scenery in repertoire to solve. I suspect, ironically, it may be true to say that in mainland Europe, particularly in Germany which pioneered the stage wagon for mechanical handling in repertoire, that there is a move against the traditional wagon. Perhaps they are being influenced by Anglo-Saxon musicals. On the other hand, here in the UK, where we have less opera houses and less money, there's been little demand for wagon systems generally, but one of the largest systems in the world has recently been installed in the Royal Opera House and we'll probably hear that this works better than many people may have imagined.

Today we have four experts to let you know their current thinking on the technologies involved. I'm very pleased to introduce, first, Dr Peter Lutz of Batik to describe the chain drive system which is installed in Barcelona. I know this one works because I've seen it. He will be followed by Clive Odom who was involved with the design of the Royal Opera House system. Maths Nyström and Ingemar Carlsson will describe their 'truck' system and Eiji Nishimura will then speak about the Mitsubishi 'wagon' system installed in many Japanese theatres.

First speaker: Dr Peter Lutz

I want to speak about the stage wagon system we have built in the Gran Teatre del Liceu in Barcelona, in Spain. The system is a multi-level, multi-access system with passive wagons. We use rigid chains to drive the passive wagons, and the wagons can be moved in both axes onstage and also at the basement level. This system has a lot of advantages: we have passive stage wagons; there are no motors and no batteries on the wagons; and therefore no need for trailing cables or any other related problems. The wagons have minimal height and a low deadweight. The wagons in the Liceu in Barcelona are 30 cm (1'-0") high. They can drive at a speed of up to half a metre per second (approx 19" per second) and they can operate at two or even more levels. They can easily and quickly change their direction of movement between transverse and longitudinal travel without any movement of the wagon during change of direction.

How does it work? We need a special type of chain: rigid chain that can push and pull forces and transmit these to the wagons with minimal elongation and minimal play. And we need a chain channel, inside which to guide the special chains under the floor. Another main element of the system is the chain drive unit. This consists of a geared motor, the drive unit itself and the sprockets to drive the rigid chain. The drive unit includes a geared limit unit which provides the emergency limits, one positioning

Dr Peter Lutz studied at the Vienna University of Technology where he gained a diploma in Electrical Engineering, going on to complete his Doctorate in the Department of Communications and Radio Frequency Engineering. He joined Waagner-Biro in Vienna and became Head of Electrical Engineering, responsible for a wide range of industrial machinery and control systems. He now works for Batik (a wholly-owned subsidiary of Waagner-Biro), a firm providing specialised control systems for stage and auditorium equipment.

The special wagon drive chain, and this in place in a section of the guide channel.

The chain drive unit showing the motor, gearbox and limit box, and the two encoders.

encoder system on the drive and, now, an interesting point, we also have a second positioning encoder system. This is connected to a rope drum position measurement unit, and the end of the fine wire-rope is attached to the end of the chain to give us information about the exact position of the head of the chain attached to the wagon.

Why do we need this second encoder? I can explain by means of the system overview. There are a number of chain storage areas where the unused part of the chain is stored. The drawing indicates the drive units and the wagons with their couplings; these are the points where the wagons are fixed to the ends of the chains.

Photo: Waagner Biro

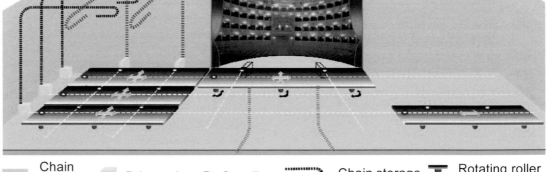

System overview diagram showing stage level. Note that there are actually four side stage wagons, rather than the three shown, and only half-wagon space on stage right.

| ▤▤ | Chain channel | ▨ Drive unit | ⬭ Coupling | ▱▱⮑ Chain storage | ⬬ Rotating roller construction |

There are four for the separate wagon sections which travel across stage. For the other direction of movement (up- and downstage) we have two chains running parallel and therefore we need two coupling elements.

The dimensions of the wagons for the Liceu are 4m × 15m (13'-1" × 49'-2"), and we have to travel from one side stage over some compensator elevators to the main stage and then over to the other side stage.

The difference between chain positions can be significant and we've experienced that the combination of elongation of the chain and of play in the chain elements adds up to an amount of about 6 cm (2½"). On the other hand, our position counting system should be able to give a position accuracy of about ± 1 mm (0.04"). Therefore we need a very sophisticated control algorithm, and a combination of the information from the positioning encoder attached to the head of the chain on the stage wagon and from the position of the drive unit, to ensure a smooth movement for the total travel of the wagons. This also ensures we achieve an exact positioning with an accuracy of ± 1 mm at all intermediate positions.

Another important element of the system is the rotating wheel device underneath the passive wagons. With this construction of three twin-castors mounted on a rotating carriage, the wagons can be moved freely on the flat surface anywhere on stage. These roller units are also known in the theatre industry as 'turtles'.

Diagram of the Gran Teatre stage layout showing the two levels and indicating some of the extensive wagon movements possible.

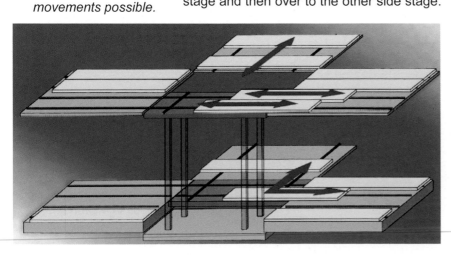

We use a pin as the coupling element to connect the wagon to the end of the chain when lowered. At the same time a guide roller is also lowered and engages in the slot in the top of the chain channel in the floor surface, and this is used to guide the wagon in the desired direction of movement. The same elements exist with a 90° offset for the other direction of movement. Large stage sets can be moved easily and comfortably by means of combining a group of such wagons and using the possibilities of the control system for synchronous movement.

The wagons are transported from stage level down to the basement level and back by means of the large stage platform elevators. There are two main stage platform elevators, 8m × 15m (26'-3" × 49'-2") each. On top of each of these elevators there are two platform elevators, each able to carry one stage wagon. These can only move a short distance on their own mechanisms but are carried on the main platform elevators to the basement level. There is a side stage for four stage wagons on stage left, and a right side stage which can take four half-sized wagons. There wasn't enough space available for the theatre to have full-sized wagons on this side. The wagons can travel to the rear stage area too; there are compensator platforms, and at the lower level there are two side stages for four full-sized wagons each, and one backstage area, also accessible by wagons.

Now I will show you a short movie in which you can see that the system really works very well! It shows a wagon coming from the side stage onto the main stage; at the lower level, the wagon is pushed by the two parallel chains from the stage area to backstage; and now a group of wagons is entering the stage from the side stage; this shows the view on top of one wagon, and running from the side stage you can see the chain and the chain channel, and the floor, now at stage level. The movie also shows a wagon coming to its end position, where some details of the coupling mechanism can be seen. Our sophisticated control system can offer a range of special effects; here a group of wagons is started with an offset of half a wagon, and runs to the pre-programmed target position. More details about the control system will be presented by one of my colleagues in one of the next Conference sessions.

The system offers a lot of possibilities. It's very flexible for various types of stage sets that have to be moved between the two levels and side stage areas, and on to the main stage. When a group of wagons is travelling from main stage area to side stage, as soon as one of the wagons has cleared, the wagon in front can start to move immediately over the stage area and go to the backstage area. When a wagon has been driven into the backstage area, we have to retract the chains and then the side wagons can re-enter the stage area again. That was the short presentation of the movie from the Liceu and I thank you for your attention. I will be glad to answer your questions. Thank you. Ω

Left: a cut-away view of the Gran Teatre showing the main stage elevators and the basic stage planning. Above: a view down into the basement areas with the main stage elevators lowered.

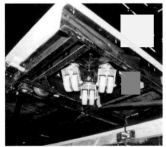

Triple-swivel castors underneath a wagon and a major set ready for movement on wagons.

Photos: Waagner-Biro

Clive Odom: With a background in stage management, prop-making, carpentry, sound, lighting design and equipment maintenance in various theatres in the UK and Asia, Clive became Stage Director at the Royal Exchange Theatre in Manchester and Production Manager for the Tyne Theatre Company before being appointed Technical Manager (Engineering) at the Royal Opera House. He became a senior member of the ROH Theatre Consultant Team for the recent development, with responsibility for the design and co-ordination of the stage installations. He now works with Richard Brett in the Theatreplan consulting group.

Second speaker: Clive Odom

I'm just going to talk briefly through the wagon system at the Royal Opera House: why we came up with the system we did, and how we implemented it, and I too have a video to show you.

The aims of the Royal Opera House development were pretty straightforward: obviously we were going to build a modern opera house on a site where an old opera house had existed and which had very little technology in it. We wanted particularly to allow more time for rehearsals and lighting sessions on the stage, and that meant we needed to get the scenery on and off the stage much quicker than it had been done in the past. In fact, up until the redevelopment started, we would rehearse on stage in the morning and then spend from 1 o'clock at lunchtime, right through until, sometimes, a minute before curtain up, setting up for the evening performance. We needed to be able to extend the time spent on stage for rehearsals and reduce the time spent for set changes. A great part of the concept of stage wagons for scenery was so that we could build scenery on the wagons once and then keep it built. This would enable us to move the scenery around into the rehearsal rooms and onto the stage, and then, obviously, move it off the stage quickly later with the wagons so that we could set up for the evening performance, this again being achieved rapidly by moving scenery on stage using further wagons. We also wanted to improve health and safety conditions and to make the theatre a better place to work in, with less manual handling.

Our brief for the wagon system was fairly simple. We wanted it to be flexible. We increased the total working stage area in the Opera House; there is now the main stage, a side stage, a rear stage, a rear side stage, and also a large fit-up area which is some way off to the side, and there are two rehearsal rooms into which we can put stage wagons. We wanted to be able to group at least three wagons together. In the Opera House there are six stage elevators; each elevator is 14.9 metres (48'-6") wide across stage and, running up and down stage, 2.44 metres (8'-0"). The wagons are 14.9 metres × 4.88 metres (48'-6" × 16'-0") so that one wagon fits on two stage elevators. We needed to be able to move up to three stage wagons together as a group. We also wanted to have a flat stage at all times. We didn't want to have wagons sitting above floor level in the side

stages because they just stop you doing anything else, and we wanted also to be able to use traditional scenery on trucks, because a lot of productions in the Opera House repertoire use these. Productions which pre-date the redevelopment comprise a lot of sets that wouldn't require the wagons but would require a flat floor. So we needed to make sure that we kept the stage floor as flat as possible. We didn't want any guide tracks or slots and the ballet company, in particular, was very keen that we didn't have wide grooves in any of the stage areas which might cause dancers to trip or twist their ankles or otherwise cause injury. And for the same reason we wanted very small gaps, very close tolerances, between the wagons and the surrounding floor and any adjacent wagons. In our investigation of existing wagon systems we found that most had what we considered to be rather large gaps between the moving elements.

So to the solution. During the development of the Opera House we were lucky enough to have an engineer, Mike Barnett, working with us. Some of you may know or have heard of him; he is a very talented mechanical designer and he's done a lot of work in the West End, and has designed many of the amazing sets that are used in the West End – the helicopter in *Miss Saigon* and similar things – and also many of the shows in the Royal Opera House that have moving elements. Mike considered the problem, and he came back with a scheme which is the basis of the system that we developed.

The pictures on the next page show the side of an elevator with a drive cassette in it, and it's a tooth-belt drive. It drives on the side of the wagon. At the time it was rather an unusual solution to the problem because it means that the surface of the wagon is at stage level. The wagons don't come up onto the surface and drive along; when they're moving they drive with the surface of the wagon level with the surface

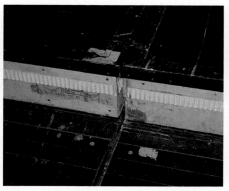

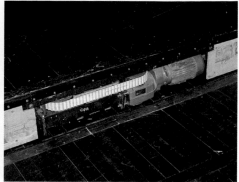

of the surrounding floor, and the only part of the floor that is not at stage level is the area which the wagon is approaching. Once the wagon has moved, we then bring up a compensating elevator behind it to fill in the space.

Now I'd like to show a video which will explain the drive system in operation. We made a prototype of the wagons, and this is some film of that prototype running. It shows the elevators and wagons with no floor on them so it's easy to see what's going on.

"Stage wagons complete with sets will be capable of moving in all areas of the stage. This diagram represents movements of wagons in the stage area. For instance, at the end of the rehearsals, part of Mayerling could be moved to the side stage, Bohème could be moved into the rehearsal room, and Tosca made ready in the rear stage. The remainder of Mayerling could then be removed off the stage to be replaced by Tosca for that evening's performance.

"Here are pictures of the full-width, half-depth wagon being tested in the workshop. The test weights on it are equivalent to the maximum scenic load it would be required to carry. There are also half-width but full-depth wagons. The wagons auto-matically slow down and stop at the end of their travel. The wagons are powered by toothed belt drive cassettes located beneath the floor. These in turn mesh with equivalent toothed belts fixed to the side faces of the wagons.

"Special triple-swivel castor units ensure that the wagon can be reversed accurately without being pushed off course. Self-lubricating polythene guide strips allow the wagons to operate with a very small clearance gap.

"It is extremely important that the stage floor remains level at all times. This is achieved using compensating elevators. In use, the compensating elevators in front will be lowered, the wagons moved, and then the compensating elevators behind returned to stage level, thus ensuring a safe working stage level at all times.

"Building the prototype has shown that the proposed system will be effective."

The prototype equipment was made back in 1996, primarily to show to those people who doubted that the system would work, and the video was made by amateurs during the construction of the prototype. You can see that the driving of the wagons is done using nylon belts which are fixed to the sides of the wagons, so the wagons are completely passive. They use turtles, or triple-swivel castors, similar to the ones in Barcelona, which allow the direction to be

A drive unit exposed for maintenance, the toothed belt attached to two adjacent wagons and a drive unit in normal use, with a lowered compensating elevator in front.

Three images from the prototype test, the video of which was shown at the Conference.

Photos: Techplan, courtesy Royal Opera House

Photos: Techplan, courtesy Royal Opera House

changed without the normal off-centre kick that you get with a single castor. The compensating elevators in the Royal Opera House are hydraulic and they are simply a system of levers with rollers which lift the top platform by lever arms. The guides for the elevators are passive scissors mounted underneath, one in each direction at right angles. This all seems to work very well mechanically. To carry out a move of a wagon, you simply drop the compensating elevators that form the route in front of the wagon and run the wagon in the gap, or 'canal', that has been formed.

One of the secrets of the system is the guides which are described in the video as polythene guides; it's actually ultra-high molecular polyethylene, which is a type of plastic which has got a very, very low coefficient of friction against itself. We formed an edge to all the wagons, all the compensating elevators and all the stage elevators out of this plastic. It is actually quite a nice way of finishing off wagons, because the timber fits inside it so you don't see any timber edges; it's black, and

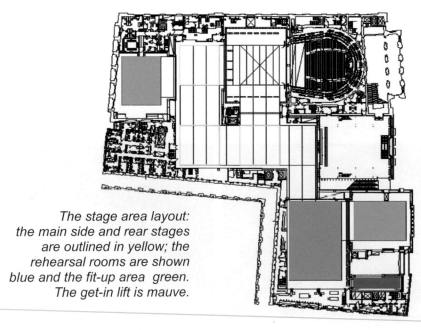

The stage area layout: the main side and rear stages are outlined in yellow; the rehearsal rooms are shown blue and the fit-up area green. The get-in lift is mauve.

we work to a very small tolerance gap, which was a minimum of 1 mm and a maximum of 5 mm at every join; ± 2½ mm (0.1"), something like that. And in fact we found during the prototype tests that the tighter we could keep the gaps the better the guidance worked and the better the wagons ran.

The layout of the stage in the Opera House shows the six elevators in the main stage and around it; on stage right, there is a side stage and upstage a rear stage. Off to the bottom of the picture there is a space which is what we call the fit-up area. This is adjacent to one of the rehearsal rooms. Scenery being delivered or collected is brought to the fit-up area by the get-in lift. When the scenery is constructed, it can be moved into this rehearsal room or moved around the corner and into the side stage and rear stages, ready for movement onto stage.

There was a problem with the planning of the Opera House because of the shape of the site – Bow Street runs down the front of the building, and the Piazza cuts in backstage – and we have a pinch point where we could only fit two wagons. So scenery, if it's built in the fit-up area, has to be able to break down to fit on two wagons only. Some sets have to be brought round onto the main stage area before final assembly. But once on the main stage area, you can run a group of three wagons around, and obviously they can go both up and down and across stage.

We divided the stage area as efficiently as possible. We had just enough room to get the width of three wagons side by side, so we actually have a sort of parking position between the side stage and the main stage and between the rear stage and the rear side stage. And the space at the back is particularly useful for storage of scenery in the rep. This is often quite full, and the space between the stage and the side stage is also useful because sometimes you need to push a set out of the way to get something past it, for which this space is particularly helpful.

At the rear of the stage there is another rehearsal room. This was built some 20 years before the main redevelopment and has been kept. Its floor is at stage level, so when we take wagons in there they have to be lifted up to stage level and roll in on top of this floor. Fill-in rostra elements are then placed around the wagons to get a level floor with the wagons in place. This was a disappointment because it would have been much better to have driven them straight in. This room is also not on the stage centre-line, so all the wagons have to do a dog-leg to get in there, which makes it a far more complicated operation.

Although the wagons are always at floor level, in order to drive an adjacent wagon you have to lift the wagon beside it to get the drive cassettes, which are in the sides of the elevators, level with the wagon you want to drive. This is indicated in some of the pictures and does require the compensators to be able to lift the full load of wagon and scenery.

I have a couple of minutes more video which shows the set for *Traviata* being moved from upstage onto the main stage and lowered into the floor when it gets on stage. You can see the elevators are lowered by the depth of the wagon to allow the wagon to be moved. The wagons in the Opera House are, again, as in Barcelona, 300 mm (1'-0") high. The main stage elevators are being used to bring the set right down to stage level, and in this show, *Traviata*, the chorus enter from underneath the stage, up through the elevator structure onto the set.

That's all I've got to say at the moment, but we'll have the questions afterwards. Ω

Backstage at the Opera House:
1 Rear-side stage with set on wagon raised to allow those in front to be driven,
2 Rear-side stage from rear stage,
3 The complicated set for "La Clemenza di Tito" built on wagons,
4 Scenery on boat trucks in rear stage,
5 The set for "Der Rosenkavalier" built on wagons,
6 Tractors delivering scenery in pallets to the fit-up area,
7 More built pieces on wheels showing the need for a level stage floor, and
8 The tilting and rolling platform for "The Flying Dutchman" which is built on wagons and then lowered 4 metres (13'-1") into the floor.

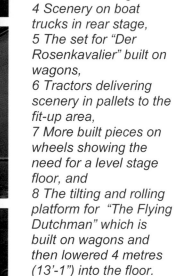

Photos: Techplan, courtesy Royal Opera House

Göteborgs Operan by night and day, a picture of the foyer spaces, a view into the fly tower from a lowered stage elevator and, a scene from "Les Misérables".

Ingemar Carlsson is the Chief Construction Engineer at Gothenburg Opera House and an owner of NovoScen AB, a stage equipment design company. In addition to his work in the Opera, he has undertaken stage equipment designs for the Hannover Opera House, The Århus Theatre in Denmark, the Royal Opera House in Stockholm and the Tröndelag Theatre in Trondheim in Norway. Before working in the theatre, Ingemar was involved in the engineering of radar and steering equipment for merchant shipping.

Third speakers: Maths Nyström and Ingemar Carlsson

Maths Nyström

Let me introduce the Gothenburg Opera. It is a repertoire theatre that plays around 200 to 220 shows every year. We play opera, ballet and some musicals. When we started planning this project in the early '90s we wanted to combine the heavy scenery change-over system with that which can be used for scenery movements in the actual shows. That's why we tried to combine the two different layouts; wagons for scenic use in shows that can move around scenery in all directions, and also to provide the changeover systems.

Ingemar Carlsson

I'm going to talk about the stage wagon system that we are using in the Gothenburg Opera. The Opera was opened in 1994 and one idea we had at that time was to create a system with the maximum of flexibility in order to provide artistic freedom as well as a transportation system.

The architecture is strongly influenced by the ship-building tradition in Gothenburg. In fact still we have one of the biggest shipyards in Sweden, on the other side of the river. The theatre was to be, as Maths said, not only for opera, but also for ballet and musicals. In the production of *Les Misérables* we used the wagon system a lot, not only for transportation, but mainly for the artistic use, as part of the performance. The fact that we are not only making productions, we are operating the opera in repertoire, means that we need a lot of machinery for transportation, not only the stage wagon system, but also extensive lower-stage and upper-stage machinery.

The theatre has a traditional cruciform layout with a main stage, wings (side stages) left and right, and a rear stage. We have a scenery assembly space; we also have an experimental stage, and we have the workshops, all at the same level. We wanted to transport scenery in all these areas with wagon systems. So we started by installing a big electrical wire in the floor which it was possible for the wagons to move along. We have eight small wagons, 3.5 × 3.75 metres (11'-6" × 12'-4") and four big wagons which are 8 × 3.5 metres (26'-3" × 11'-6").

The première of Verdi's opera *Un Ballo in Maschera* (*Masked Ball*) is in September this year and it's a very big production. It is

Photos: courtesy Göteborgs Operan

on a revolving stage that is moving in and out at stage level and there is only the secret office coming from the side. The size of the setting is 10 metres (32'-10") high and 20 metres (65'-7") deep. So without a stage wagon system it wouldn't have been possible to have this in the repertoire together with other musicals and similar shows. The pictures were taken just before coming to this Conference; we are building part of the system in the rear stage right now. The revolving stage on the top is 8 metres (26'-3") in diameter. This is on one of the large stage wagons, the big one, 3.5 × 8 metres, and around it is additional structure because of the overall size required. The wagon has the timber on the top and the additional structure on the bottom, with a turtle (triple-swivel) castor. The revolve operates on a rake.

In another production, *Jesus Christ Superstar*, the facility of using the wagon units to move anywhere was employed. One of the ideas is that we can move these units in any direction anywhere in the opera house. There is no limitation, either at stage level or in the basement. The drive units are not stage equipment; they are standard truck components, similar to those which might be delivered to Volvo next week.

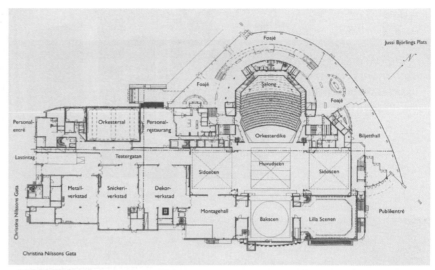

Photos: Techplan, courtesy Göteborgs Operan

Stage level plan, the timber workshop and paint shop (with a viewing bridge).

Plans for "Un Ballo in Maschera" ("A Masked Ball") together with photographs of the set in construction. Note the single castors on these triple-swivel units.

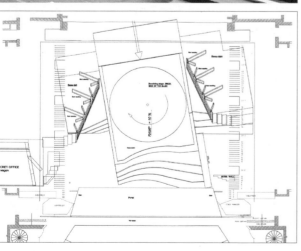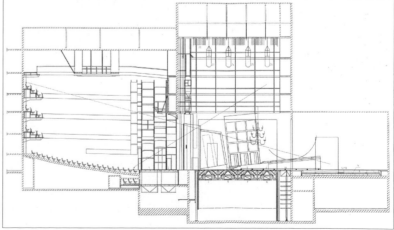

Photos and drawings: courtesy Göteborgs Operan

Stage wagon systems

A decorated wagon for "Jesus Christ Superstar" and, below: the drive and control components and a view on a wagon with the flooring removed.

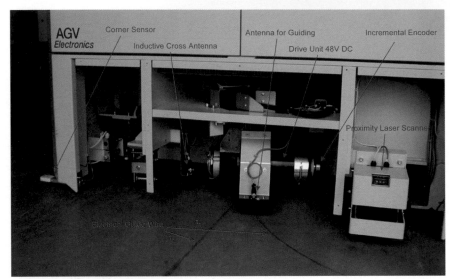

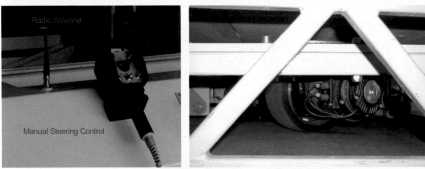

All the components shown on the annotated picture below will also be found in our wagon system. The system that we use has electrical wires in the floor, but we also have additional sensor systems for navigation by means of gyro and laser navigation, magnets and so on.

The drive unit operates on 48 volt DC, it's a standard unit used in every truck everywhere in the world. We have, at the front, one antenna for guiding; that antenna will follow the wire in the floor. If we use different signal frequencies, we can choose which track the wagon will follow by means of changing the frequency. We have an incremental encoder for the speed control of the motor, we have a steering motor that rotates the drive unit, and we have a laser scanner for safety. This works like a radar system; it can measure distance and angles to something ahead of the system and start warning, saying, "Walk away, I'm coming," and when you don't walk away, it will stop. We also use an inductive cross antenna, to guide the wagon and determine the distance travelled. A proximity sensor on each corner completes the system.

For the steering we rely on two systems. radio antennae, which are most commonly used in the performance, but during setting up and technical works we are moving normally with a manual steering control.

A drive unit is installed in each wagon and uses a wheel of 200 mm (8") diameter. That makes the height of the wagon 250 mm (10"). In reality, the height of the wagon is governed by the size of the batteries.

If we examine a wagon without any floor, the batteries are on the left, and the drive unit in the centre. This wagon has some counterweights in it because the scenery decoration that had to be fitted was very high – it was for *Les Misèrables*, a very high structure of 6 or 8 metres (19'-8" or 26'-3") – and there were people running up on the set, so we needed to stabilise the system.

In the side of the wagon frame is the fitting for a docking unit, because this wagon was connected and disconnected mechanically to another wagon, which means that we had to have a very high degree of accuracy in the system.

The idea from the very beginning was to use components that were standard in industrial work; well-proven, reliable components. At this time, it was in 1992, lasers were on the market but were not

Photos: courtesy Göteborgs Operan

very well tested, so we decided at the basic level to use a developed industrial antenna using the wire in the floor. The electric current in this creates a magnetic field, and because of the bar-antenna format the position of the wagon along this antenna can be measured very accurately, within half a millimetre. It is possible to have a single wire slot for the cable, or a multiple-wire slot with many different frequencies, and both are only 20 mm (¾") deep.

I truly believe in redundancy, because once you use this system in a performance it has to work. And every human being has two eyes and ears; therefore if somebody cuts my wire I have to rely on another system, so we use a lot of small magnets for positioning wagons during a performance. These are rare earth, cobalt samarium magnets, very small, strong magnets. We put them into the wood of the stage floor in a pattern, like a magnetic lighthouse. Then we measure the magnetic field and you can determine your position very accurately. In addition to these magnets we need a gyro and, of course, the distance measurements. We are using a gyro sensor, it's a rate gyro, not a north-seeking gyro compass, and outputs a signal equivalent to degrees/second. The type we use is from British Aerospace and is very expensive. You can buy these components for 10% of the price we pay, but their accuracy is not as good. This is a very good component and it helps us a lot.

And as you have two eyes and your ears as well, we add a third system by using a laser, together with a number of reflectors around the stage area, as a third system for navigation.

For communication we are using two channels on 430 MHz radio for the data link. And when the performance finishes and everybody wants to go home, it's very important that you don't forget the batteries. And we learnt very early that it was not easy to teach people to think about that. We have a navigation system in the wagons and therefore we have the facility to charge them up automatically by means of charging plates in the fixed stage flooring that are connected to the charging contacts on the wagon.

So, in summary, we have remote control wagons with full freedom of movement in two dimensions. We cannot fly – but we can move in any direction on stage level. We have a multi-sensor system for navigation, and this is really a matter of

redundancy. We do not have redundancy in every step of the system, but our experience is that motors themselves and also the batteries, if they are well monitored and kept in a good condition, give no problem. But the sensor system and incremental encoders, the different sensors in a system, are the most important, and we like to work with these. And we have also, for safety, a multi-sensor system for collision avoidance; and the wagons are battery-powered, but with mechanical limitations. I am not going to talk too much about batteries. Much has happened with batteries in the last 10 years, so we rely totally on batteries, we have no problem with them, and using batteries gives us the flexibility to move anywhere.

What I am saying is that this is not for every theatre, but for our theatre where we have to combine musicals with opera and ballet, we need a lot of flexibility. Regarding musicals – I think more than 50% of the visitors coming to the opera come to the musicals, so we have to play musicals in a repertoire form. My view is "get off the rails". With this system, like a sailing boat, you can move in any direction; I mean, loosen the moorings, lift the mainsail and sail away and enjoy the freedom of the seas! For this system we must thank Volvo who started our thinking, because all those wagons go back to the technology used by Volvo at that time, and also today, of course. Thank you very much. Ω

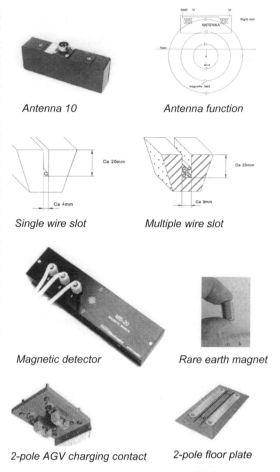

Antenna 10

Antenna function

Single wire slot

Multiple wire slot

Magnetic detector

Rare earth magnet

2-pole AGV charging contact

2-pole floor plate

Gyro sensor

Laser unit

430 MHz radio modem

Some of the components used for control of the stage wagons in Göteborgs Operan.

Theatres equipped by Mitsubishi Heavy Industries (top right): Shanghai Grand Theater; Act City Hamamatsu; New National Theater in Tokyo and the Aichi Art Theatre.

Eiji Nishimura is the Manager of the Mechanical Design Department for Stage Engineering within Mitsubishi Heavy Industries. He was the leading Engineer on the Aichi Arts Theatre which was the first fully automated opera house in Japan. He has also worked on the New National Theatre in Tokyo, Shanghai Grand Theatre and the Esplanade Theatres on the Bay in Singapore.

Fourth speaker: Eiji Nishimura

Mitsubishi Heavy Industries Ltd (MHI) has delivered various kinds of stage machinery to a number of Japanese and overseas theatres and has also delivered the stage machinery installations to most of the opera houses in Japan. Significant projects include Aichi Art Theatre, Act City Hamamatsu, New National Theater in Tokyo, Shanghai Grand Theater and the Esplanade Theaters on the Bay in Singapore.

Taking this welcome opportunity to introduce MHI to a wider audience, we would like to present mainly our driving method for the ultra-thin side stage wagon and for large sliding rear stage wagons which we have designed and delivered.

As shown in the plan diagram below, in a typical opera house there may well be side stage wagons, (red) and a rear stage wagon, often a so-called sliding stage wagon (blue). When the side stage wagon is required to move, firstly the main elevator and side compensator are lowered (just over the same depth as the side stage wagon), and then the side stage wagons are able to move.

These wagons can be both individually and synchronously operated. The sliding stage wagons can only move after the mainstage elevator and compensator are lowered.

The side stage wagons cannot move without the floor for running on, but the sliding stage wagon in the rear stage does not require a floor as it spans across the opening and runs on the rails which are installed at both sides.

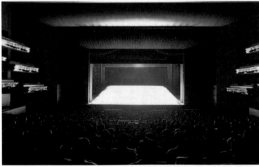

Photos: Mitsubishi Heavy Industries

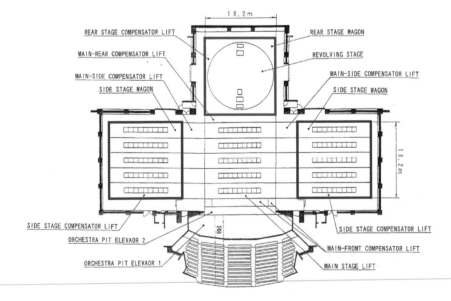

The key features of the side stage wagons which Mitsubishi construct are as follows.

- Ultra-thin.
- After moving onto the top of main stage elevator, they can be raised and lowered with main stage elevator.
- Low noise level.

The table at the bottom of the next page shows a list of the parameters for the side stage wagons in two theaters which Mitsubishi has recently completed.

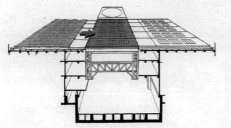

SIDE STAGE RIGHT
Stage wagons move when main and compensator elevators are lowered by wagon depth

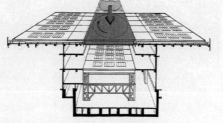

REAR STAGE
Rear sliding stage with turntable (revolve) can move downstage when main stage elevators are lowered

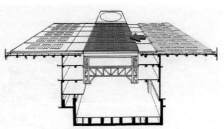

SIDE STAGE LEFT
Stage wagons move when main and compensator elevators are lowered by wagon depth

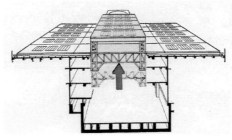

MAIN STAGE
Double deck elevator allows understage settings to be raised into view

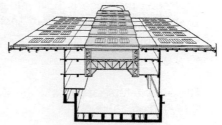

MAIN STAGE
Elevators can be raised or lowered as required and can also form steps or slopes

Facilities offered by typical opera house stage floor machinery.

We call our stage wagon drive system the 'chain-pusher driving method'. Driving equipment cannot be built into the wagon because this wagon is so thin. The drive mainly consists of the drive sprocket, chain return sprocket, chain, pusher connection device and pusher. The pusher is connected to the chain which is installed under the wagon and pusher connection device is fitted to the side stage wagon. The side stage wagon is driven by the chain running and moving the pusher.

Once a side stage wagon is moved on to the main elevator, the pusher is released which means this wagon is perfectly free. Alternatively the pusher can be retracted and can wait in preset positions. When the pusher goes to catch the side stage wagon, the pusher is connected automatically, by itself.

All driving equipment is installed in the pit under the side stage compensator. The pit depth is 1.55m (5'-1") for theatre A and

reduces to 1.5m (4'-11") for theatre B. The drive consists of a reduction gear, chain, chain sprocket, pusher and chain tension adjusting device.

The actual pusher configuration is like that shown. The lower part of the pusher is rigidly fixed to the chain. Two low-noise roller chains are used. The connecting plate has to penetrate the side stage compensator and this requires a slot in its surface.

Table of parameters and a drawing showing the mechanisms of the Driving Chain, Pusher and Pusher Release.

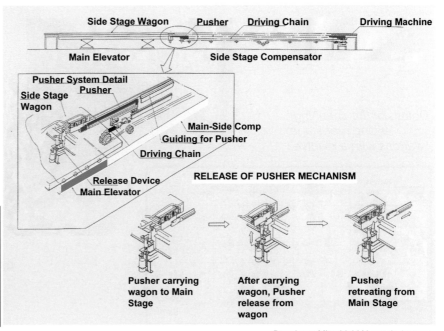

RELEASE OF PUSHER MECHANISM

Pusher carrying wagon to Main Stage

After carrying wagon, Pusher release from wagon

Pusher retreating from Main Stage

Drawings: Mitsubishi Heavy Industries

Theatre	Dimension (m)	Depth (mm)	Travel (m)	Q'ty	Power (kw)	Load (kg/m²)		Speed (m/s)
						Dynamic	Static	
A	18.2 x 3.6	150	23.8	5	5.5	200	500	0.06~0.6
B	18.2 x 3.6	180	23.6	10	5.5	167	167	0.06~0.6

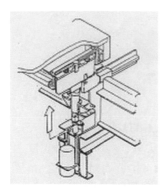

Blow-up of the pusher connection device for the side-stage wagons.

Limit switches for stopping and interlocking the system and an encoder for detecting position are provided. Locking pins for position-keeping are provided on each main stage elevator, and there are receptacles in each side stage wagon. Operations can be done individually and/or simultaneously and smooth starting and stopping are carried out electrically.

Next we consider the sliding stage wagon in the rear stage. Features of this sliding, spanning stage wagon are as follows:

- It enables dynamic scenery change
- Revolving stage is built into the sliding wagon for various performances
- Can be used as complete second stage
- Low noise level

The parameters for these stage wagons are shown in the table.

The diagram shows driving mechanism for rear stage sliding stage wagon and revolving stage. The driving system for sliding stage wagon is a self-drive method of a wheel on the rail, and a chain friction method is used for the revolving stage.

The span of the rear wagon is about 18.5 metres (60'-8") and main spanning beams are designed to carry the loads over this distance from side to side. The number of wheels is 16, of which 8 are drive wheels.

Two drive wheels are connected via one motor at each corner therefore requiring four motors. These four motor are independent; they are not connected mechanically, but are electrically synchronised. Position control is done using a cable reel or rack and pinion device. A cable busbar system is installed for feeding power to the wagon for the revolve.

The positioning of the revolving stage is achieved by a pinion and gear system around the center bearing and limit switches are arranged for certain basic stopping positions.

Lastly, taking this opportunity of showing some of our special skills, we have illustrated (on the right) some of our other projects and characteristic theatrical equipment and installations. Thank you for your kind attention. Ω

Details of the spanning, sliding rear stage wagons with a revolve.

Theatre	Dimension (m)	Depth (m)	Travel (m)	Q'ty	Power (kw)	Load (kg/m²) Dynamic	Load (kg/m²) Static	Speed (m/s)
A	18.2x18.2	1.0	23.7	1	11x4	200	500	0.06~0.6
Revolve wagon	Φ16.4	-	∞	1	30	200	500	0.2~2.0 (rpm)
B	18.2x18.2	1.0	21.9	1	7.5x4	100	100	0.06~0.6
Revolve wagon	Φ16.4	-	∞	1	22x2	100	100	0.2~2.0 (rpm)

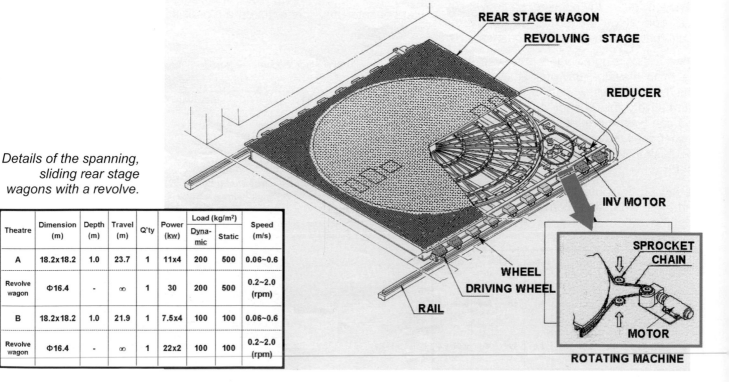

REAR STAGE WAGON
REVOLVING STAGE
REDUCER
INV MOTOR
SPROCKET CHAIN
WHEEL
DRIVING WHEEL
MOTOR
RAIL
ROTATING MACHINE

Stage wagon systems

The Concert Hall in the Esplanade in Singapore, during commissioning. The building also contains a lyric theatre and concert hall with equipment by Mitsubishi Heavy Industries, in their first collaboration with Bytecraft Automation of Australia.

The chain-operated main stage elevators shown lowered in the Aichi Art Theatre.

Top left and clockwise: Acoustic reflector for concert platform; small revolving stage elevator platforms; a mechanised shade louver and a traditional Japanese "NOH" stage.

Photos: Mitsubishi Heavy Industries

Questions and discussion

David Taylor, Theatre Projects Consultants

Can Peter Lutz describe the mechanisms for the elevators in Barcelona?

Peter Lutz, Speaker

The drives for the two mainstage elevators are rack and pinion and are mounted in the elevator pit. On each of these large elevators are two small elevators which are raised and lowered by chains. These mechanisms are mounted in the gap between the small 'plateau' elevators and the mainstage platforms.

Question from the floor

I have two questions concerning the stage wagon mechanism in the Royal Opera House. How can you ensure that those two belts, one on the wagon and the other on the drive cassette, are perfectly synchronised with each other? The second question is: How many drives are there?

Clive Odom, Speaker

The simple answer is that we don't synchronise the drives. The whole of the Royal Opera House wagon system is designed to be a sloppy, loose control system. In other words, all the drive motors – and there are some 230 drive cassettes around that whole stage area – every one of them has a variable speed drive, but they're all open-loop and there's no position control done with the drives. The positioning of the wagons is achieved purely with sensors built into the floor and when the wagon approaches and passes over a sensor, that's when we know where the wagon is.

The drive cassettes are spring-loaded and they are pushed out slightly to contact the toothed belt on the wagon by a number of springs. There is a little hydraulic ram that pulls them clear when the elevators move up and down. Once the elevator has completed the movement, the hydraulic pressure is released and the springs push the cassette out so that it meshes with the toothed belt on the wagon. As a wagon approaches a cassette, if the teeth don't mesh it doesn't matter. All the drives are given the same speed command and the unmeshed drive belt isn't actually driving anything, so it will tend to go just a little bit faster than those that are pushing the load, and the teeth then slip past each other and engage. The belts have only a 10 mm (0.4") pitch. So after a very short time they then drop in, locate, and start driving, and its speed adjusts to match the others.

And I have to say it works very successfully like that. We did this really to save costs, to reduce the number of encoders required, and associated processing. The system is used at least twice a day, every day, in the Opera House to change the settings around, and with no problems at all.

Alan Russell, Chairman

We had a good explanation from Mitsubishi about how their chain connects and disconnects from the wagon; how does this work with the system in Barcelona? Do you have an automatic system?

Peter Lutz, Speaker

Very simply. You have to put a crank into some positions on the wagons; there are holes to put the crank into on top of the wagon and in some side places to avoid problems if stage scenery is set up on top of the wagon. You just do a few turns and this lowers the pins manually, the pins and the guiding roller together.

It was intended to have an automatic system in the first runs, but then this was deleted due to cost reasons and the client agreed to have a simple manual system. It was thought possible to do this automatically but probably you would have to find a solution for driving the coupling mechanisms from below, for instance, or you would have to connect the wagon to some source of energy for the drive. Ω

British Standards and Model Conditions

Chairman: Jeff Phillips, Project Manager and Consultant, Royal Opera House
Speakers: Paul Mathews, Director, Evans Stage & Studio Engineering
          Ray Carter, Theatre Consultant, Next Stage
          David Adams, Chairman ABTT Safety Committee
          Peter Angier, Theatre Consultant, Carr & Angier

Introduction: Jeff Phillips

The Standard that we are looking at in this session covers the '*specification for the design and manufacture of lifting equipment for performance, broadcast and similar applications*'. When I was invited to join the Briefing Committee for this Standard, which is BS 7905, I was quite pleased; I thought, "That's just the thing I'll need for the equipment in the Royal Opera House when we rebuild it." Wrong. We actually used a lot of experience of what we were doing during the development of the Opera House in the Standard because it didn't get published until after the House was built!

Paul Mathews really identified the need and this gap in the Standards. He started the whole ball rolling and he's going to tell you about how he got the British Standards Institute to let us prepare BS 7905.

BRITISH STANDARD   BS 7905-1:2001

Lifting equipment for performance, broadcast and similar applications —

Part 1: Specification for the design and manufacture of above stage equipment (excluding trusses and towers)

ICS 53.020.00

NO COPYING WITHOUT BSI PERMISSION EXCEPT AS PERMITTED BY COPYRIGHT LAW   **BSI**

First speaker: Paul Mathews

For the last 21 years I've been involved in design of lifting equipment for television studios and a few theatres. Before that, I was in general engineering, designing machinery for industrial, nuclear and aerospace applications.

I want to start by talking about lighting hoists as used in television studios. The hoists illustrated employ helical winding; there are two wire-ropes, one being wound onto each end of the long winding drum. The wire-ropes each support one end of a lighting barrel (framed bar which carries the luminaires). These are employed in quantities of up to 100 in a television studio and much assorted equipment is loaded onto each barrel.

A number of lighting hoists with helical grooved winding drums installed in BBC television studio TC4 in Television Centre in London.

Photos: courtesy British Broadcasting Corporation

Drawing of a pile winding drum prepared for the British Standard and a theatre pile-winding hoist mounted on an overstage grid.

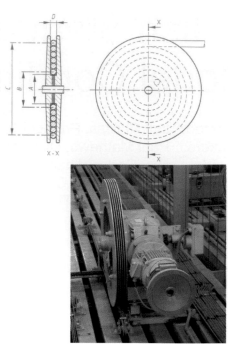

Paul Mathews was educated at Imperial College and served a Graduate Apprenticeship with WH Allen after national service in the RAF. He then travelled widely throughout the world, designing industrial, nuclear and aerospace machinery, before becoming involved in theatre and television equipment with Evans Stage and Studio Engineering. His company provides a number of standard products and also provides a design service for companies requiring special new machinery products.

A television studio requires a lot of suspensions, and so each hoist is required to be as simple as possible, or the overall complication is multiplied to almost unmanageable proportions. The hoists illustrated are all *two-wire* hoists. That means there is one wire-rope supporting each end of the lighting barrel. This type of hoist works well and has been proved to be reliable over more than 40 years.

These hoists are *helical wind* hoists; we will now consider *pile wind* hoists. For the benefit of anyone who has not yet met the *pile wind* hoist, the illustration on the right shows the arrangement. The wire-rope starts on a small diameter, and winds in ever-increasing circles on top of the previous turns. The rope leaves the drum and goes off to the load from the largest diameter. Obviously when the lighting barrel is at floor level with all the wire-rope paid out you have a small winding diameter. As the hoist is raised, the winding diameter increases, and the torque requirement on the motor increases quite substantially; therefore you need a bigger geared motor unit than you would need for helical winding. The pile winding drum, which is also known as the 'yo-yo' drum in America, produces a severe crushing force on the wire-rope at the centre of the drum due to the tension in the layers above. This and the resultant side forces on the drum have to be taken into account in the design. So from many points of view, helical wind is the better method of supporting these loads.

To alleviate the problems with pile winding, a pair of smaller diameter wire-ropes are sometimes used side by side in place of one substantial wire-rope. This enables the drum size to be reduced so that a more reasonable size of gearbox can be used. This doubles the number of wire-ropes in the studio and can increase the risk of snagging. Some continental countries had a law insisting on at least four wire-ropes being used on all lighting hoists.

At the time when the Machinery Directive was being introduced to our industry, there was a suggestion that the necessary supporting standards would be provided by adopting existing national standards from individual countries and imposing them throughout the European Union. This would have meant that we all would be forced to have four-wire lighting hoists. This was not wanted and is not necessary.

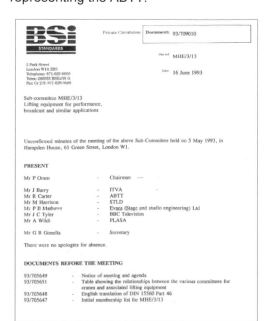

Photo: Techplan

The upshot of this situation was that a group of industry leaders in the UK approached the British Standards Institution (BSi) with a view to producing a standard for our industry, The procedure was highly logical, starting with a form provided by the Institution that I had to complete. Documentary evidence of support for the proposal was required from many organisations involved, including the ABTT, the Society of Television Lighting Directors and the BBC. The British Standards Institute agreed to proceed and we started 1993. Peter Oram was the Chairman for just that first meeting, and Ray Carter, who's here today, was representing the ABTT.

The Committee has the designation, MHE/3/13, Lifting Equipment for Stage and Studio. There were many other people involved in the Cranes Subcommittee, and all these people were meeting and writing the standards for all the different sorts of crane. It's a huge task to get standards written so that equipment can be made to be sold throughout the European Union on a level playing field where everybody works to the same rules, so that you can make machinery in this country that can be sold in any of the other European countries and vice versa.

At the time we started the Machinery Directive hadn't actually become cast-iron law. The Machinery Directive is supported by 'harmonised' standards, and there are A standards, B standards and C standards. We're looking at a C standard; we haven't got a C standard, but at least we've got a British Standard now, eight years after the start. The three types are:

'A' Standards – general standards applicable to all machinery.

'B' Standards – general standards applicable to a range of machinery, and specific standards for individual safety devices for machinery.

'C' Standards – standards for individual types of machinery.

Note that a member country can propose its national standard either for adoption as the CEN Standard, or for use as the basis of discussion. The Machinery Directive also specifies the *maximum* requirements for machinery products to ensure that nobody can specify more, and in doing so, create a barrier to trade. It should also be noted that the Use of Work Equipment Directive specifies the *minimum* levels of safety that are required for workers to enjoy.

We have now got this national Standard for flying for use within our industry. This is what the work over the last eight years has been all about. It's interesting that the Machinery Directive specifies a maximum requirement for machinery products, to ensure that nobody can specify more. So if you conform to the Machinery Directive, you can sell your equipment throughout the European Community.

Peter Oram, the first Chairman of our Committee, came to our very first meeting, and advised us on the way to proceed. Then we went our own way from there. He wrote a piece on 'European matters' which is interesting in that it explained the role of CEN/TC147 and its working group.

'CEN/TC147 is the parent committee for all standards work on the subject of the safety of cranes and it is responsible for a work programme containing various standards to be written, with respective targets for the completion of various stages. CEN/TC147 has delegated this work programme by setting up various working groups to write the individual standards. All of this work is required by CEN to provide some of the standards to support the EC Machinery Directive and its amending directives. When each harmonized standard is published, each EC country has to withdraw its corresponding national standard(s).

'On 1st January 1993 various UK Regulations came into force which legalised the Machinery Directive and certain other directives (including the Use of Work Equipment Directive). From 1st January 1993 to 1st January 1995 there is a transition period, whereby manufacturers of machinery must either comply with the Essential Safety Requirements (ESR) of the Machinery Safety Directive itself, or comply with the appropriate national standards of the purchaser. If the manufacturer chooses to comply with the ESR's in the Machinery Directive he must declare his belief that he has complied by attaching a CE mark to his product. After the 1st January 1995 the manufacturer will have two options open to him: compliance with the ESR's in the Machinery Directive <u>or</u> compliance with the national standards that support the Machinery Directive. If the product is a crane or a winch, the standards will be those under the control of CEN/TC147. (Unfortunately not all of the CEN/TC147 standards will be published by then, so for a time after 1st January 1995 manufacturers will only have one option - compliance with the ESR's in the Machinery Directive).'

Note carefully that he says 'After 1st January 1995' – that was two years ahead at that time – 'the manufacturer will have two options open to him; compliance with the ESR's in the Machinery Directive', which we've got, 'or compliance with the appropriate standards that support the Machinery Directive', that's a C Standard, which we still haven't got.

If the product is a crane or winch, the standards will be those under the control of Standard TC 147; that's us. So since 1st January 1995 – that's seven years so far – manufacturers have had only one option. It's not really an option, but there you are; we have got to use the Machinery Directive.

A little thing to finish up with; everyone has so far chickened out of writing a standard for theatre elevators. The standard that we've got does not apply to theatre elevators. The term *theatre elevators* was used at the meeting of the Council of Ministers of the European Communities in discussion of the second amendment of the Machinery Directive. We're now on to the third and fourth amendments, and there's another one in draft. The current wording begins: '*Theatre Elevators: devices for the lifting of persons which are installed permanently or temporarily in theatres and which enable persons, be they actors or stage hands, to move from stage to places adjacent to the stage (basement, flies, wings, orchestra pit, scenery) and vice versa*'.

So that's where we are today. Thank you for listening. Ω

Second speaker: Ray Carter

Ray Carter trained as a Mechanical Engineer but his lifelong interest in the arts led to him becoming a theatre consultant and designing stage machinery and rigging installations for performing arts centres in some 18 countries. Ray was responsible for the preparation of the ABTT Code of Practice for Flying Equipment in the Theatre Industry, published in 1993, and has been the ABTT representative on the British Standard Committee compiling BS 7905. His theatre consultancy practice operates under the name *Next Stage*.

This standard, BS 7905 – 1:2001, does not try to re-invent the wheel, nor does it attempt to impose unrealistic restrictions on the use of overhead flying equipment; it is the combination of the best practices within the industry brought together in a form which may give the basis for a common yardstick. It is intended to aid, not restrict, allowing scope for innovative design and the use of solutions which may not yet have been thought of.

When Paul proposed the preparation of this standard in December 1992 it was estimated somewhat optimistically that a first draft could be expected in May 1993 with completion in 1994; in the event it was published in 2001, so we took nine years, not two.

At the time of the original proposal, the Safety Committee of the ABTT was close to publishing a Code of Practice for Flying, which had been in preparation for several years. As I was editing the Flying Code, it was suggested (by David Adams) that I would be the logical person to represent the ABTT on the BSi sub-committee. This is how I came to be attending the first meeting on 5 May 1993.

In the absence of any better format it was agreed that the draft ABTT Flying Code should be used as a starting point. A cut-and-paste operation took place with suggestions for changes and additions coming initially from Joe Barry (Granada TV), Adam Wildi (PLASA), Paul and myself. From then onwards, information and documentation was received from various quarters, which was processed and edited into the present document. This included receiving comments from the public following publishing of the draft.

From the beginning we wanted a Standard that could be used wherever overhead equipment is used to support performance, not just in theatres but in TV studios, conference halls, outside broadcasts, whatever. This means that some sections have little relevance to a particular technician; for example few stage-hands in the Royal Opera House have to worry about the use of TV monopoles. There was, of course, the problem of different terminology and working practices to overcome, particularly between theatre venues and television studios.

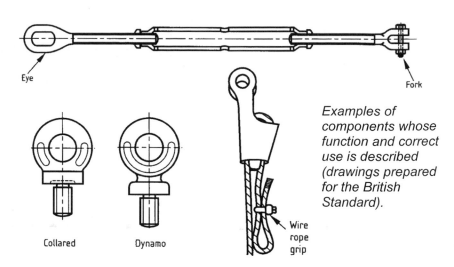

Eye

Fork

Collared   *Dynamo*

Wire rope grip

Examples of components whose function and correct use is described (drawings prepared for the British Standard).

Throughout all our discussions we were very aware that the Standard should be of assistance to both the person designing the equipment for performances and to the crew member on the stage floor who has to use it. Whenever the text appeared to be getting too theoretical, Rikki Newman (Master Carpenter at the Phoenix Theatre in the West End and a member of the Committee) could be relied upon to bring us back to earth (or stage floor level) with a vociferous appeal to make it understandable to the guy on the stage or in the fly gallery.

As briefly as I can, I would like to summarise what the Standard does, using the section headings as an *aide-memoire*:

1. Scope
'This British Standard specifies the requirements for the design and manufacture of components and systems used to lift and traverse equipment and personnel for the following applications:

a) film
b) television
c) theatre and similar entertainment events
d) conferences and exhibitions

Lifts and elevators are not covered by this standard'.

2. Normative references
This is a list of standards which are referred to in the text and therefore constitute part of the Standard.

3. Terms and definitions
Explanation of various words and phrases used throughout the standard.

4. Structural stability
However well designed, manufactured and installed, any overhead equipment must be attached to an adequate structure, be it fly tower, studio ceiling or even a truss structure set up in a park. This section requires that the load-bearing capacity of the structure shall be checked.

5. Components
This section deals with items or sub-assemblies forming part of a complete installation. General strength requirements are noted and relevant factors of safety given.

Items covered include fasteners, fibre ropes, wire ropes and their terminations, chains, clamps, connectors, rigging screws, clews, eyebolts, shackles and suspension bars.

6. Machinery
The requirements for various items of machinery are covered: for instance, the angle of deflection of a wire rope as it leaves or enters a winding drum or pulley, which is known as the 'fleet angle'. Guidance relating to winding drums and pulleys, such as the form of the groove, is given as well as the specific requirements for pile-winding (yo-yo) drums.

Chain drives and gearboxes are dealt with and guidance given as to when secondary brakes should be fitted.

7. Traverse equipment
This section covers such items as tab (curtain) tracks, trolleys, track point systems and drop-out sections.

8. Lifting machinery
You may think that all over-stage lifting equipment is Lifting Machinery. However, in this Standard the term refers to machines used to suspend loads over people. This includes manual rope hauling, manual winches and hoists, powered winches and hoists, and items like donkey motors and secondary drives.

Here guidance is given regarding block and tackle, hemp sets, counterweight flying, winches, Tirfors (wire-rope gripping mechanisms), chain hoists and television equipment such as pantographs and monopoles. The section on counterweight flying, for example, gives recommendations about rope locks, weights, guarding and loading notices.

The manual winch section includes the requirements for an automatic self-

It is particularly important that the building structure can support the loads imposed upon it!

Photo Romualdi, Davidson & Associates, Inc

Further examples of items that are defined in BS 7905: fleet angle to drums and pulleys, groove form, multiple purchase ropes and various curtain tracks.

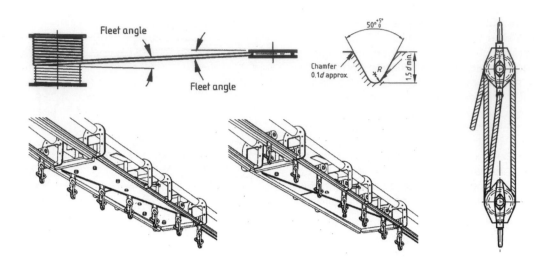

locking device and states that all ratchet and pawl devices be enclosed. The powered winch and hoist section refers to overload and travel limit sensors and gives general guidance on electric and hydraulic drives.

9. Flying of performers
This was one of the most difficult sections to produce, as there are strong advocates of several proprietary methods of 'personnel flying'. However, we believe that this text, covering safe working loads, documentary records required, and the form of in-view flying wires and harnesses, should be applicable to all installations.

10. Controls
This covers the control of lifting and lowering by manual effort or by the control of motive power such as electricity, hydraulics or other non-manual sources. Control stations, emergency stops, operator vigilance, monitoring systems and group control are all included.

11. Marking
Information as to what should be displayed relating to safe working load (SWL), and where loads may be applied is given, as well as the rating labels required on every machine and notices relating to safe operation of remotely-controlled machinery.

Examples of loading notices are also given in an Annex A at the end of the Standard.

12. Documentation and information
Manufacturers are required to supply comprehensive operating instructions and a description of the machinery. Installation instructions are also required, as well as repair and maintenance instructions.

We have tried to produce a Standard which gives guidance and help to all those involved with lifting equipment for performance and broadcast applications. This summary has, of necessity, only touched on a number of aspects. We would be delighted to have comments and questions from anybody here, particularly from those who have read the standard! Ω

Editor's note: BS 7905–1:2001 is strongly recommended reading for all those involved with the use of any overstage or television studio machinery. Copies may be obtained from BSI Customer Services: tel: +44/0 20 8996 9001, fax: +44/0 20 8996 7001, e-mail: orders@bsi-global.com. Standards are also available from the BSI website at http://www.bsi-global.com.

Copies of the ABTT Flying Code of Practice and other theatre Codes relevant to theatres and places of public assembly can be obtained direct from the ABTT office by e-mail: office@abtt.org.uk.

Questions and discussion

William Conner, Schuler & Shook

Just a quick question; I'm working on several standards for rigging in the US, as part of the ANSI standards of the American National Standards Institute which is not a governmental agency. And I was curious; is the BSI a governmental agency?

David Adams, Speaker

No, it's not. The BSI was originally set up by the iron and steel industry in order to sort out the confusion of railway lines, and railway line sections, at the end of the 19th century. It has now got a Royal Charter. It's probably getting close to being a quango – that's a quasi-governmental organisation. It's funded by the Department of Trade and Industry, but it receives only 40%, approximately, of its expenditure from government; the rest it receives as support from industry and support from members and from the sale of its publications. So the short answer is, it has a close link with government, but it isn't government.

Anders Larsson, Drama Institute, Stockholm

Are people aware that we have a Swedish standard also in this subject for lifting equipment in the stage? The British Standard looked quite similar to the Swedish standard, so that was the reason I thought maybe you'd seen it. It took a long time to develop our standard. They started in 1981, I think, and it was completed eight years later.

Paul Mathews, Speaker

I believe we've seen that standard. I've seen many standards from different countries – certainly Norwegian and American standards, and I'm sure a Swedish standard as well. We tried to look at as many as we could find and we tried to include various aspects of opinion that had come out of reading these standards, so hopefully what we've put together is not objectionable to any other member state.

Introduction: Jeff Phillips

Now we're going to move on to conditions relating to the operations and management of performance buildings. There were rules and conditions set out for managing places of entertainment years before the Health and Safety at Work Act came into force, but they set out best practice and conditions to try and ensure the safety of audiences. They've been revised from time to time, but we have recently seen some quite major revisions and some new thinking. David Adams was elected as the editor of those new revisions, and he's here to tell us all about it.

Third speaker: David Adams

The licensing of premises for public entertainment in the United Kingdom is handled locally. The decision whether to grant a licence is determined by locally elected representatives who are accountable to their electorate for their decisions. Entertainment licences are granted after considering planning issues and local morals concerns – after all, what's acceptable in Soho may not wash in Harrogate. It's a good principle. The UK is not unique in this.

However in the UK *all* aspects of entertainments licensing are dealt with locally. This includes the safety standards required both for the design and construction of the building and for the management of the premises. Safety requirements are therefore likewise the subject of local interpretation. This system works extremely well when the authority and its officers are well versed in the problems of entertainment premises, and it permits a great deal of flexibility. But many authorities, particularly in rural areas, lack this expertise and tend to compensate with onerous decisions founded on ignorance. Whether to permit table dancing is no doubt best left to the burghers of Nether Wallop, but should their officers also decide the number and width of the fire exits?

David Adams is a Fellow of the ABTT who has been active as Chairman of its Safety Committee for many years and is retained as its Safety Consultant. He is Joint Chairman of the Committee that produced "*Model National Standard Conditions*", Editor of "*Technical Standards for Places of Entertainment*" and also serves on a number of British Standard (BSi) committees. He was instrumental in getting the important BS on panic devices created and has since contributed to many others. Prior to this, he had a long and active career in the theatre having been both scene and lighting designer, production manager, administrator and licensee.

A SUMMARY HISTORY OF UK SAFETY REGULATIONS

- Manual of Safety Requirements in Theatres, etc Home Office 1934 replaced by:-
- Guide to Fire Precautions in Existing Places of Entertainment, etc, Home Office 1990
- Places of Public Entertainment Technical Regulations, Greater London Council 1965
- Current BS 5588 Part 6 Places of Assembly

Standards can, and do vary, widely throughout the UK – some might even say wildly. There are around 464 different licensing authorities in England and Wales alone. And each authority sets its own requirements as it chooses. Local decision making allows individual risk assessments and provides the possibility of enormous flexibility. Consistency it does not provide.

Even in London, adjacent theatres may be required to operate to different standards – one right wing authority basically leaves all operational matters to the theatre management apart from one annual inspection, whilst its left wing neighbour requires to consider everything in triplicate – that's three inspectors as, and I quote, 'the Council would be held responsible if the set caught fire during a performance'! Some rural areas have no requirement that scenery should not readily ignite in village halls, whilst in Westminster gaffer tape has been considered a dangerous fuel on a fully protected stage.

Theatre operators and particularly touring shows suffer from a wide range of conflicting requirements because of this local decision making.

There clearly is a need for some nationally accepted standards and regulations for places of entertainment. For these to be successful it is important to remember that good governance depends upon the consent of the governed.

This talk is about a unique initiative, headed by the Association of British Theatre Technicians (ABTT) and the District Surveyors' Association, which seeks to address these issues. This initiative unites regulators and the industry in addressing the problems posed by entertainment premises. It takes the form of two reference books backed up by two Standing Committees.

Entertainments Licensing Regulations should be:
- *Consistent*
- *Necessary*
- *Proportionate*

and should offer:
- *Certainty*
- *Clarity*
- *Efficiency*

The two publications referred to in this paper.

MODEL NATIONAL STANDARD CONDITIONS FOR PLACES OF ENTERTAINMENT and Associated Guidance

The Association of British Theatre Technicians
The District Surveyors Association
The Local Government Licensing Forum

TECHNICAL STANDARDS FOR PLACES OF ENTERTAINMENT

The District Surveyors Association
The Association of British Theatre Technicians

Background

- Formation of Local Government Licensing Forum Working Party
  - Setting up and composition
    - Licensing officers
    - Legal officers
  - Scope of review
    - Exclusion of outdoor events
    - Exclusion of cinemas

LGLF Working Party

- Inaugural meeting (February 1998)
- Approach adopted – broadly drafted Standard Conditions + Explanatory Notes
- Draft Conditions and Notes circulated for comment (January 2000)
  - LGA Circular 49/00
  - LGA website
  - direct circulation to interested parties
- Final version of Conditions and Notes (July 2000)

Model National Standard Conditions Working Party

- Recent issue in London of Model Rules of Management for Places of Entertainment following review by Entertainments Licensing Working Party
- Formation of MNSC Working Party comprising members of LGLF Working Party and nominees from London Licensing Co-ordinating Committee (August 2000)
- Scope of review – cinemas included

Approach of Working Party

- Model conditions generally applicable to all premises
- Appendices relating to particular conditions
- Additional model conditions relating to the particular use of premises
- Exceptions where more restricted model conditions apply

Draft conditions and consultation

- Draft Conditions circulated for comment (December 2000)
- Four month consultation period (April 2001)
- Final version of Conditions (July 2001)
- Production version of Conditions (October 2001)
- Publication of Conditions (January 2002)

The first publication may not much concern the people here today. The Model National Standard Conditions for Places of Entertainment were first published in January 2002. They deal with operational matters, including some technical issues mainly to do with scenery and special effects.

These Conditions have been produced in the interests of providing national minimum standards. The basic 41 conditions cover the simplest premises, to which may be added additional conditions dealing with, for instance, cinemas or theatres. Appendices help licensees and the inspecting officers with safety procedures. Each local authority may then add its own specific requirements in respect of a particular premises as deemed necessary. And even if a particular local authority has not adopted the Conditions, they provide consultants, architects, licensees and technicians with a yardstick with which to measure and even question the local authority.

However, most licensing authorities are expected to adopt the Model National Standard Conditions, although this will take a while to achieve given the need for local consultation as a result of the Human Rights Act. A large number of professional bodies have recommended the adoption of the Model National Standard Conditions by all licensing authorities including the bodies listed at the top of the next page. The responsible Secretary of State, the Rt. Hon. Tessa Jowell, MP, also supports the initiative.

Of particular interest to us today is Condition 11 (a). This brings me to the second publication, the Technical Regulations detailed in Appendix 1 of the Model National Standard Conditions which originated in Technical Standards for Places of Entertainment first published in April 2001.

Now some of you may feel that, what with the Building Regulations and the activities of the Health & Safety Executive, not to mention Brussels, we could do without any more regulations. You may even side with Brunel's comments to the Royal Commission in 1848: '... *the Commission ... will ... lay down ... 'rules' to be observed or, in other words, to embarrass and shackle the progress of improvement tomorrow by recording and registering as law the prejudices or errors of today ...'*

BODIES SUPPORTING ADOPTION OF THE MODEL NATIONAL STANDARD CONDITIONS

The Association of British Theatre Technicians
The Association of Building Engineers
The Association of London Government
The British Entertainment & Discotheque Association
The British Institute of Inn-Keeping
The Chartered Institute of Environmental Health
The District Surveyors Association
The Local Government Association
The Local Government Licensing Forum
The Royal Institute of Chartered Surveyors
The Society of Entertainment Licensing Practitioners
The Trading Standards Institute

Remember, however, that in Birmingham in the mid-nineteenth century there were at least 128 different thread forms. In 1965 you could still buy sacks of handmade nuts and bolts in Clerkenwell and have to search to find the single nut that fitted the bolt to hand. No one, I suggest, seriously doubts the value of equipment standardisation. The same economies of effort must surely apply to safety.

Most decisions regarding safety can be made by reference to agreed common standards. These standards should allow a freedom of choice when this is important but also provide a common basis between users and enforcers for the mundane decision.

Almost all local authorities have issued some form of technical requirements, frequently buried within their operational procedures. Many do not go much further than fire precautions – along with banning female mud-wrestling on Good Fridays! The best regulations were based directly on or derived from the Greater London Council's (GLC) Technical Regulations of 1965. Although excellent in their time – the ABTT helped to write them! – the GLC's Regulations were highly prescriptive and excessively detailed, which have led to a number of problems.

Condition 11 (a)
The Licensee shall ensure that the premises continue to comply with the Technical Regulations as set out in Appendix 1. No alterations shall be made to the approved arrangements except with consent.

The problems with the GLC Regulations were mainly that:

- They were far too specific – with the result that the detailed technical requirements were often out of date and frequently inappropriate to a particular situation.
- The expertise and resources available to individual licensing authorities varied enormously – consequently regulations were inconsistent between authorities and enforcement was extremely variable.
- This meant that the regulations were not always understood or respected by the entertainment industry with the consequent threat to safety that this implies.
- Unnecessary expense was frequently incurred because of local variations which could not be readily resolved given the absence of any central resource to resolve matters of interpretation or dispute. This particularly affected touring productions and transfers between venues.
- The regulations were often too narrowly concerned with the safety of the public, and ignored risks to staff and performers.
- The regulations were based upon a mandatory approach that frequently totally ignored the concept of assessment of risk.

Let me tell you a brief story about John, our local fire inspector. We had a weight-operated release held in the 'on' position by a tracker wire. This served to turn off the gas boiler in emergency. It used to jam regularly – that is, on every inspection by the theatre surveyor, the insurers, during the fire brigade annual survey and with the gas board – and would probably do so in a fire as well. The problem was the tracker wire was thin and stiff and the brass pulleys had very shallow grooves so the wire used to jump off the pulleys and jam in their mounts. But the installation complied with BS 483 or some such number. My chap decided to change the system for a robust nylon string on deep groove pulleys as used in hospitals and everything worked wonderfully. Until John arrived – "I cannot permit that string. Boiler release mechanisms must use a metal wire." Why? This works. "No – the string might melt in a fire." And? "The rule is quite clear." "But the gas would be turned off if the string melts – don't you see it fails

safe?" Now John was no fool, so he let the string remain!

There were regular problems with the GLC's Technical Regulations, which were usually ameliorated by the exercise of discretion by the enforcer. But discretion – risk assessment – implies understanding and a readiness to accept responsibility. And that's the problem. Many enforcement officers lack specific training and rely on excessive prescription to cover their ignorance and thus avoid the possibility of criticism for a wrong decision. And some are even judged by their number of successful prosecutions.

The acceptance of responsibility also implies the competence to make decisions. This entails an understanding of the actual intention behind a safety recommendation rather than just concentrating on the form of words. Back to my friend John, the fire inspector!

Risk assessment is an excellent tool but it needs to be based on knowledge. And risk assessment involves making choices. These choices involve the concept of reasonableness and the acceptance of responsibility. The concept means accepting that different people will come up with differing resolutions to safety issues; the concept of responsibility also implies the possibility even of (honest) error. Absolute safety is a chimaera – or perhaps rather a siren luring mankind to madness. The only way to ensure that no one can die in a theatre is to close all theatres. But staying at home is much more dangerous.

The Technical Standards come from a collaboration between enforcers and the industry who have each recognised that the one has an imperfect understanding of the other's problems and are prepared to learn from the other. The Technical Standards provide the guidance that is appropriate to the needs of the entertainment industry, guidance that remains flexible enough for performance needs but allows some commonality of approach between the various protagonists involved in safety issues. Advice is offered on safe standards and good practice for all types of entertainment premises.

The Technical Standards are firmly based on the philosophy that regulations should be goal-setting, rather than prescriptive, that recommendations should not be regarded as mandatory and that the proper

---

Risk assessment enables solutions which are:
- *Necessary*
- *Proportionate*
- *Efficient*

Solutions should be:
- *Certain*
- *Consistent*
- *Clear*

Collaboration – agreement, not enforcement.

Goal-setting – not prescription.

Model Conditions generally applicable to all premises

- Part I : General
- Part II : Applications requiring a specific consent
- Part III : Particular responsibilities of the licensee
- Part IV : Safety (including fire safety) conditions
- Part V : Sanitary, heating, lighting and ventilation conditions

Additional model conditions relating to the particular use of premises

- Closely seated audiences
- Film exhibitions
- Door supervisors
- Special effects
- (Keeping good order)
- Hypnotism
- Performances for children
- Scenery and properties
- Indoor sports entertainments
- Striptease or similar entertainments
- Stage performances

Appendices relating to particular conditions

- Technical regulations
- Specimen form of licence
- Staff training
- Fire log book
- Specimen staff duty register
- Maintenance of fire equipment
- Specimen check list for safety checks
- Certificates to be submitted

Exceptions where more restricted model conditions apply

- Subsidiary films and videos
- Films and videos in hotels
- Premises used occasionally for public entertainment

assessment of risk should illuminate all decisions regarding safety. The Technical Standards avoid prohibition, and replace the prescriptive rule by guidance, and the requirement for absolutes by moderation. Some will find this upsetting, even unhelpful. But responsibility implies a willingness to make decisions. And decisions need to be based on understanding.

The Technical Standards offer a unique approach to licensing requirements which marries the British Standards format of Commentary + Recommendations with the Building Regulations approach of Regulation + 'deemed to satisfy' Approved Documents.

The book deals with the physical requirements for building or converting, equipping and maintaining any entertainment premises through a series of related discussions. The book is concerned with the safety and well-being of all users of the premises. Disabled access considerations are addressed within the main body of text rather than regarded as an add-on. The scope is very wide, with sections ranging from considerations of site to hygiene, from structure to special effects, from fire safety to stage engineering. Problems of conversion of existing premises and smaller premises are also addressed.

Each section starts with a *Commentary* that sets out a particular issue with respect to places of entertainment.

A *Technical Regulation* follows, which gives a clear functional requirement that should apply to any premises used for entertainment. As functional requirements, these Regulations are not likely to need frequent revision.

Recommendations come next, which detail ways of meeting the requirement of the Technical Regulation. Advice is offered on safe standards and good practice for all types of entertainment premises. Whether or not a Licensing Authority has adopted the Technical Regulations, the advice is apposite to any operator of an entertainment premises. These are Recommendations, and other ways are possible. The format is not intended to stifle innovation.

Updates are the responsibility of the Standing Committee, which is drawn from experienced enforcers and from the industry. Users of the Technical Standards can advise the Committee of difficulties of interpretation, new products and new ideas. The Committee continues to meet regularly to consider any issues raised. Revisions are quickly incorporated in the book and posted on a web site for those who have already bought the publication.

To give an example of the general approach we can look at Regulation 35: '*Any mechanical installation shall be arranged so as to minimise any risk to the safety of the public, performers and staff.*'

This is dealt with under sections K1 dealing with mechanical installations for use by the public and K2 on stage engineering. For instance let us take K2.31 on secondary suspensions:

K2.31

'*A minimum safety factor of eight is recommended for all flying installations. Therefore, provided the equipment has been rigged and tested appropriately, secondary suspensions should not normally be necessary. If there are any doubts about the quality of the installation it should be re-inspected by a competent person and rectified if necessary. Providing a secondary suspension to an inadequate installation could easily promote a false sense of safety. However, non-combustible secondary suspensions such as chains or steel wire bonds, should always be provided:*
a) for equipment such as luminaires and loudspeakers hung on bars using hook clamps or similar fittings where an accident with a piece of moving scenery might cause the equipment to be dislodged from the bar;
b) where equipment is rigged temporarily;
c) where a combustible suspension, for example a fibre rope or a textile sling, has been used for convenience when rigging equipment.'

This is followed by a Note:
'*This does not apply to backcloths, drops and similar items rigged in a 'hemp house' where combustible suspensions are acceptable for all bars other than those used to suspend luminaires.*'

Some of you may not see relevance of the Technical Standards to existing premises. However, these Technical Standards will inform your risk assessments. You can identify to what extent the premises, installations and equipment meet desirable standards and take compensatory steps where necessary and also plan for improvements. They can also solve production problems. To give an example, let us look at F2.39:

F2.39

'*Where there may be operational problems with light spill or glare from internally-illuminated signs it is important that the correct escape route sign is used. This sign is specified in BS 5499 as suitable for use with internally-illuminated signs and uses a white figure in a green doorway.*'

We all know you shouldn't turn off the escape route signs (EXIT signs until they became a running man) although they may cause problems with light spill – so what can you do? F2.39 discusses the problem. By the way, the ABTT pioneered and tested the reverse format for the internally illuminated running man sign specified in BS 5499.

F2.39 concludes with this Note:

'*Where light spill or glare from internally-illuminated escape route signs still proves to be a problem, it may be necessary to reduce their light output. This may be achieved by the use of neutral density filters. Where the normal lighting may be dimmed, it may also be appropriate to dim one or both supplies to the internally-illuminated escape route signs as the normal lighting is reduced. Where dimmers are used they should be arranged so that:*
a) the luminance of the signs is at least 2 cd/m^2; and
b) the signs automatically return to full brilliance when the normal lighting is restored; and
c) in the event of the failure of either supply, the remaining lighting to the signs is immediately and automatically restored to full brilliance.'

And now a quick story. Many years ago, we made some alterations to provide a small office for the stage doorkeeper who had previously occupied a cupboard. At the request of the GLC Theatre Surveyor, I provided an adjustable air grille – what's known as a hit-and-miss ventilator – over the doors leading to the dressing-room corridor. This, he suggested, would assist the stage doorkeeper by improving the ventilation of the stage door office in hot weather. Three months later the chap from environmental health came round and required the hit-and-miss to be replaced by an air brick to guarantee at least 3 air changes per hour – and probably 75 when the wind was westerly! Just before licence renewal the London Fire Brigade came round and – horrors! – the air-brick was connecting the dressing room corridor and stage door areas and could lead to smoke transfer in case of fire. The air-brick was bricked up. On licence renewal the Theatre Surveyor "requested" the hit-and-miss ventilator be replaced. For the next few years at each of the many inspections we changed the hole or the air-brick. Then I got the three conflicting parties into the same space, together with two bricks, a ventilator, a hit-and-miss grille and some sand and cement.   And I left them to it ... Now ... I am not saying that the Technical Standards would have immediately resolved that problem but they would have helped – and the Standing Committee could have solved it. For the record the Fire Brigade won, but – and it's a very big BUT – they all quite failed to notice that the stage door office was lined in 2" exposed cork – disastrous in a fire – and totally a product of my ignorance – and quite contrary to Recommendation E2.07.

All parties need to be educated.   The Technical Standards will help. Thank you for listening. Ω

Editor's note: Copies of the documents discussed by David Adams, the Technical Standards for Places of Entertainment 2001 and the Model National Standard Conditions for Places of Entertainment 2002 can be obtained direct from the ABTT office by e-mail: office@abtt.org.uk.

Introduction: Jeff Phillips

When these Standards were published, a Code of Practice was sent out for comment to various people in the ABTT and selected people in the industry. Since David is the Chairman of the Safety Committee and would therefore normally receive the document he had just edited, we asked Peter Angier if he would chair the ABTT Committee to review this Code of Practice. Peter has come to tell us about this review.

Fourth speaker: Peter Angier

I'm a theatre consultant and so I am particularly interested in the design and planning of theatre buildings, and I have a slightly different slant on all of these regulations, standards and guidelines. And I'm also not like David Adams, and I don't share his passion for sitting on committees. But I've done it, starting with BS 5588, because I had my own particular aims. Those are fairly unexceptional aims and include removing all unnecessary restrictions – and by that I mean things which are out of date. People often don't realise that these regulations, standards, etc all start from something. They are very rarely written from scratch, and as time goes on you accumulate things that are just out of date. So they have to go. Even now, the Technical Standards have clauses in them that have a sort of flavour of the 1930s.

Just consider the anomalies; by which I mean things which have, again, accumulated over time. People put in a particular sort of clause to deal with a particular problem without looking at the Standards overall. And those too produce contradictions. They have to go. And then there are the issues of increased design and planning freedom. You have to try to use this when you get the chance. I've got one relevant example, rather a nice example, although it goes back a long time. There was a time when the GLC had a rigid rule that if you had 500 seats or more you had to have a safety curtain. I've actually been involved in planning an auditorium where the seat numbers were tweaked to get them just under 500 so that they didn't have to have a safety curtain. That restriction was removed in BS 5588,

Peter Angier is Principal of Carr & Angier, Theatre Consultants. He started in the theatre at the Cambridge Arts and was Technical Director at the Mermaid before taking up the post of Production and Theatre Manager at the National Theatre School of Canada in Montreal. He was Editor of the Journal of the ABTT and has been an active Committee member on ABTT and British Standards Committees. He also organised a previous Conference for the ABTT.

Learning Resources Centre

and it was an achievement which everybody takes for granted now. So you can have a safety curtain or not as you choose, with suitable safeguards.

My other main aim is to stop things getting any worse. And it isn't done with malign intent, but these committees don't always work. They get an assembly of people from the Home Office, fire officers and so on, and they all think of things which would be a nice idea to have. And if you aren't very careful a committee produces things which are very restrictive on the theatre, and we all need to be vigilant.

Fifteen years ago I think that the legislative threat really centred on construction. These days, because what has been produced in terms of guidelines is so good, it's more likely to be an operational problem produced from the sort of stream of Health and Safety rules which are coming though, but that's actually a different story.

The committees that produce these things are usually based in London – in fact I think they are invariably based in London – and they have a metropolitan outlook. For them, advisory standards are not a problem. They understand the difficulties overall, and they can see that people should be able to produce other solutions. I can remember clearly the BS 5588 committee. They would get immersed in some wrangle about a detailed point and they'd always fall back on the comforting thought, "Oh well, it's only advisory; people still have the freedom to propose something else." That is just about all right in central London. It wears a bit thin in the wilds of Islington and Hackney and in the rest of the country it's not what they want at all. What the rest of the country wants is rules. They want rules in a book and they want to be able to administer with the sort of time-honoured phrase '*It says here ...*' and if they're in any sort of doubt they tend to fall back on the Building Regulations; and in theatres, using Building Regulations can cause trouble.

The great achievement of the new Technical Standards book, in my opinion, is that its contents look like rules and feel like rules, but actually they're still advisory. And they're still advisory because they are not being formally adopted. In my experience they are being accepted and they're being used, but they're not being adopted by local authorities so they don't actually have the force of rules. I've been

wondering about why this should be so, and it isn't just their comforting appearance; I think it's because they have authoritative tone which is based on real knowledge, and they give the reasoning behind a recommendation. The old standards, the British Standards, always have an introductory commentary which tries to explain what is behind a rule, but the new Technical Standards have taken that much further and they are very informative indeed in the commentary, which is extremely useful and helps considerably in dealing with building control officers and firemen.

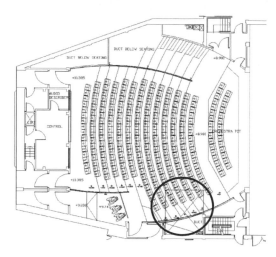

I've just got a few examples of theatres being special cases. The auditorium with a stepped gangway shown above doesn't have much similarity with a conventional staircase, but in building-control terms people have often tried to apply the rules for a staircase to a stepped aisle, and it's extremely useful to have a Technical Standard which states absolutely plainly that the step gangway is not a stairway.

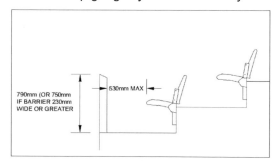

Above is a section of an auditorium showing the relaxed standard for guardrails at the front of a tier. This has got a long history, goes back to a very early British Standard which was modified by, I think, the ABTT Theatre Planning Committee's request, so that you could lower the rail to improve sightlines from a tier. It's gone through a lot, including BS 5588 part 6, and it has been reinterpreted and more clearly expressed in the current Technical Standards. Very useful indeed – absolutely crucial for sightlines from balconies.

The 3-D sightline viewed from a particularly bad seat in a new auditorium shows the effect of an 1100 mm (3'-7¼") high guard-rail which is next to a gangway and therefore has to be at that height. I think of that seat as being more or less saleable. But if you apply the Building Regulations to that guard-rail, you would have to make the gap below it small enough so that a 100 mm (4") diameter ball wouldn't pass through it. The Technical Standards have now brought in a relaxation of that, so that you are allowed a 225 mm (9") ball, and that is what this hand-rail complies with. And it makes the difference for that particular seat between it being saleable or not saleable.

The plan of the auditorium balcony is just to remind us all that boxes still exist, even in a modern auditorium; the Technical Standards have taken further the guard-rail rule and they have allowed a box which has loose seating to have a low rail which people can look over. It is absolutely essential to have a low rail, over which people can see easily, in such a location close to the stage. Previously, no Standard had dealt with the fact that you had a low rail and loose seating in theatre boxes. And now we are actually permitted that, although it doesn't define the number of people you can have in a box – it just says *small,* which is still open to interpretation.

My last illustration is slightly personal; the old GLC rules had a bit of a grey area about whether or not you could open store rooms, prop rooms, that sort of thing, directly off a stage, and how they should be fire-separated. We managed to get into BS 5588 that they were permitted; then I had to wait for a theatre where I could put this relaxation into practice. This was the first one, which was actually Milton Keynes Theatre, and you can see, on the stage right side (left of the picture), there is a prop room and an electrical store opening straight off the stage. And very handy these rooms are in that location.

I would now like to say a little bit about the operation of a safety curtain. This is drawn from the Technical Standards and it shows how the informative commentary can be helpful.

Image: Carr & Angier

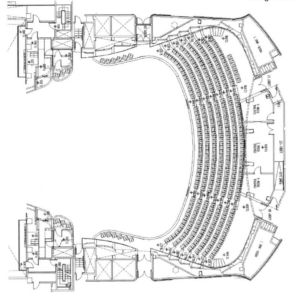

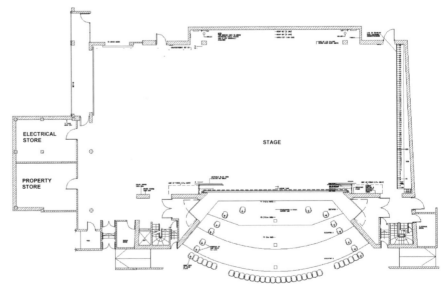

Above: the restricted view from a seat adjacent to an aisle, centre: near-stage boxes shown on a balcony plan, and bottom: the stage plan of the Milton Keynes Theatre showing, on the left side, the prop room and an electrical store opening directly off the stage.

ELECTRICAL STORE

PROPERTY STORE

STAGE

The effects of air pressure on a safety curtain and of make-up air being allowed into a fire on stage from under the safety curtain.

If we look at a theatre in which there is a fire developing on the stage, it has smoke vents at the top of the fly tower, which are open, but there's no safety curtain, and it's highly likely that smoke, fumes, flame, will get out into that auditorium very quickly indeed and smother the people in the top tier (**1**).

If you add a safety curtain and you have absolutely no air supply into the stage, you get a rapidly reducing pressure in the stage area, which is fine; it ensures that the air movement, if it's going anywhere at all, will be from auditorium to stage. The difficulty is that if you have no air supply at all, the reduction in pressure is probably excessive. The neutral pressure plane (NPP), shown where the dotted line is, is probably even a bit low, and in those circumstances it would be up near the smoke vents. The potential hazard is that the safety curtain will bow under this air pressure and might even pull out of its guides (**2**). The remedy would be to have a safety curtain so excessively thick that it would get in the way of the theatre rigging.

So if you introduce air from outside the stage, the safety curtain is relatively okay, but the neutral pressure plane sinks to below the top of the safety curtain (**3**). As a result, there is a chance that smoke will leak around the safety curtain and get into the auditorium.

So the right answer is to introduce a small amount of air into the stage from the auditorium, the neutral pressure plane moves above the safety-curtain line, and you continue to maintain a flow of air from auditorium to stage, leaving the auditorium safe for people to escape (**4**). And that's why, if you've got a safety curtain at all, it would be better with a few holes in it! Ω

The safety curtain and protecting the audience and the building is discussed more fully in **OSCR 2** *Audience Safety.*

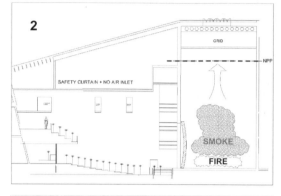

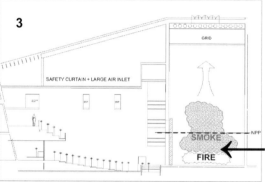

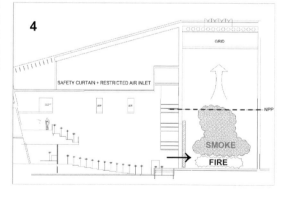

Questions and discussion

Jeff Phillips, Chairman

Well, I've learnt a few things as well! Do you think we should have all these standards; are there standards we don't have that we ought to add to the list? Has anybody got anything to say about additional areas to cover or any questions on the technical aspects?

David Wilkins, Lancelyn Theatre Supplies

I've started to work a lot with architects in the design of theatre spaces and I've found that the Technical Conditions are very much a common-sense document, as are the Model Conditions, and I commend very much its use. I do lack a little guidance on electrical phasing requirements, because there is an old Health & Safety Executive (HSE) document which stipulates that there shall not be more than one phase on a lighting bar, and I haven't seen anything recent that says whether this is still a requirement or not.

Various comments from the floor

I don't think it is! I do know of lighting bars with three phases on them. I don't think it's banned, is it?

David Adams, Speaker

I think the problem is that, as Peter Angier said, there is a tendency for these committees to be London-based, and this has not been a London problem for quite a long time. This was because there was a guidance note sent out by the HSE stating that where the three phases were not accessible to the public then it would not be regarded as a problem. I will make a note that when we're looking at that area to consider whether to add something on three-phase supplies. One of the things I would stress about this document is that it does depend on the industry coming forward and saying what they see the failings and omissions to be. If we are not careful we will get the enforcers saying, "This isn't clear enough; we would like to insist upon ..." and it's up to the industry to press for greater freedom. But I will certainly make a note to see if we can pick up this point about three-phase supplies.

Alan Russell, Theatre Projects Consultants

One of my great concerns is this three-phase business. Let everybody remember that, before they have the privilege of killing themselves on 415V, they could readily kill themselves on 230 and 240V as well. The 415V is still only 230V to earth, anyway.

William Conner, Schuler & Shook

I was curious about the matter of the aisle stairs or gangway with steps; what would you like to permit that is different from a stairway?

Peter Angier, Speaker

Principally the different 'goings', and also a variation in tread height.

William Conner, Schuler & Shook

I take it that different 'goings' refers to uneven tread depths?

Peter Angier, Speaker

Front-to-back, referred to here in the UK as the 'going'. Because where a seatway joins the gangway we sometimes like to have a wider section.

William Conner, Schuler & Shook

Just as a point of information, most of the theaters in the US have recently, or in the past decade, moved towards requiring uniform tread depths – or equal goings, I guess would be the translation.

Peter Angier, Speaker

Well, I think you're making a big mistake.

William Conner, Schuler & Shook

Having unequal tread depths (goings) is not right for the person that's coming from the top row down or from the bottom row up. It's irrelevant that there are intermediate rows of seats. To that person it's a stairway.

Peter Angier, Speaker

Well, that's not the view in this country. And for good reasons; you would make it very difficult to design a good auditorium if you insisted on that rule. Isn't there a problem getting into the seating row or out of the row? And such a restriction would rule out certain shapes of auditorium.

William Conner, Schuler & Shook

We permit unequal risers for reasons of sightlines, but still require the uniform tread depth. I don't think accessing the rows has been a problem. I don't know if you're familiar with the work of Jake Pauls (a consultant from Silver Spring, Maryland), but he's done quite a bit of study of people moving in aisles, including filming many hours of it and observing it. I'm convinced by his research that equal tread depths result in fewer stumbles and fewer falls, and fewer injuries. And I haven't found that auditorium shaping has been affected. But I'd be curious to see an example how that would happen.

Peter Angier, Speaker

I am familiar with some of Jake Pauls' work, though not all of it, and indeed with that of Jonathan Simes. I think the UK view is that the junction between the seat way and the aisle is a critical place for stumbling, and to get that junction perfect or as near perfect as we can, we accept a reduction in standard in the gangway aisle itself; that's the thinking behind it. But clearly you have a different approach. I don't think from what I've seen that it's possible to obtain a perfect junction and a total continuity of tread depth and rise uniformly through an auditorium.

Jeff Phillips, Chairman

Okay. Are you all satisfied? You're all happy about that sort of difficulty? Was producing these Standards a waste of time? How many people are going to use BS 7905? Are you going to use the Standard? Is it going to be helpful? From that reaction, it's hard to say! Well, we've given you an idea about them, anyway. The Technical Standards and Model Conditions will be available at the ABTT stand at the Theatre Show after the Conference or from the ABTT office. Thank you all very much. Ω

Safety in motion

Chairman: Alan Russell, Director, Theatre Projects Consultants
Speakers: Ted Fregon, Chief Executive Officer, Bytecraft Automation Pty Ltd
            Dave Ludlam, Power and Control System Consultant, Theatreplan

First speaker: Ted Fregon

I'm going to start with a joke – it's always a good thing to do! I was talking to my wife last night and I said, "I've got all this preparation done, but I haven't got a joke," and she reminded me of an engineering joke that I was told about two weeks ago. The question is posed: *How do you send an engineer into complete despair?* And the answer is: *You tie him (or her) up in a chair, and you put a map, incorrectly folded, just out of his reach.* I actually think that was completely appropriate for this subject! About two years ago when Richard Brett asked me if I'd participate in this Conference, he asked me what I'd like to speak about. The thing that I wanted to address was international safety standards. And the other thing that can drive an engineer into complete despair is trying to understand and work out the labyrinth of international standards that are appropriate to our industry.

I've got two warnings to start with. Firstly, this is a really superficial view of a very complex area. I don't profess to be a safety engineer or an expert in this discipline, but I'm a practitioner in the stage-machinery control field, and I'll give you my best interpretation of the standards scenario. The other thing is that this technology is absolutely littered with TLAs (a TLA is a Three-Letter Acronym) and we have actually coined another phrase called a PLA, which is a Poly-Letter Acronym, because lots of the terms that you're going to hear have got five characters in them! In fact, the one that I'm not going to refer to during this presentation is SOUP. Does anyone know what SOUP is? SOUP is Software Of Uncertain Pedigree. At that point I think we'll move on!

Around the world there are lots of different standards regimes which we could talk about. The United States has a regime; there are some industry-promoted standards regimes. But the ones I'm going to address today, briefly, are in the European scene, including the EC Machinery Directive. Dave Ludlam is going to go into that in quite a lot more depth, when he follows on. I'm going to talk a little bit about the German DIN regime, and if I go wrong, I hope our German friends in the room will explain where I've gone wrong, so we will all know for the future. And then I'm going to focus on the new standard that my company has done a lot of work on, which is IEC 61508.

Introduction

To embark on the construction of any modern theatre is to undertake one of the most complex and potentially compromising of all construction projects. A development on the scale of a national opera house presents the added opportunity, and responsibility, to build a socially significant monument with the very best architectural and engineering values. But, foremost, a theatre must be a functional, efficient and safe space for both the performers and audience.

Among the many challenges faced by the designers of such a prominent project is adopting the latest technology whilst ensuring reliability, low risk and reasonable cost. Around the world, national and international standards continue to emerge which impinge on most aspects of theatre design.

Stage Automation: Functional Safety

Safety and reliability are the highest priorities for an engineer when commencing the design of any new machine. Next is the engineer's natural desire to employ the latest innovations and to achieve a certain elegance of design. The compromises that inevitably arise are essential components in the evolutionary process of developing ever better solutions to what are often old problems. Just as society's expectations advance, so to does technology's capacity to deliver and vice versa. The micro-

Ted Fregon is Chief Executive Officer of Bytecraft Automation Pty Ltd, a privately owned and operated company which he co-founded in 1984, and which is the only company specialising in both lighting and automation control system solutions. Ted has formal qualifications in Electronic Engineering and more than 20 years in stage machinery and stage lighting control system design and development. He has a particular interest in international codes and regulations.

A summary of the many features that contribute to 'Functional Safety'.

"Measures intended to reduce risk of injury resulting from a hazard"
- Emergency Stop
- Brake control & monitoring
- Over-speed detection
- Limit switches
- Crossed wire
- Overload
- DMB (Dead Man's Button)
- Synchronisation
- Clear User Interface (MMI)

Historically, electronic and software solutions have not been recommended for Safety Critical Systems

processor has enabled engineers to build control systems of incredible complexity when compared with the electro-mechanical solutions of previous years. But until quite recently, safety functions have still been implemented with the old electro-mechanical technology.

Perhaps predictably, until recently, Germany has been the source of much of the acknowledged 'best-practice' in the field of measurable machinery safety. In particular, the German standards for electronic control system safety were unique and were adopted by many stage-machinery control-system designers. However, after a decade of development a new international standard has emerged which significantly advances the state of the art for control-system safety.

Overview

A stage machinery system should be designed according to the most appropriate contemporary safety-design principles. Usually these principles are codified in national standards or codes of practice which may be variously industry, national or international documents.

One of the most difficult problems facing consultants, manufacturers and owner/operators alike is the determination of the appropriate standards environment for a given project. The choice of standards is often not straightforward and can be dependent on territory, industry segment and individual interpretation. In some territories, for example in the European Community, law mandates compliance with certain standards, whilst in other countries the situation can be entirely voluntary and unclear.

Even in the highly regulated European environment, there can be conflicting national and international standards and literally hundreds from which to choose. Nevertheless, in an increasingly litigious and safety-conscious world, determination of, and compliance with, the most appropriate standards is critically important. The following discussion will deal with the current international standards regime in relation to control-system design.

Electronic Control Systems

Machinery control systems are responsible for the safe and reliable coordination of the components of a machine so that they collectively perform the desired function. The earliest control systems were constructed from electromechanical (relay) logic whereas today's systems have evolved into often-complex arrangements of electrical, electronic, and programmable electronic components (E/E/PE). This evolutionary process continues still, and is the natural by-product of technological developments. The last 50 years have seen quantum leaps in technology: from the transistor in 1947 to the first microprocessor in 1971 and thereon. As this evolution took place, the safety-related parts of the control system were implemented using the older electromechanical technology, whilst the non-safety critical 'control' functions were migrated to newer electronic and programmable-electronic systems. This was because of a belief among the engineering and regulatory community that electromechanical systems were more reliable, hence safer, than the electronic or programmable (software-based) equivalent. The fundamental reason for the preference for electromechanical solutions, especially for safety-critical systems, is that, quite literally, one can see and confirm the correct operation of the relays involved. There is a basic mistrust of programmable solutions where (a) it is impossible to see what is going on internally and (b) exhaustive verification of design and implementation is either difficult or even practically impossible.

Many of the control-system safety standards in force around the world today have evolved over this period and are, arguably, no longer relevant in the 21st century. For example, until its update in 1997, the European standard EN60204 demanded an electromechanical solution to safety-critical control gear. But new standards, which have evolved over the last 10 years, since the late 80s deal with using complex programmable systems to provide safety features.

European Machinery Directive

The Machinery Directive is a law of the European Parliament; it was launched in 1989 and updated in 1998. The Machinery Directive is one of three directives with which I guess most people are familiar, the other two being the Low Voltage Directive and the Electromagnetic Compatibility (EMC) Directive. The Machinery Directive lists some essential safety requirements, and then it defines how to implement those requirements by directing the user to a list of standards. The list of standards are actually listed in a document called OJEC – or Official Journal of the European Community – which I took the liberty of printing out from the internet. There are actually 340 standards included, so compliance is a nightmare. The particular standards, though, that generally apply to the areas in which most people in this room are going to be interested, are listed. These include EN 954, EN 418 and so on, about which David is going to speak a little more later.

Classifications 4 and 5

I'm going to leave the EC system for the moment and just take a quick look at the DIN (Deutsches Institut für Normung) Standards. Since the early 1980s, first in Germany and then in the international community, standards have been developed to guide engineers in the design of safety-critical electronic and, especially, programmable control systems.

Within the stage machinery community, the German control-system safety-standard regime is commonly referred to as the TÜV Class IV or V Standard, where TÜV stands for Technischer Überwachungs-Verein. This is in fact a misnomer because TÜV does not *publish* standards, but rather, *they test and certify compliance* with external standards. In fact, the Class 5 designation refers to a requirement of DIN V 19 250-1989.

The Standard 19 250 is a publication by DIN, and TÜV is one of the organisations who can test for compliance with it. They're not the only one, by the way. Another interesting thing that's not widely known is that this standard has never actually been published as a formal, final standard; it's a preliminary standard, as is its complement, which is 0801. I believe the reason for this is that DIN does not publish national standards when there are international standards which cover the same area.

Law of the European Parliament

- Launched in 1989 as 89/392/EEC
- Currently version: Directive 98/37/EC

| "*ESRs*" Essential Safety Requirements
| Mandated standards are updated regularly in the OJ: "Official Journal of the European Community"
| References "harmonised" standards only
| Standards for Control Systems include:

- **EN 954-1** — Safety of machinery. Safety-related parts of control systems. General principles for design.
- **EN 418** — Safety of Machinery. Emergency stop equipment, functional aspects, etc.
- **EN 1050** — Safety of machinery. Principles for risk assessment.
- **EN 1037** — Safety of machinery. Prevention of unexpected start-up.
- **EN 60204** — Safety of machinery. Electrical equipment of machines.

About the time when this standard was being developed, the new international standard, IEC 61508, was coming into existence, so the work on this one was never completed. That's my interpretation; I believe it to be true, but I'm happy to be contradicted on that.

From the point of view of control system safety for stage machinery, there are actually six relevant DIN documents:

- DIN V 19 250: Control Technology: Fundamental safety aspects to be considered for Measurement and Control Protection Equipment (MSR).
- DIN 19 251: Guiding technology: MSR safety devices; requirements and measures for the secure function.
- DIN V VDE 0801: Principles for Computers in Safety Related Systems.
- DIN 56921-11: Backdrop Hoists.
- DIN 56925: Scenery Hoists.
- DIN 56940: Stage Elevators.

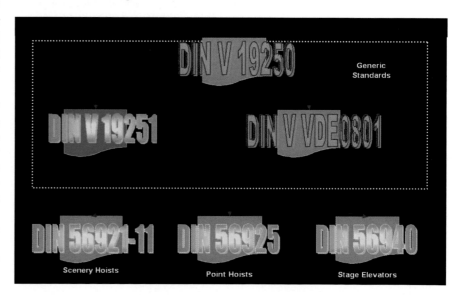

DIN V 19 250 (1989)

Essentially, DIN19 250 provides a means of assessing and quantifying the risk of injury resulting from the malfunction of a safety function in a system. The output of the process outlined in the standard is a 'Risk Class' or *Anforderungklassen (AK)* in the range 1 to 8. Importantly, for a given system, say a stage machinery control system, the Risk Class is not uniform for every function of the system but is assessed case by case for each safety function. Class 1 is the lowest risk category and 8 is the highest risk category.

As discussed later, it has been determined that the highest AK applicable to stage machinery safety-critical functions is 4 or 5: thus the phrase: TÜV Class V. The uncertainty (4 or 5) results from the subjective nature of the standard where, for example, one must make an assessment of 'Occurrence Probability' being high, low or very low.

Once the Risk Class has been determined, two further standards, DIN19 251 & DIN V VDE 0801, provide guidelines for the techniques necessary to reduce the risk to tolerable levels. These measures vary according to the Risk Class. As the Risk Class increases, so too does the complexity and rigour of the design solution.

DIN 19 250 tells us what risk category applies to our application – for example, 7 or 8 would apply to a nuclear power plant or something like that and 1 is a trivial case. Once we've determined the risk category (and for theatres it's been agreed generally that Risk Class 4 or 5 applies), then we take that Risk Class and we apply it, and look up the rules according to DIN Standard, VDE 0801, and that tells us what are the things that we have to do to actually comply with that Risk Class.

DIN 56921-11(1997)

- Covers electrical & mechanical aspects of backdrop hoists
- References more than 30 external standards
- Leaves some specifications to be determined by "agreement"
- Provides guidance in application of DIN19250 in determination of AK#.

DIN V 19250 (1989)

- "Control Technology: Fundamental safety aspects to be considered for Measurement and Control Protection Equipment (MSR)"
- Defines Risk Classes or "Anforderungklassen" and use of *Risk Graph*
- Misnomer: *"TÜV Class IV or V"*
- Preliminary Standard

DIN V 19251

- "Guiding technology: MSR safety devices; requirements and measures for the secure function (of)"
  - *"MSR"* Measurement and Control Protection Equipment

DIN V VDE 0801

- "Principles for Computers in Safety Related Systems"
- Preliminary Standards
  - DIN VDE 0801 (1990)
  - DIN V VDE 0801/A1 (1994)
- Prescribes Hardware and Software measures necessary to protect against errors.

One of the earliest standards I mentioned, DIN 56921-11 which is for batten hoists, has got a very interesting appendix to it, which explains how to assess the risk in a theatre and come up with 3, 4 or 5, or whatever the Risk Class is. I recommend it; it's good reading.

Risk Classification

The diagram at the bottom of the previous column is a risk graph according to DIN 19 250. Those familiar with EN 954 will recognise this similar diagram, but they are different; EN 954 only relates to results in five levels – B1, 2, 3 and 4 – whereas this risk graph results in eight levels.

Working out your risk category is really a very subjective process. The first thing you have to do is look at the situation and make an assessment of the extent of any resulting damage. Is it going to be low, medium, severe – say, one death or many deaths? These are the terms that are in the Standard. It's really very unclear in use.

DIN V 19250 AK# Risk Graph

S   Extent of Damage
- S1: Low
- S2: Severe
- S3: Several Dead
- S4: Many Dead

A   Length of Exposure
- A1: Rare
- A2: Frequent

- G1: Possible
- G2: Hardly Possible

W   Occurrence Probability
- W1: Very Low
- W2: Low
- W3: High

While there is some guidance provided, the example that I mentioned of the batten (flying) hoist, actually shows us that the recommendation of DIN is that it should be level 3: severe. This is actually the situation which occurs if something goes wrong in the synchronised movement of a number of power-flying hoists that are supporting a rigid load over a stage full of people. As several people might die as a result, DIN has determined that this is a severe, level 3, risk.

The next decision to make is whether the length of exposure is rare or frequent, and after that whether the event is likely to occur, or very likely to occur, or very unlikely to occur. In this case it's been determined that it's actually unlikely, which gives us this risk-class determination. This, confirms how Class 5 is derived.

What is really important to understand is that the Risk Class doesn't apply to every function of the control system or machine. It's necessary to analyse the system with a diagram like this one for every kind of risk that you can identify, and you will derive different Risk Classes for different types of situation. There are some examples of that actually in the DIN standard for your reference.

DIN 19 251

This standard specifies the design principles necessary to meet the Risk Class identified in DIN V 19 250. It applies essentially to hard-wired systems of relay logic, limit switches etc. It deals with issues such as fail-safeness of wiring, redundancy, fault detection, self-test etc.

DIN V VDE 0801 (1990/1994)

DIN 0801 must be read in conjunction with amendment A1 published in 1994. This standard is aimed directly at guiding the design of computer-based, safety-related control systems. As stated earlier, software based systems are inherently much more complex to verify. Usually, for practical purposes, it is impossible to exhaustively explore, test and verify every possible path through, and outcome of, a computer programme. Further errors can result from areas outside the application system programmer's control such as from faults within the COS Operating System, drivers or computer hardware. COS refers to 'Commercial Off the Shelf'; for example, a standard third party product like Linux or Lynx OS^{TM}, Windows^{TM}, etc.

Microprocessors themselves may have internal errors in their design which show up only under rare circumstances: after all, the modern microprocessor comprises more than 20 million transistors. Faced with this reality, the authors of DIN V VDE 0801 have set out comprehensive rules designed to reduce the chances of undetected systematic and random errors occurring and rendering the safety function unavailable.

DIN 56921-11 (1997)

The preceding standards (DIN 19 251, DIN V VDE 0801 (1990/1994) & DIN 19 250) are 'generic' in so far as they can be applied to a broad range of applications. DIN 56921-11 is an industry-specific standard developed by a sub-committee within DIN for theatres and multi-purpose halls. This particular standard applies to scenery hoists with multiple suspension lines.

DIN 56921-11 deals with all aspects of scenery hoist design including mechanical, electrical and control-system design, implementation, operation and testing. It cross-references about 40 other standards including DIN V 19 250 and DIN V VDE 0801.

The appendices to DIN 56921-11 are particularly useful because they provide examples of the application of DIN V 19 250 and the determination of Risk Class. For example, failure of group synchronisation safety systems is determined as posing the highest risk at Class V.

Interestingly, DIN 56921-11 does leave some really important specification requirements undefined. When I found these standards, I thought, "Oh, this will tell me what the German requirements are for a synchronisation error," for example. But it doesn't give that. It actually says that this parameter is to be agreed between the parties who are building the system. So it sets the broad-brush requirements, but it doesn't actually pinpoint your other requirements – it still leaves a lot of that to be worked out by the design team.

DIN 56925 1997 and DIN 56940 (2001)

These two standards are companion documents to DIN56921-11, and deal with the specific requirements for point hoists and stage elevators respectively.

IEC 61508 – The International Functional Safety Standard

IEC 61508 was published in seven parts between 1998 and 2000 with the rather long title of 'Functional Safety of Electrical/ Electronic/Programmable Electronic Safety-related Systems' (EEPEIS). Actually, it's a very big standard and it's seven volumes; it's 400-odd pages. It was finally published in 2000 as an international standard, and that's when we, and a lot of other people around the world, really took notice.

This standard has been adopted and published by several nations including Australia, Britain, Germany and some other European countries. Work commenced on the standard within IEC Standards Committee 65A in 1985, and various drafts were published between 1991 and 1997. IEC61508 borrows heavily on many of the aspects of DIN V 19 250 and DIN V VDE 0801. The reverse is also true because the 1994 amendment to DIN V VDE 0801 was in fact published to bring that German standard into line with the then draft IEC 1508.

Even though IEC 61508 has many similarities with the DIN regime, it has some clear distinctions. Principally, it stands alone. Unlike the earlier DIN standards that must be cross-referenced extensively to obtain the full picture, IEC 61508 uses the 'Safety Lifecycle' concept as a fundamental framework. The standard nominates 16 phases of the lifecycle, which range from concept through to eventual decommissioning. Adoption of the lifecycle concept is mandated by the standard, which is one reason why the standard cannot generally be applied retrospectively to legacy systems: safety must be built-in from the beginning, not added later.

What's really important about it is that it stands alone; it doesn't refer to any other standards as far as compliance is required. It does refer to other standards for guidance, but there are no other standards that are brought into it for compliance. It's a totally generic standard. That means that you can apply it to anything. It can be applied to a theatre; equally it can be applied to a push-bike, if that push-bike's got a computer in it, or to a nuclear power plant or something similar. It defines what's called the Safety Lifecycle, so it identifies the fact that safety has to be built into something, not added on top. What that really means is that the safety lifecycle

IEC 61508

Functional Safety of Electrical/Electronic/Programmable Electronic Safety-related Systems
- Development commenced 1985, published as an International Standard 2000
- Comprises 7 parts
- **Stands-alone**
- **Generic**
- **'Safety Lifecycle'**
- **Conformance:** must be designed-in.
- **International:**
  - Adopted and/or accepted by many countries.

- Complex & not easy to apply
  - 400 pages
  - Interpretation
- Requires Independence
- Does not replace industry specific standards and established good practice
- Does not guarantee safety but makes it more likely.

starts at the time you conceive of building something, right through to defining it, specifying it, building it and decommissioning it in the end of its life. And IEC 61508 actually guides us on how to manage that whole process, which is called the safety lifecycle. Conformance must be designed in; which conversely means that conformance can't be applied afterwards.

A lot of the complexity of applying this standard flows from the fact that it's generic and, because it's generic, it doesn't give us prescriptive solutions to the problems that arise in the design of stage control systems. It also requires a lot of independence in assessment. When we set about developing a stage machinery system to this standard, we knew we needed an independent consultant to assist our work; we've now had to get a further independent assessor to assess the consultant who's helping us. And that was because during the process our consultant got a bit too close to us. He became part of the design team rather than independent, and as the assessment has to be completely external, we needed another consultant.

IEC 61508 doesn't replace industry-specific standards or established good practice; in fact it expects us to use such things. So just because you comply with IEC 61508 doesn't mean you can't go and comply with IEC 60204 or EN 954 or any of these other standards as well. Most importantly it doesn't guarantee safety – it just makes it more likely in the outcome. It remains very

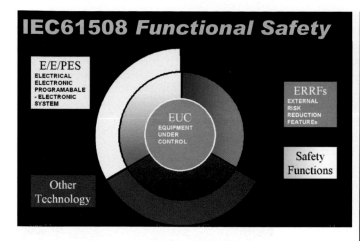

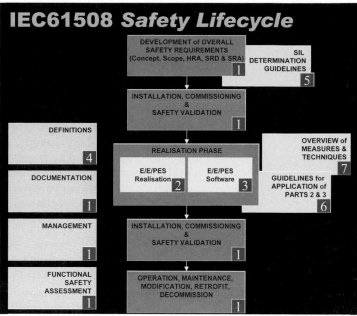

Functional Safety Diagram and references to the Safety Lifecycle of IEC 61508.

hard to guarantee that all products are going to work perfectly every time but, if the rules in IEC 61508 are followed, it's much more likely that they will.

I have prepared the diagrams above to try and illustrate one of the concepts of IEC 61508. There are more acronyms in here; EUC, which is Equipment Under Control, and the plant, motors and drives in a flying system for example. The 'other technology' is equipment that's external to the control system. So this might be instrumentation that's attached to the control system – it might be limit switches or brakes and suchlike that form part of the plant that is under control, but not the actual plant. It also includes an earth, as correct grounding is an external risk-reduction feature. And it might even be training, if only well-trained operators are allowed to use the system.

Everything that's inside the circle is part of the functional safety system, and that's the part that's covered by IEC 61508. It's actually like the safety lifecycle; the 16 or 17 steps defining the safety lifecycle inside the standard. The right-hand diagram shows what the various volumes of the standard cover. The main process starts with conceptual design and preparing the scope of the project, doing a HRA (Hazards and Risk Assessment), an SRD (Safety Requirements Definition), and an SRA (Safety Requirements Allocation). Red numbers represent the volume of the standard which defines these various features.

These parts tell us, as engineers, what we have to do to comply with the standard. What IEC 61508 includes is a thing called a SIL that's roughly equivalent to the DIN *AK*. SIL is 'Safety Integrity Level', and in this standard there are four of them, levels 1 through 4, so it's not as finely tuned as the DIN system. The Safety Integrity Level is actually an inverse measure of the probability of failure of a safety function. So if you've got a safety function inside your control system its SIL is the probability that that function will fail. The higher the number, the lower the probability that it will fail, if it's allowed to fail.

Being an engineer, the next part is really the part that I like of the standard. It's that IEC 61508 allows us to use a quantitative technique to determine what the safety integrity level is, rather than the subjective technique that I mentioned earlier. It gives us a diagram which actually refers to DIN 19 250 and tells us how to use that Risk Graph to get the SIL level. If we use this graph and the same guidelines that came from the DIN standard and we go through the same path, we actually get to SIL 3 – so that means that just purely on a quantitative approach and using the same guidelines from the DIN regime, we get a SIL 3 requirement for synchronisation of overhead batten-hoists.

Then there is the 'possibility of prevention'. The quantitative approach is what I prefer. It means we don't have to go and make determinations as to how many people might die; it allows us to use mathematics to come up with a SIL for everything; and that's what we've done. But before you can do that you have to understand the term 'Tolerable Risk'. That's the risk which is accepted in a given context, based on the current values in society. I underline 'current' because that points to a key factor in this standard; you've got to keep reviewing your approach to it because things change. That reverts to this matter of lifecycle; you are making a decision today based on one set of values, and five years hence these values might have changed, so you have to review your approach.

IEC 61508 acknowledges zero risk isn't attainable. That disappoints some people, because some people think that if there is a standard and they apply it, they will be perfectly safe. Well, the real world just isn't like that. To use this quantitative approach we have to come up with what's called a Tolerable Risk of a Fatality occurring in our venue. In the case of a flying system in a theatre it would require us to determine the probability that we're prepared to accept of a fatality occurring on a stage as a result of the use and operation of the flying system? That's a pretty hard decision. Society accepts in general that road trauma will affect about 100 in 1,000,000 every year. So we have to come up with some measure like that of what's acceptable in a theatre. I'm not going to tell you what that is today. I don't want to go there.

Safety Integrity Level (SIL)

Safety Integrity Level is a measure of the probability of failure of a safety-related function within the E/E/PES safety related system. The higher the SIL, the lower the probability of failure.

IEC61508 provides for just four SILs: 1, 2, 3 and 4, with 4 having the highest integrity. The SIL concept is broadly equivalent to the Risk Class (Anforderungklassen) of DIN V 19 250 although the DIN system has 8 levels.

So the first step in this quantitative approach (shown on the opposite page) is to make a list of all the hazards that might occur in your venue as a result of using the total plant, in this case the flying system. And this can include things like a machine started by an operator without warning, which is actually operator error. Once we've listed all the hazards, we work out a mitigation measure for every one of them.

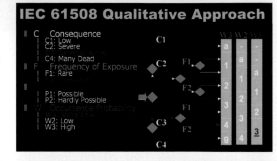

You might have lots of different way of mitigating a hazard; it might be that training is important, or the control system might feed back the operator's input, and ask him to input it again, that sort of thing; so these are all mitigating factors. You then build up a table which has got the list of hazards and the mitigating features, the safety features, of the system. The probability of failure of that part of the system is also entered, and the SIL that results from it. All this information is put into a spreadsheet; the hazards, the probability of that hazard occurring per hour, the hazard-probability per demand – that is how likely is this part to go wrong every time it's used? The hazards are things that go wrong – and the safety functions are the features that will stop these things going wrong, or at least stop them propagating to the output and causing an injury to somebody.

The safety functions each have a SIL, and we then get a mitigated probability per hour, which is then reduced by a number of safety factors to get a lower probability.

IEC 61508 Quantitative Approach

Step 1

"HRA" Hazards & Risks Assessment

· Identify Hazards

Step 2

"SRD" Safety Requirements Definition

· Identify Risk Mitigation Measures

Hazard	Safety Requirement (SR)
Operator-caused hazards during "Bump In" or "Technical Rehearsal"	
1 Machine started by operator without warning (e.g. while load being attached by others)	1 ERRF (Supervision, Operator training, OHS procedures, etc) 27 Ability to selectively disable machines by means of CS command ("exclude")
2 Overshoot of intended stopping position during manual movement (using joystick or similar control)	1 ERRF (Supervision, Operator training, OHS procedures, etc) 7 Soft limits (end-of-travel "deads") 8 Limit switches (inputs to ACM processor) 9 Overtravel limit switches 35 Soft limits (ACM safety parameters)
3 Wrong machine started (manual or profile motion)	11 Operator data entry feedback (ergonomic display) 3 DMB ("Dead-man button") function. 1 ERRF (Supervision, Operator training, OHS procedures, etc)
4 Wrong group of machines started (manual or profile motion)	11 Operator data entry feedback (ergonomic display) 3 DMB ("Dead-man button") function. 1 ERRF (Supervision, Operator training, OHS procedures, etc)
5 Wrong pre-programmmed action or cue started	11 Operator data entry feedback (ergonomic display) 3 DMB ("Dead-man button") function.

Step 3

Determine SILs

"SRA"

Safety Requirements Allocation

11	Operator data entry feedback (ergonomic display)	0.100	no SIL
12	Operator data entry feedback from system controller or ACM	0.100	no SIL
13			
14	Dynamic load monitoring (CS)	0.010	1
15	Safe-edge sensor	0.100	no SIL
16	Safety gates (stage elevator)	0.100	no SIL
17	"Look-ahead" sensor (wagon)	0.010	1
18	Limit available output power of machine to safe level (rabbit)	0.010	1
19	Incremental encoder integrity check (Z-mark)	0.100	no SIL
20	Secondary brake	0.100	no SIL
21			
22	Safety sensors, e.g. belt/chain break, crossed-groove, slack cable.	0.010	1
23	Monitor drive status, e.g. fault signal.	0.100	no SIL
24	Motor over-temperature sensor	0.100	no SIL
25	Data packet integrity and timing checks, i.e. CRC signature, preset time-out and packet sequence field.	0.100	no SIL
26	Broadcast 'start' command in ACM network protocol	0.100	no SIL
27	Ability to selectively disable machines by means of CS command ("exclude")	0.100	no SIL
28	Common "System Monitor" (processor) and redundant comm's network, to supervise ACMs in synchronous group motion	0.010	1
29	Monitoring by System Controller CPU	0.100	no SIL
30	ACM "Safety Processor" (smart watchdog)	0.010	1
31	"Brake Fail Monitor" (uses motor-drive to hold load and raise alarm)	0.100	no SIL
32	Brake actuator state feedback (to ACM input)	0.100	no SIL
33	Redundant position measurement sensor	0.010	1

The first 3 steps in a quantitative assessment under IEC 61508. Steps 4 and 5 are over the page.

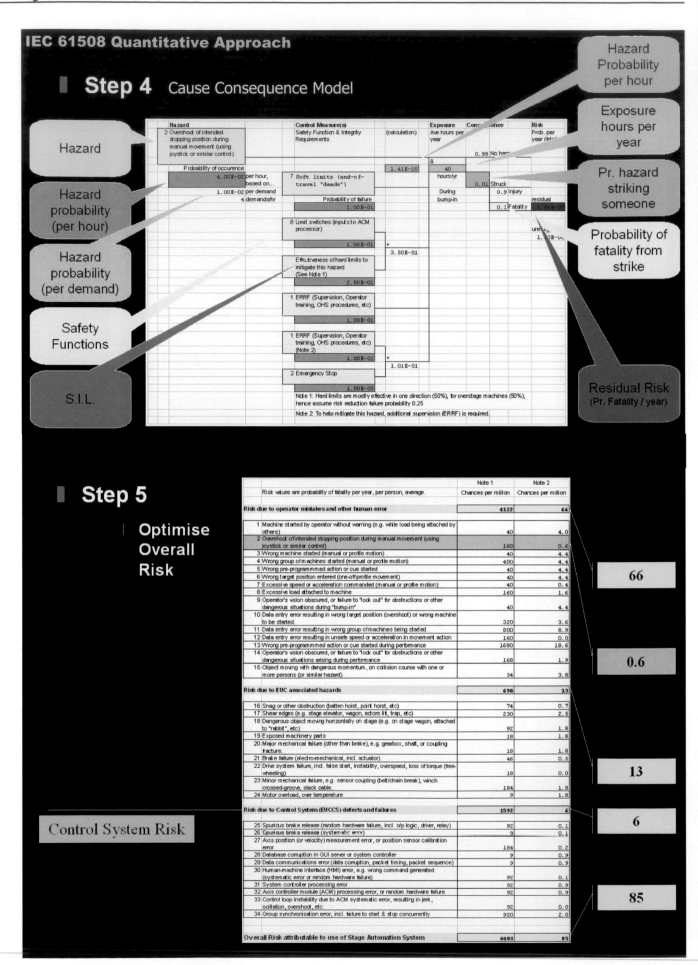

We also have to work out how many times the user is exposed to this hazard each year, because in the end we need to get a per-year reliability. We have to examine the probability of this hazard actually occurring, getting through all the safety measures, and actually striking someone, because most of the time something falling will probably miss, or it will be a near-miss. Then there is the probability that, if it does strike someone, it causes a fatality. The final figure is what's called Residual Risk. With this model you can fine-tune the SILs of all the safety features to get a Tolerable Risk for the total system. We believe that operator errors are a dominant factor in a stage control system, and we can reduce this risk by putting in more safety features to get the total down to a tolerable number. That is the process to go through, which eventually gives you a SIL requirement for every one of your safety functions.

Each safety function, for example group synchronisation error detection, might be performed by a combination of software and hardware, and we might have determined that it requires SIL 3. The standard includes a number of tables which refer to the processes, such as software

IEC61508: Realisation

▌ SILs lead to hardware and software requirements
▌ All stages of lifecycle are effected
  ▌ Design, Implementation, Testing, Maintenance, Modification etc.
▌ Part 2 provides general requirements, Part 3 dictates software
▌ Hardware must have highest common denominator SIL, Software may have varying SIL only if independence can be proven.

Technique/Measure	Ref	SIL1	SIL2	SIL3	SIL4
Structured Methods including fir example: JSD, MASCOT, SADT and Yourdon	C.2.1	HR	HR	HR	HR
Semi-formal methods	Tbl. B.7	R	HR	HR	HR
Formal methods including for example: CCS, CSP, HOL, LOTOS, OBJ, Temporal logic, VDM and Z	C.2.4	-	R	R	HR
Computer aided design tools	B.3.5	R	R	HR	HR
Defensive programming	C.2.5	-	R	HR	HR
Modular approach	Tbl. B.9	HR	HR	HR	HR
Design & coding standards	Tbl. B.1	R	HR	HR	HR
Structured programming	C.2.7	HR	HR	HR	HR
Use of trusted/verified software modules and components	C.2.10 C.4.5	R	HR	HR	HR

Ref: IEC61508-3 Table A.4 pp79 (simplified)

design techniques, that have to be used. In this case we find that for SIL 3 we've got to use 'semi-formal' methods. Any software engineers know that semi-formal methods make life hard. Formal methods, as applied in SIL 4, can shift the cost of your software development by one or two orders of magnitude. So these are the kind of processes that are bound up in this standard.

IEC61508 SIL3 System Architecture

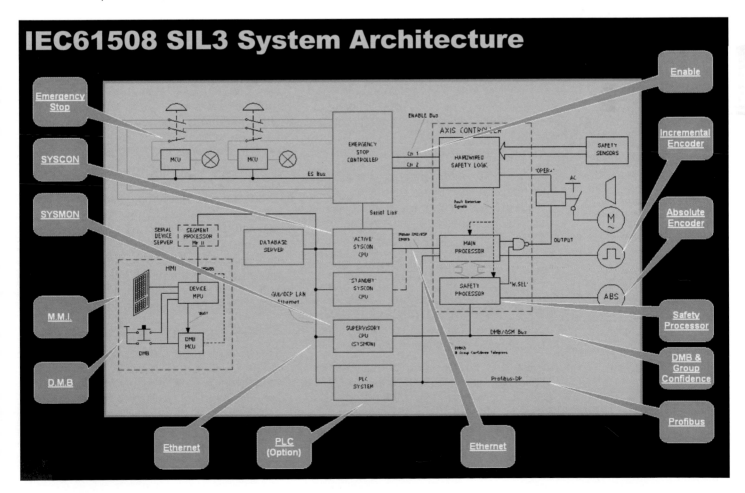

Derivative Standards

It has already been stated that IEC 61508 is a generic standard. This means that it can be applied to any industrial sector including theatres and extending to any imaginable control system where functional safety is a requirement. If there is a downside to generic standards it is that their application to a specific task is made more difficult because of the amount of interpretation that is required. For this reason IEC 61508 will spawn industry-specific standards and one example is IEC 61511, which is being developed for the process control industry. However it is unlikely that such an industry-specific standard will emerge for theatres in which case the generic standard can, and should, be used.

Austrian Standards

Austria is one the few countries with a set of national standards developed specifically for stage machinery. In addition to these industry-specific standards, Austria has adopted many of the European Machinery Directive standards plus the German DIN V 19 250, 19 251 & VDE 0801.

The Austrian theatrical standards are:

- ÖNORM M 9630-1 General
- ÖNORM M 9630-2 Over-Stage
- ÖNORM M 9630-3 Under-Stage
- ÖNORM M 9630-4 Fire Safety
- ÖNORM M 9631 Maintenance Instructions
- ÖNORM M 9632 Test Procedures

United States of America

In the USA and Canada, the Process Control industry uses ANSI/ISA S84.01. This standard was designed to be compatible with the draft versions of IEC 61508 (that is IEC1508). Now that IEC 61508 has been published, ISA S84.01 is likely to be revised. ANSI/ISA S84.01 uses only three SIL levels (SIL 1 to 3) which correspond with the same levels in IEC 61508. Unlike IEC 61508, S84.01 does not address the complete product lifecycle from design to decommissioning.

Whilst IEC 61508 is a generic standard applicable to all industries, ANSI/ISA S84.01 is intended only for use in the Process Control industry. Whilst not mandated, IEC 61508 can be used on a voluntary basis for Functional Safety in USA and Canada. Another standard used in the

USA is UL 1998 'Software in Programmable Components'. It has recently been slightly revised, but the main content is quite old.

European Standards

The Machinery Directive applies within the European Community. There are three 'Directives' or laws of the EC which impact on products sold there. The Directives mandate compliance with certain standards but they do not list those standards; instead, the standards lists are published from time to time by the EC in the 'Official Journal' or OJ. Currently more than 340 standards appear in the OJ for the Machinery Directive, of which about 60 are relevant to control system design. The principal standards from a safety standpoint are:

- EN 418 Safety of Machinery. Emergency stop equipment, functional aspects, etc.
- EN 954-1 Safety of machinery. Safety-related parts of control systems. General principles for design.
- EN 1050 Safety of machinery. Principles for risk assessment.
- EN 1037 Safety of machinery. Prevention of unexpected start-up.
- EN 60204 Safety of machinery. Electrical equipment of machines.

It is clear there is really a jumbled minefield out there when trying to determine which standards to use. We really have a choice; we can choose national standards or regional standards – and I have lumped the DIN standards and even the Machinery Directive into that category – or we can choose truly international standards. As an international manufacturer from a foreign country a long way from anywhere, down under, for me international standards have a great advantage. They really level the playing field as far as I'm concerned because I'm trying to market my products into a lot of different countries. So I say more power to them! Let's have everything by international standards; let's get rid of all these regional and national standards.

Safety Level Correlation

There are three standards in common usage, EN954-1, DIN V 19 250 and IEC 61508, which provide a quantitative measure for 'Safety Level'. All three standards use differing criteria to arrive at the safety level so it is not strictly correct to equate them. This is particularly so for EN954-1, whereas the correlation between the DIN and IEC standards is more accurate. The ANSI system is almost the same as the IEC system.

Industry Codes of Practice

In addition to government-regulated standards there have been initiatives from industry bodies to develop codes of practice for use by their members. Two such organisations are the ABTT and ESTA. The ABTT in the UK and ESTA in the USA both have projects under way for the development of Codes of Practice for rigging systems. The ABTT does publish such a code but it is subject to updating following the availability of BS 7906 which has been discussed at this Conference.

Bytecraft's 'Camelot' System

Bytecraft has customers in many countries and so it is important that our systems meet the standards in those countries and the special requirements of particular projects. Bytecraft's engineers have been watching the development of these international standards for many years.

Our *'State'* control systems have been available since 1990, with dual-channel architecture as required by DIN V 19 250 & DIN V VDE 0801. However these are national standards and are not really internationally applicable. The emergence of IEC 61508 was an important development because it meant that now there is a truly international standard, published in many languages, to which we could develop our systems and that would be accepted worldwide. In 1999 Bytecraft committed in total A\$3m (\$2.05m, £1.25m, 1.75m) to the development of a new generation of stage automation control systems. The result of that investment is *Camelot* which implements all of the necessary safety functions in accordance with IEC 61508 and with Safety Integrity up to SIL 3.

Summary: IEC 61508 – Functional Safety for the 21st Century

On every continent, in almost every technical field, there is an undeniable trend toward the adoption of harmonised, international standards. There are many drivers behind this trend, not least of which is the desire for uniform and fair international trading conditions. In the functional safety arena, IEC 61508 and its derivatives are the clear benchmarks and are certain to be adopted internationally. There is clear evidence that this process is in progress and is gathering pace.

Safety Level Correlation

IEC61508	DIN V 19250	ANSI/ISA S84.01	EN954-1
SIL	AK (Risk Class)	SIL	Category
	1		B
1	2	1	1
	3		2
2	4	2	3
3	5	3	4
	6		
4	7		
	8		

Note: Direct correlation is not valid: provided for discussion only

Summary: Functional Safety

- IEC61508 – Functional Safety for the 21st Century
  - International
    - Already adopted by many countries
  - A single, stand-alone document
  - Comparable and arguably better than other standards in the field
  - Manufacturers, Customers and Users alike can rely on it.

So that's it. My message is: I think the world would be a better place with both a level and safe playing ground, and I think that compliance with an international standard like IEC 61508 is the way to go. It's a decision we made in our company many years ago and we've invested a lot of money in developing this product. We get a better product as a result, we get the opportunity to sell our product everywhere, we're more confident with the product and we think that the users out there get also a more reliable product. I'm done! Thank you. Ω

David Ludlam has been Engineering Manager for the Royal Shakespeare Company at the Barbican Theatre for the past 14 years. Responsible for design and management of the stage machinery, he has followed development of the relevant standards and legislation. He has direct experience of both 'in-house' and Notified Body certification processes under the EC Machinery Directive, and has overseen an upgrade to the control system of the powered flying system in the Barbican Theatre. He is a Chartered Electrical Engineer with experience in instrumentation and high integrity real-time software for the medical diagnosis and industrial control fields. He is currently working on a number of major theatre projects with consultants Theatreplan.

Second speaker: Dave Ludlam

I've been in this business for over 14 years now, and I've had the excitement of working on safety applications both as a designer and as a specifier, so I have quite a broad view of the requirements of safety standards.

Because Ted and I were unable to review each other's presentations before the first performance, as it were, I shall try not to repeat too many things that have been covered, but I will repeat some because I would really like to ram them home in terms of understanding the very different direction from which IEC 61508 is coming.

First of all, a question: How many people present are aware of a significant incident – although not necessarily a fatality – involving some powered stage machinery? Can I have a show of hands? A few, and I'll put my hand up also. How many would say that the primary cause was some sort of hardware failure – not mechanical, but some failure in the control system, including its design? Two. Not many, so not too bad. We need to get a perspective before we start, and it appears we're not doing a bad job. However at the same time, we would all agree that stage machinery is potentially extremely dangerous, and that added complexity, the inclusion of far more electronic and programmable electronic systems, means that we have to have some way of ensuring that the safety functionality is actually going to be there when we need it.

I'm going to cover, in about half an hour, what safety-related systems are. I'm going to explain why we should even bother with IEC 61508, a little bit about the methodology itself, quite a bit about its limitations – I think we have to be honest – and I'm then going to talk about the developments that are springing from IEC 61508; the next few years will see some major changes.

Definition of a safety-related system

- IEC 61508 only covers E/E/PES

- Hardware, software and human elements

- Carry out safety functions where failure would give rise to risk (Functional Safety)

- Stand-alone or integrated into EUC

Remember that IEC 61508 only covers electrical, electronic and programmable electronic aspects of the safety system. It doesn't cover the mechanical strength of the system or anything like that, and of course it cannot be practically applied retrospectively. There's an awful lot of it, and I think Ted's done a magnificent job of even beginning to explain how 61508 is applied. The important point is to be clear that a safety function is delivering functional safety, and the failure of a safety function gives rise to an increased risk.

Functional safety as defined by IEC 61508 can be implemented in two forms. It can be either part of the Equipment Under Control (EUC), embedded into the primary control system – for example, the synchronisation functionality on flying systems is a safety function – or it can also be external, like an overspeed monitoring system, which is in parallel with the main system.

Example: Safety Functions

- Prevent contact with dangerous moving parts

- Prevention of unexpected start-up

- Prevent loss of axis synchronisation

- Prevent danger from Operator incapacitation

- Prevent danger due to mechanical failures

- Emergency stopping

It is important to think 'safety functions'. When many people consider designing a hoist, they think, "I want some limits, I want a cross-groove detector, I want an overload sensor," and they create a list like that. But in fact what they should be thinking is, "What are the hazards that we need to control?" This different way of viewing things is fundamental to IEC 61508.

Safety integrity, and I want to press this home again, is a probability. It's a new way of thinking about things. It's a probability that the safety-related system will perform to the required safety function under all stated conditions within a stated period of time. In simple terms, when you hit the emergency stop it works. In more complicated terms, if one hoist in a synchronised group is lagging and you want absolute synchronisation, something will happen to make that situation safe.

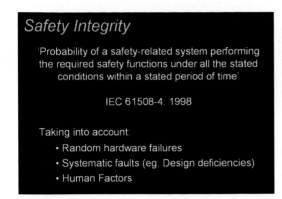

Safety Integrity

'Probability of a safety-related system performing the required safety functions under all the stated conditions within a stated period of time'

IEC 61508-4: 1998

Taking into account:
- Random hardware failures
- Systematic faults (eg. Design deficiencies)
- Human Factors

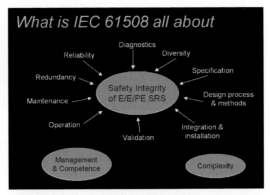

What is IEC 61508 all about

And we need to deliver safety integrity taking into account certain major factors. One hazard is obviously random hardware failures. And this is historically how many people think of safety: "What happens if a component goes wrong? Where's the safety?" But that is actually, in many ways, the easy bit.

The harder bit is systematic faults. And, basically, systematic faults have their basis in design deficiencies. Somewhere along the line somebody has made a mistake and you don't know about it, and it's only going to stick its ugly head up when you demand that safety function and it's not there. And the other important approach with IEC 61508, where it's making a major step forward, is that it includes the concept of human factors – people – as being in the safety loop. I'll return to that later.

Safety Integrity Level (SIL)

- Is a property of a safety function
- Defined as one of four levels
- Each level represents a target likelihood of failure of a safety function
- SIL is not directly comparable to an EN 954-1 Category (B, 1, 2, ,3, 4)

Let's just repeat that a safety integrity level is a property of a safety function; it is *not* a property of an entire system. You must understand that. As has been said, it's defined as four levels, and each level represents a target likelihood of a failure of that safety function; it's what we call the 'probability of failure on demand'; that is, what's the probability it will be there and working when you need it? And again, it's very dangerous to make any direct comparisons with, for instance, EN 954 categories B1, 2, 3 and 4, because they are for categorising *entire systems*, and safety integrity level is about categorising

or parameterising a *safety function*. Another way to look at this is that a Safety Integrity Level expresses your willingness to accept a risk for the hazard being controlled by the particular safety function.

The diagram setting out what IEC 61508 is all about is really to give an indication of how this standard views the world. And what it's saying is that IEC 61508 has an opinion, so to speak, on everything that could possibly have a bearing on the safety of a piece of equipment. And what it also attempts to address are two things that most other safety standards don't even try and get close to. They are (1) how you deal with complexity, and (2) how you deal with management and competence throughout the entire design lifecycle of the machine.

The Safety Lifecycle diagram below is in a different form to that which was described earlier by Ted. The point about this is that it's an incredibly rigorous approach to designing and safety. As you see, it goes from concept to decommissioning; I don't believe there's anything that isn't talked about. What you do need to understand is

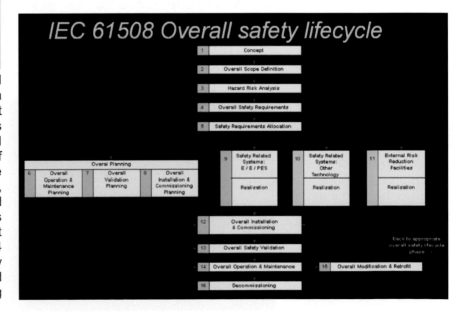

IEC 61508 Overall safety lifecycle

IEC 61508 Methodology in brief

Safety lifecycle Participants

- System definition
  - End user / Consultant
- Realisation phase
  - End user / Vendor / Contractor
- Operation and maintenance phase
  - End user / Contractor

that in any safety lifecycle there will be a number of parties that have to participate. If we look at this in very simple terms, the key ones are System Definition, some sort of Realisation Phase, which is design right through validation and test, and then the third phase is obviously Operation and Maintenance. From the perspective of people who might be running theatres and wanting to buy equipment or build equipment in-house, who's involved in all those stages? You are, as end users. If you're end users, you have to have some appreciation of IEC 61508, because in fact you are in many ways the key player.

So why do we need to bother with IEC 61508? There is an interesting bit of research done by the UK Health and Safety Executive. They looked at the primary cause of 34 incidents in various classes of control system. This shows that specification errors are a major cause of incidents, as well as errors in design, implementation, installation and commissioning. There are some problems with operation and maintenance; and, rather as expected, 20% due to changes after commissioning. It's always worth knowing that changing something after you have got a system into service is often where increased risk or even new hazards can be introduced. The major point about

this chart is that it shows you've got more than 60% of the primary causes of failures actually built into the safety-related systems before they were even put into service. That is saying that we need a standard, a methodology, that can reduce that number of mistakes effectively.

So why do we need *more* standards applied to theatres? My personal feeling is that the major reason is that stage machinery is getting more complex, and I don't see an end to this. We have more axes, more moves, more reliance on synchronisation, and we're now getting into areas like having multiple operators. This particular aspect can be quite worrying; there's been some recent research which basically says that the understanding of human factors is fairly good for a single operator working a single piece of machinery, but there's been very little research done on the situation where you have multiple operators controlling many pieces of machinery. This is what we're beginning to see in high-capability systems with multiple control desks and operators scattered all over the theatre.

With this level of complexity you have to consider more than just random failures. Using the American standard MIL-HDBK-217F (Reliability Prediction of Electronic Equipment), you can calculate the failure rate of just about anything *except software*. This is a well understood system. The problem is, because it's well understood, people tend to focus on the hardware reliability. In fact, as you get more complex systems, especially both complex hardware and complex software, it will be the systematic, designed-in, failures that will be the major issues. And therefore we need a full safety lifecycle standard, one standard covering the whole of the development of this sort of equipment.

> "If you're an end user you have to have some appreciation of IEC 61508, because you are, in many ways, the key player."

> "… more than 60% of the primary cause of failures are actually built into the safety-related systems before they are even put into service."

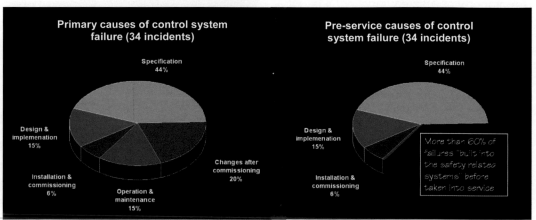

Source: 'Out of Control' HSE. ISBN 0 7176 0847 6

Do we need more standards?

- Stage machinery is getting more complex
  - More Axes required
  - More complex moves
  - More reliance on sychronisation
  - Multiple operators

- Move from random failures to systematic failures when complex hardware and software is used

- Need full safety lifecycle in one standard

- Best defense argument

Limitations of IEC 61508

- Very COMPLEX

- Will NEVER be a mandatory standard

- Does not address Human Factors

- Too 'Process' orientated

- No competency framework for practitioners

IEC 61508 and EN 954-1 Compared

	IEC 61508	EN 954-1
Safety management	✓	
Concept	✓	
Hazard & risk analysis	✓	✓
Functional safety assessment	✓	
Integration	✓	
Validation	✓	✓
Modification	✓	
Verification	✓	
Competence of persons	✓	
Operation & maintenance	✓	✓
Decommissioning	✓	

The other reason for using IEC 61508 is that it is becoming recognised as the future of this sort of standardisation, and to have compliance with something like 61508 will be your best defence in any court of law.

I am going to say a few words about EN 954 as a comparison. IEC 61508 has just got CENELEC approval, so it's actually now a European standard; it has an EN number and it has to be in place by August 2002. This doesn't make it a harmonised standard; it just means it's a European standard. You can however use it legitimately anywhere; it's an international standard. It has been argued that for large European public contracts above a certain limit, I think it's around €200,000 ($234,000, £142,000), which are paid for by government, there is a requirement to use European standards where they are available. One aspect of this is that it's making EN 61508 compulsory by the back door. But I believe, and I will expand on this later, it's going to become harmonised anyway in the future with later standards.

If we look at all the various aspects of safety management, they are all covered by EN 61508, but only three effectively appear in EN 954, which is the existing primary standard in Europe used for designing the safety-related parts of control systems. These are hazard and risk analysis, validation and operation and maintenance, but all the other factors are not really addressed by EN 954.

The biggest limitation, with which I think Ted would agree, is that IEC 61508 is unbelievably complicated! This is because IEC 61508, is an *IEC base standard*, so it's basically a standard that you can use to apply to equipment now, or you can use it as a basis for subsequent standards, or for what are called *sector standards,* and I'll describe these later. As a *base standard* it will never be mandatory, it will never be harmonised, because there isn't the concept within the European standards framework for such a broad-ranging standard to become harmonised. For obvious reasons it would just cause too much complexity.

When I said earlier that IEC 61508 addresses human factors, there is only about half a page, in its 400 pages, on human factors. There are quite sweeping statements about human factors, but at the moment the content on human factors needs some expanding, and while the content is not great, the concept is in there, and that's important.

Another difficulty is that the standard is also too process-orientated. Most commentators on IEC 61508 agree that a lot of the early input was from the processing industry, and by that I mean chemical plants, which is partly why some of the terminology is difficult to understand. External risk-reduction facilities, even safety integrity levels, safety lifecycle, demand, continuous modes of operation, all these sorts of things, they really all come from the processing industry. We have to go through a learning phase to understand how that applies to stage machinery.

My big personal bugbear with IEC 61508, especially a standard as complicated as this and without any new *specific standards*, is that there is no competency framework for practitioners. No competency framework has really been developed yet. We have to understand what 61508 is saying as a core part of the requirement to meet the

Functional Safety Assessment

"investigation, based on evidence, to judge the functional safety achieved......"

- Critical activity

- Requires **_competent_** person(s)

- With adequate **_independence_**

- For **_each_** phase of **_every_** lifecycle

standards of a functional safety assessment. It says you must investigate based on *evidence*, not just, "I think it's okay." That is evidence to judge the functional safety achieved by your system.

This is a critical activity. The standard says that it requires a competent person or persons, and that these persons must have adequate *independence*. For the lowest level, SIL 1, that independent person could be in the same organisation; but it can't be the designer, it's got to be somebody separate, so for a one-man outfit that's quite difficult. Where are you going to find your independent assessor, even if you just design SIL 1 systems? At SIL 4, the highest level, we're talking about an independent organisation, a completely separate body. And in between you really have to make a judgment on the recommendations. It will depend on the complexity of what you're trying to do, the novelty of the design, if you're breaking new ground. Your experience will dictate how much of the assessment you could do independently in-house and how much you'd have to put out to a third party.

If the assessment is done in-house it's important also that you have independent ways of managing that group of people and their resources, and that you make sure that they're not becoming responsible for the development itself. If you find that your independent assessor is suddenly becoming a designer, then he or she can't be an independent assessor any more.

Work in the UK at the moment on assessing the assessors is being done under the CASS scheme, which is being kicked off by the IEE (Institution of Electrical Engineers), with a number of industry bodies. It is using as a base Standard EN 45013; this is a general criterion standard for certification bodies who handle the certification of personnel; a standard for how you run a certification scheme. Based on this they're setting

down the requirements for either individuals or companies to offer functional safety-capability assessments, that is: to offer independent assessing services. It's important to notice that the two main things we're talking about here are a common set of academic and professional qualifications for the people doing this work, and a need for a structure to demonstrate their personal and behavioural skills. That's interesting; what are they talking about, personal and behavioural skills? This is something that's really come from the software industry; recent work by the IEE and BCS (the British Computer Society), in the form of an assessing framework for safety competency and commitment in the software-engineering field. This is recognition that as you move away from hardware design, where the processes are well understood, into doing software engineering, unless you go into really formal methods, a lot of the final quality of the software is down to personal discipline. How well you write software is down to your attitude and competency.

There's an anecdote here about the software group that were handling the launch system for the NASA shuttle, so it was quite safety-critical. They were writing the basic software systems to prevent the shuttle, with the engines running, from toppling over at the launch. They did a lot of work trying to find out what it is that makes low-error software. In fact this shuttle-launch software group are recognised throughout the world as writing some of the most reliable software ever. They did an analysis, and they used formal and semi-formal methods, and investigated all sorts of parameters. And they found that the biggest single factor in writing good software was to achieve a method of judging the competency of the people actually doing it. And this is a new way of thinking, to actually find ways of measuring competency and measuring personal and behavioural factors. They found that this actually had more bearing on the quality of their software than any number of formal methods.

So where is IEC 61508 going? It's just come out, and it's already gone into a 'maintenance program', as it's called in IEC-speak. I want to talk about the maintenance programme a bit, a proposed guide that's coming out, and then cover two sector standards, 62061 and 61800. Sector standards are where you take IEC 61508 and use that as a base standard to

"Assessing the Assessors"
The CASS Guide -
www.cass.uk.net

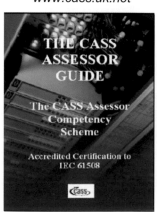

THE CASS ASSESSOR GUIDE

The CASS Assessor Competency Scheme

Accredited Certification to IEC 61508

Future Developments of IEC 61508

- Maintenance programme

- Proposed Introductory Guide

- IEC 62061 Implementation for machinery sector

- IEC 61800-5-2 Programmable Drive Systems

- UK HSE Contract Research Report on Low Complexity Systems

produce something that's more sector-specific. By sector-specific, I'm saying there are similar standards for the nuclear industry sector, the railway sector and the chemical-industry process sector. And finally I'm going to touch on a HSE report on low-complexity systems, because there is a recognised problem with IEC 61508 for low-complexity systems: it really is a sledgehammer to crack a nut.

IEC 61508 Maintenance Programme

Target date March 2006

Main issues:
- COTS / SOUP
- Alternative design methodologies for:
  - Low SIL (1/2)
  - Low complexity
- More help with SIL determination
- Criteria for low, high and continuous demand modes
- Functional safety requirements for digital communications
- Human Factors

The maintenance programme should deliver the next revision of IEC 61508 by March 2006, which is a fair way away. The main issues it's going to look at are SOUP, Software Of Unknown Pedigree, and COTS, Commercial Off-The-Shelf software. There's a lot of work going on in international committees to give much more guidance into the use of pre-existing software. It's going to look at some alternative, hopefully simpler, design methodologies for low-SIL systems – this is SIL 1, SIL 2 – and also some guidance on low-complexity. There's going to be a lot more help on determining SIL, so more guidance on how you link hazard and risk assessments through safety function definitions to a SIL level. It's going to also explain the criteria between what is a low-, a high- and a continuous-demand mode.

And this programme has obviously got to address the function of safety requirements in digital communications which is something that's important to our industry, because all our modern theatre control

systems are network-based. This will require all networks to be deterministic and to have known failure modes, and to have a calculable probability of failure on demand. This will ensure that you've got some real numbers to design around when you rely on a signal shooting across a network. And it will expand on some of the work on human factors. There's not much I have been able to find out about where that's going to lead, but they are promising to address it in a fairly thorough way.

Because the powers that be recognise that everyone's who is going '61508' is wringing their hands and wanting to go into a darkened room with a wet towel over their heads, they are planning to produce a guide aimed at helping people to understand, or at least appreciate, what IEC 61508 is about. The main issues are to explain better the concepts of functional safety.

IEC 61508 Proposed Introductory Guide

Target audience:
"those needing to understand IEC 61508 together with those who need to have an appreciation of IEC 61508"

Main issues:
- The concept of functional safety
- Basic concepts and methodology
- Subsystem integration into complete systems
- SIL determination
- 'Proven in use' concepts

Be warned - It will **not** be a *'Silver Bullet'*

They want to cover the methodology and the basic concepts that underline the whole standard, the whole way of thinking. They're going to give some guidance on how you integrate sub-systems. You might have sub-systems of a known SIL level; what happens when you join them together with other SIL levels, and how do you find out what the total SIL level is? And also they are expected to provide more help with determining a SIL level.

They intend to expand on the application of previous experience, because people are saying, "I've got an experienced company. I've been building this equipment for all these years. I know it's good; I haven't killed anyone with it yet. How can I bring that prior knowledge into EN 61508?" This is the Proven-In-Use concept. At the moment there's a split between the parties; one side really thinks that proven-in-use is dangerous because it counters the completely rigorous approach of IEC 61508. The other side, perhaps more commercially-minded people, are saying,

"Well, you can't just ignore it, there are all those working systems out there. You've got to have some way of bringing existing equipment, existing design work, maybe hundreds and hundreds of thousands of man-hours of design work, into the fold – you can't just throw it away overnight." So proven-in-use is going to be quite an interesting debate, but again I have no feel for where it's going at the moment.

But be warned that the guide is unlikely to be a silver bullet. One of my contacts at HSE stressed that it sounded great, a proposed introductory guide; but what you can't do with any standard is produce a guide which undermines the standard. It can only be a guide. They will have to be very careful about the language used so that they don't end up undermining the original intent of IEC 61508. So don't expect it to make everything simple.

> ## IEC 62061: Machinery Sector Standard
>
> Target date September 2004
>
> Main issues:
> - Calls up EN954-1 in an instructive way
> - Not a design standard
> - Provides methods for checking to see if control systems meet target safety requirements
> - Will not cover SIL 4
> - Second CD due now
> - Plan to harmonize under the EC Machinery Directive

The target date for the machinery sector standard is 2004. This is taking IEC 61508 and essentially distilling it into a standard, specifically for machinery. It takes a lot from EN 954, which is good, because a lot of people understand that already. It's not a 'design' standard, but what it will do is provide, in a simpler form, methods for checking to see if the control system can meet a target safety requirement. And it's going to be an attempt to simplify that process. It will not cover SIL 4, and there are two reasons for this. The flippant reason that was given to me was, "Well, no one would trust software at SIL 4 anyway," which is a common view. Some people would just not go to SIL 4 with software, but I think you eventually have to trust it enough to do that. The other reason is that SIL 3 corresponds to approximately a 10^{-3} probability of a dangerous failure per year. And that aligns pretty well with what is commonly regarded in the UK at least, through the HSE, as the maximum tolerable risk for workers. That's the view

in the UK anyway. This standard is now in second Committee Draft (CD in IEC-speak). One very interesting point is that the road map for this standard indicates that it will harmonise with the Machinery Directive. This means, in Europe at least, you will have to comply with EN 62061 if your machinery is covered by the Machinery Directive, which means that the thinking, the ethos, of EN 61508 is effectively going to become law in Europe.

> ## IEC 61800-5-2: Power Drive Systems
>
> - Designated safety functions
> - Defined fault reactions
> - Will lead to SIL rated drives
> - First CD due later this year
> - Plan to harmonize under the EC Machinery Directive
> - Backed by UK HSE for crane and machinery control

We should consider IEC 61800 on power-drive systems; this is an exciting standard. It's in its very earliest days, and the idea is that some of these sector standards can be as focussed as appropriate within a sector. There are no rules on what they can cover, so the plan is to have a sector standard for variable-speed drives. Often when you try to do a safety assessment, the first thing you look for is the reliability of this lump called a drive, and you just can't find out. You may end up designing lots of things around the drive because you just can't trust the drive.

So the approach is to create a standard which will designate safety functions for power-drive systems and define the fault reactions. This means that in a given fault situation the result is defined, a certain function must happen; normally, I would imagine, this is that the drive stops. This will lead, in theory, to manufacturers who meet IEC 61800–5–2 being able to quite legitimately claim a SIL level for their drive. Within that they'll have to say whether it's a SIL 2 or a SIL 3 drive, provided that it is used in a defined way. This is a major step forward because for a lot of more simple projects the whole safety system could be built around a drive. As this is road-mapped to harmonise under the Machinery Directive, we can expect it to have a wide uptake from the drive manufacturers.

This standard in particular is being backed very heavily by the HSE (Health and Safety Executive), in the UK because they want better standards to push for improvements in the crane and machinery control industry. With this sector standard they can actually apply pressure to manufacturers to improve their systems.

Low Complexity Systems (LCS)
UK HSE Contract Research Report

Definition:
• Failure modes of each component well defined
• Fault condition behaviour completely determined

• IEC 61508 allows 'relaxation' for LCS
• Likely to apply to guard interlock circuits & similar
• Techniques for design, integration & validation
• Only SIL 1 and SIL 2 safety functions

Finally, the definition of low-complexity systems. If your failure modes of each component are well defined, your fault-condition behaviour is completely determined and you've got a very simple system about which you understand everything that could go wrong, then effectively you've got what's called a 'low-complexity system'. What does that mean? Under IEC 61508 you're allowed a 'relaxation', whatever that is. Unfortunately, it doesn't specify in detail at the moment what parts of IEC 61508 you don't have to bother about! They haven't decided yet, and there is actually a contract research report being prepared. This is determining what, in the opinion of industry generally, could be reasonably called low-complexity, and what can be effectively taken out of IEC 61508 for those situations without losing the value and the strength of the standard. This is being coordinated by a number of industry groups all over the world.

The likelihood is that it will certainly apply to things like the guarding lock circuits on presses and similar, so anything that's basically wires, relays and other types of predictable technology will certainly fit into the low-complexity category. And what it will offer is simpler techniques for designing, integrating and validating these low-complexity systems. Obviously it is only really likely to go to SIL 1 and SIL 2 levels – which is still good.

To summarise the situation: it's still very early days yet for IEC 61508. But I consider it is the best thing that's happened to safety standardisation, full stop. I'm convinced that this is the future. It's not mandatory yet, but it is widely accepted as the best-practice approach; certainly

regulatory bodies, for example the Health and Safety Executive in the UK, have already made a statement that they consider IEC 61508 to be their internal benchmark. So they will be judging other people's performance by this standard wherever possible.

IEC 61508 is very complicated at the moment – we can't argue with that, I'm afraid – but there are obviously things happening to try and simplify it. So you have two options really; you can wait for sector standards, and I think it's probably reasonable to wait a bit, especially if you're dealing with low-complexity systems because the existing standards can cover those areas fairly well. But my best advice is not to wait. You might as well start using IEC 61508 because it's going to be, as they say, 'in your face' eventually, whatever you do. And the earlier you start, the less painful it's going to be.

Human factors need a lot of attention, there's no doubt about that. As an industry, anyway, we need to pay more attention to the human-factor implications of the technology that we're introducing.

End users, theatre managers, technical directors – you are all part of the safety lifecycle, whether you like it or not. The idea of going to a third party or a supplier and saying, "Build me a safe system," is just not going to be an option, because you have to be there for the whole lifecycle; you have to get involved. There's no way out of that, although it would be possible to get your theatre or systems consultant to be involved for an extended period, I suppose.

And then, of course, I must repeat what we always say at these sessions: Make sure you are doing *something*. Just because it looks a bit scary is not a reason to run into a corner and hide. And IEC 61508 does make you feel like this sometimes! It might not be perfect, but if you start getting into understanding IEC 61508 now, it will make it less painful into the long term. Thank you all very much. Ω

Summary

• Still 'early days' for IEC 61508

• Not mandatory but becoming widely accepted as 'Best Practice' approach

• Very complex at the moment

• Option to wait for sector standards (e.g. low complexity)

• Human factors need most attention

• End Users are part of the safety life cycle

• Make sure you do SOMETHING even if it isn't 'perfect'

Questions and discussion

Anton Woodward, AVW Controls

As I understand it, IEC 61508 relates to just the safety-related part of a control system, and then only to the programmable part.

Dave Ludlam and Ted Fregon

No! It applies the electrical and electronic systems. And also to any Programmable Electronic Systems (PES).

Anton Woodward, AVW Controls

The majority – and I exclude synchronised flying here – the majority of control systems in theatres, the safety parts of the system like an orchestra pit elevator or something like that, is dealt with by hard-wired systems, virtual-stop relays, safe-edge beams, infra-red beams, working in a hard-wired manner, withdrawing power from the motor when it detects a fault. And therefore IEC 61508 doesn't apply in those situations. Do you agree with that?

Dave Ludlam, Speaker

No, not at all. It still applies because if you've got a number of safety devices, safe-edges and light curtains, it's quite easy to combine these in such a way that the overall likelihood of failure is unacceptable. You could get a situation where, as a group, the total probability of failure of a number of safety functions could become unacceptable because they all have a different probability of failure. So you have to use some methodology from IEC 61508 looking at how each of these safety functions come together to give you a satisfactory overall sense of safety about your equipment. The difference between a SIL level, where that's just looking at one channel of safety function, and combining a number of those together is quite a complex thing to do. There are a lot of standards and advice to come, and it will be easier to combine known sub-assemblies and to determine an overall known risk. But it's wrong to think that just because it looks simple IEC 61508 doesn't apply.

Anton Woodward, AVW Controls

So you don't agree that it only applies to programmable sensors?

Dave Ludlam, Speaker

No, because it applies to electrical, electronic and programmable electronic safety systems. That's the basic starting point.

Alan Russell, Chairman

I would agree with that because I've come across several so-called simple contactor-based logical control systems which have had significant safety problems.

Bert Pronk, Muziektheater, Amsterdam

I was wondering, as Bytecraft has been very much into these standards for several years, can Ted Fregon explain the way it's changed their design process and how they organised their design process to comply with this new standard?

Ted Fregon, Speaker

How long have I got? I think the important thing about IEC 61508 that both David and I have really focused on is that it applies to the whole safety lifecycle. That's from the very blank piece of paper right through every aspect of implementation, and through modification and through de-commissioning, and everything. So we don't believe you can apply IEC 61508 to everything. I can't advise a customer who's got an old system of mine, for example, what SIL that system has. There's no answer to that question. It only applies to new products, new things which are being designed from the very beginning with the standard in mind. I don't know if that answers your question.

Bert Pronk, Muziektheater, Amsterdam

I am wondering how you changed your organisation. These standards are getting so complicated, that you have to be a specialist to apply them, but they also have to be integrated into your whole design process because you have to think of these standards from the beginning to the end, and so I wonder how you dealt with that problem?

Ted Fregon, Speaker

Well, in all sorts of ways. For example, we've had to introduce a lot of case tools, like Rational Suite for example, into our software development cycle. We've had to use a number of external consultants, firstly, to help us to understand the standard, because it's really complicated, and then we also had two external consultants who worked with us. One helps us in the interpretation of the standard and designing towards it, and then we have a verification team called SVRC which actually comes in and does the compliance verification.

The simple, short answer to your question is that it's in the documentation. It means we have to provide a lot more material for assessment before we actually write software. It's turned the whole software development process upside down; it's now like the tip of the iceberg. The actual coding process is the easy part; all the work is in all the processes that lead up to the coding. For example, you can't set out to write even first line of software until you've done a hazard and risk analysis. All these steps are set out in the safety lifecycle; you're supposed to plan the maintenance and decommissioning cycle before you do the realisation cycle. So it means you can't write the software until you've worked how you're going to go in and pull the whole thing apart whenever it's worn out. It's really turned our whole process upside down.

Bert Pronk, Muziektheater, Amsterdam

One more question, please, if I'm allowed. Does this standard also deal with maintenance in operation? Now you have a whole philosophy behind your design, what happens if I want to make a modification to the design? I could go back to your company, but maybe that's not possible or not practical, so I have to know the whole philosophy and all the safety measurements inside your design. Are you communicating this to your customers somehow?

Ted Fregon, Speaker

That's actually a very good question. I hadn't thought about that. This will need some consideration immediately after this meeting!

Dave Ludlam, Speaker

The key thing there is that if you want to make a later modification, with IEC 61508 you won't get that certification unless you have all that documentation, but you've got a fighting chance of having that. Under a lot of other safety regimes the documentation requirements are less onerous and there's more likelihood that when you went back to the manufacturer there just wouldn't be the information that you'd need to make those changes safely. That's one of the things about IEC 61508, it does make sure that the information is embodied in the project records from Day One and through every stage. This means that every design step, every decision you made for safety, you would have to include in the documentation, which is called a Safety Manual.

Ian Napier, Centre Stage Engineering

Would systems like theatre elevators, safety curtains, smaller open-loop hoists be defined as low-complexity systems and therefore not come under the same rigorous scrutiny of these regulations?

Dave Ludlam, Speaker

As I said, they are still having a bun fight about low-complexity, so I can't say for certain. Something like a safety curtain, I would think, would quite probably be classified as low-complexity; but I'm not going to stick my neck out too far in public right now. We can talk about it later. I think this is one of the difficulties because as an industry we do have products that span quite a wide range of complexity. It would be nice if our industry had a better voice into this particular standard generation process, because low-complexity is probably going to be quite key in terms of delivering safe systems in stage engineering under IEC 61508, without the burden and expense of going the full distance.

Alan Russell, Chairman

Okay; I think we must draw to an end. I'm sure that you can approach our two speakers with other questions directly. And our thanks go to Ted and David for an excellent presentation. Ω

Some notes on the application of IEC 61508 to various items of theatre equipment are given overleaf.

Drawing of a major theatre with notes regarding the likely application of IEC 61508 to various parts of the installations. The drawing and notes are for general guidance only.

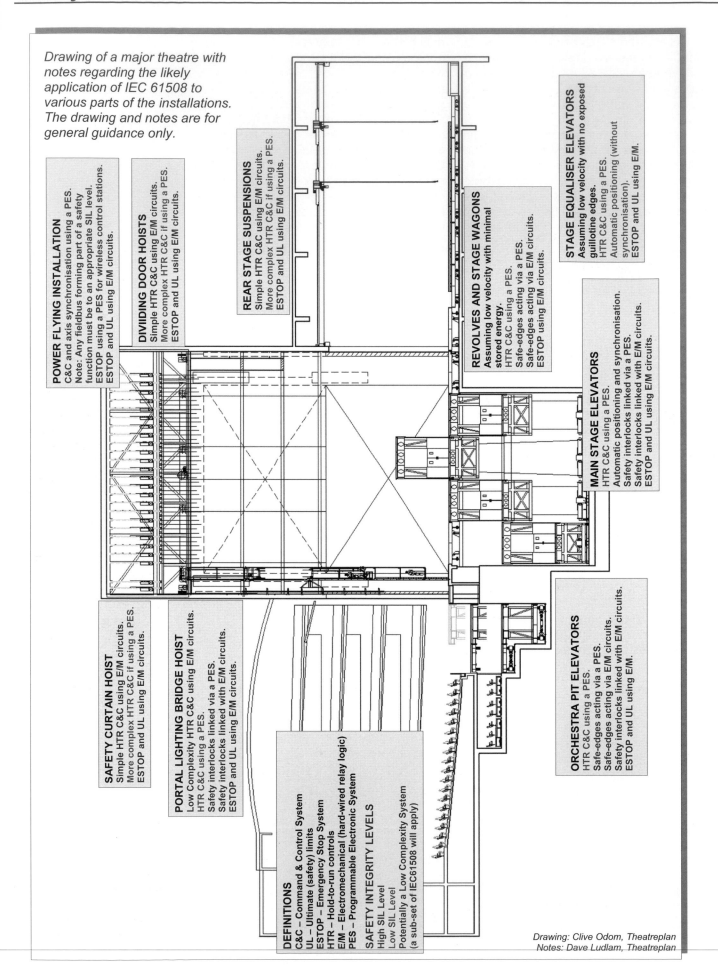

POWER FLYING INSTALLATION
C&C and axis synchronisation using a PES.
Note: Any fieldbus forming part of a safety function must be to an appropriate SIL level.
ESTOP using a PES for wireless control stations.
ESTOP and UL using E/M circuits.

DIVIDING DOOR HOISTS
Simple HTR C&C using E/M circuits.
More complex HTR C&C if using a PES.
ESTOP and UL using E/M circuits.

REAR STAGE SUSPENSIONS
Simple HTR C&C using E/M circuits.
More complex HTR C&C if using a PES.
ESTOP and UL using E/M circuits.

STAGE EQUALISER ELEVATORS
Assuming low velocity with no exposed guillotine edges.
HTR C&C using a PES.
Automatic positioning (without synchronisation).
ESTOP and UL using E/M.

REVOLVES AND STAGE WAGONS
Assuming low velocity with minimal stored energy.
HTR C&C using a PES.
Safe-edges acting via a PES.
Safe-edges acting via E/M circuits.
ESTOP using E/M circuits.

MAIN STAGE ELEVATORS
HTR C&C using a PES.
Automatic positioning and synchronisation.
Safety interlocks linked via a PES.
Safety interlocks linked with E/M circuits.
ESTOP and UL using E/M circuits.

SAFETY CURTAIN HOIST
Simple HTR C&C using E/M circuits.
More complex HTR C&C if using a PES.
ESTOP and UL using E/M circuits.

PORTAL LIGHTING BRIDGE HOIST
Low Complexity HTR C&C using E/M circuits.
HTR C&C using a PES.
Safety interlocks linked via a PES.
Safety interlocks linked with E/M circuits.
ESTOP and UL using E/M circuits.

ORCHESTRA PIT ELEVATORS
HTR C&C using a PES.
Safe-edges acting via a PES.
Safe-edges acting via E/M circuits.
Safety interlocks linked with E/M circuits.
ESTOP and UL using E/M.

DEFINITIONS
C&C – Command & Control System
UL – Ultimate (safety) limits
ESTOP – Emergency Stop System
HTR – Hold-to-run controls
E/M – Electromechanical (hard-wired relay logic)
PES – Programmable Electronic System

SAFETY INTEGRITY LEVELS
High SIL Level
Low SIL Level
Potentially a Low Complexity System
(a sub-set of IEC61508 will apply)

Drawing: Clive Odom, Theatreplan
Notes: Dave Ludlam, Theatreplan

Physical strain on stage

Chairman: Paul Edwards, Training and Safety Consultant, Professional Development Unit
Speakers: Andy Hayles, Theatre Consultant, Charcoalblue Ltd
          Jonathan Johnson, Consultant Spinal Surgeon, Royal National Orthopaedic Hospital
          Louis Janssen, Theatre Consultant, HWP Theater Advies BV

First speaker: Andy Hayles

As this is the graveyard slot, after lunch, I'm just going to try and wake you all up with a bit of audience participation, but don't worry – you don't need to do any more than raise your hand. Could I have a show of hands if you've ever loaded a counterweight cradle on a flying system? I'm impressed. Can I have a show of hands for those of you who have done that in the last year? That's still fairly impressive. In the last month? Oh, you poor things!

I'm overjoyed that there are so many of you familiar with counterweight flying systems, but I'm just briefly going to run through the problem that counterweights pose. I also have a short video that stars an esteemed member of the Conference team. We can see the basics of the counterweight system in an illustration from the *ABTT Code of Practice for Flying*.

I expect you are all familiar with this diagram or something similar. The operating fly gallery is the lower one. As we come up the diagram, we see the counterweight cradle (called the 'arbor' in the US); the loading gallery is at the top; and the piece of scenery being flown is shown on the right. There are two kinds of essentially hazardous operations involved at these two working levels: the first on the fly gallery

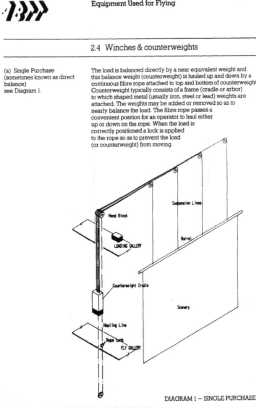

Equipment Used for Flying

2.4 Winches & counterweights

(a) Single Purchase
(sometimes known as direct balance)
see Diagram 1.

The load is balanced directly by a near equivalent weight and this balance weight (counterweight) is hauled up and down by a continuous fibre rope attached to top and bottom of counterweight. Counterweight typically consists of a frame (cradle or arbor) to which shaped metal (usually iron, steel or lead) weights are attached. The weights may be added or removed so as to nearly balance the load. The fibre rope passes a convenient position for an operator to haul either up or down on the rope. When the load is correctly positioned a lock is applied to the rope so as to prevent the load (or counterweight) from moving.

DIAGRAM 1 – SINGLE PURCHASE

Photos: Techplan

Andy Hayles has an Honours Degree in English Literature and Drama from Sheffield University. As a Chief Electrician, Andy opened two newly refurbished theatres and worked with some major touring companies, including Opera North, Scottish Ballet, Glyndebourne Touring Opera and the National Theatre. He spent a season at Stratford with the Royal Shakespeare Company in repertoire, and has been a production electrician in the West End. He joined Theatre Projects Consultants where he worked on the Royal Court Theatre and RADA, and became a Director. In 2004 Andy left TPC to form a new technical theatre design consultancy, Charcoalblue Ltd.

Left: Typical UK lever-clamp rope locks by Unusual Rigging and a rear-guided counterweight cradle by Centre Stage Engineering.

with the pulling on the hauling line and controlling the movement of the system, and the second is with the poor devil who has to load the counterweight cradle in the first place on the loading gallery.

I'll run the video now, but this is rather like a silent movie and you'll have to put up with my voice-over. We took this in the new theatre at the Royal Academy of Dramatic Art (RADA). Jonathan Johnson, our spinal surgeon, Giles Favell, the production manager from RADA, and Conference Director Richard Brett star in the world premiere of – 'Counterweight!'

"So, after a crew at RADA have rigged the bar, they call up to the crew member on the loading gallery, who then has to load the counterweight cradle. Now bear in mind that Richard Brett's been doing this for some years. Those of you who are new to the game, watch and learn. Look at that action! And the fact that not one hair gets out of place during this entire motion!

"When he's loaded the cradle, he calls down to the flyman and to the crew onstage that that bar is loaded and ready to be moved, down goes the cradle, up comes the bar – nothing on it, thank you for noticing that – and here's our flyman hauling on the line, Giles Favell from RADA. And when the set has been stopped by using his hands, on goes the rope lock.

"Now they've changed their mind down on stage; they want the bar back in. "Bloody hell," says Giles, "make your mind up! Come on – you could have called for the right bar the first time." So down comes the bar and up again comes the cradle, and Dick being the old hand he is – look at that – giving the flyman a hand. You don't get that on loading galleries very often, do you? And off come the weights. Now just have a look at the motion that Dick's having to go through in unloading all of those weights. Careful not to trap your fingers. Brilliant! And now that bar is ready to be unloaded on stage. I hope you have all understood that.

"So then we thought we'd give Jonathan a go at flying a bar himself, just to get a feel for how the hauling line worked and what it was like flying a bar. We asked him to stop the set – and that came as a bit of a surprise! And this is an unloaded bar, so that you can imagine the kind of forces and strain that are on you when that bar's got perhaps 200 kg or more on it. There goes an empty cradle back down past him. "One

day all flymen will be dressed like this, I have to tell you! And I thought ... I was very impressed actually. Considering you're a spinal surgeon, sir, that was a good effort. And I think, actually, he was secretly rather pleased with himself – as indeed we all were.

"This installation at RADA is double-purchase. Those of you familiar with double-purchase systems will know that, by a clever means of diverting the wire-ropes and using more pulleys, it enables you to give yourself more wing space at stage level. The downside is that the cradle needs twice as much weight to balance the load and is therefore twice the size of a single-purchase system cradle. Richard's just showing us here the problems of loading the very, very low counterweight, and also the one right at the top. As the rope lock finally goes on, we can summarise the problems: hauling the lines and loading the cradles."

So that you're all aware and to remind you of what a typical counterweight feels like, I've brought one along with me that I'm just going to pass round between you. Now it weighs 10 kg (22 lbs) and is quite heavy. If any of you feel that you don't like to touch it, or have any kind of trouble manoeuvring it please help each other, and in extremis I'll come and rescue you if you really get stuck! Don't  drop it on your toes; there's a Health and Safety man here! Ten kg (22 lbs) doesn't seem like very much, but it's equivalent to 10 bags of sugar, isn't it? That's quite a lot of sugar.

Two publications referred to which can be obtained by mail order from the ABTT office.

Now I'll explain the design process we go through when we're trying to pull together a specification for a counterweight system. Here's a good place to start if you're thinking about doing it yourself, the new Yellow Book published last year, a fantastic guide, not just to counterweight systems, but also to escape widths, floor loadings, ventilation requirements – you name it, there's probably a chapter on it in this book. Fantastic! What does that say about counterweight flying? Very little; I'll read it out to you: *Flying installations should comply with BS 7905–1, which is in preparation, or the ABTT Code of Practice for Flying.*

British Standard 7905 is now in existence as was described in a seminar earlier in the Conference; so what does the British Standard say? It says, in small print, *Manually loaded balance weights shall not exceed 15 kg each.* Very reasonable. What does the Code of Practice for flying say? This was published in 1993, much earlier than the Yellow Book, and again here, consistency – fantastic! How often do you see this in legislation? Only in the theatre, I would estimate. *Balance weights shall not exceed 15 kg each.* So we talked about this in our office and considered it long and hard, and thought, well, 15 kg (33 lbs) is still quite a lot – let's reduce it by 10%. 13½ kg, that's a funny weight – let's reduce it by 20%; 12 kg (26 lbs); that feels pretty good. Twelve bags of sugar? We could probably manage that. So in the specification for Stratford Circus it says: *each counterweight shall not exceed 12 kg net weight.*

Telestage Associates were the contractor lucky enough to win the contract, and they suggested that the counterweights would be far better at 10 kg (22 lbs). There are some benefits in that; when you look at a cradle you can count up the weights, you multiply by 10 kg, a nice easy sum, and you can tell how much load is on the bar.

And a weight of that size is 30% less than the recommended maximum. So we felt pretty confident, and all was going swimmingly until the licensing man for Newham turned up. He wrote a short letter about the flying system covering a number of things like the distance between the edge of the loading galleries and the ropes, but most particularly that we weren't meeting the manual handling guidelines that the HSE recommend across the country for shops, supermarkets, warehouses and theatres. And he referred

Getting to grips with manual handling

9

General risk assessment guidelines

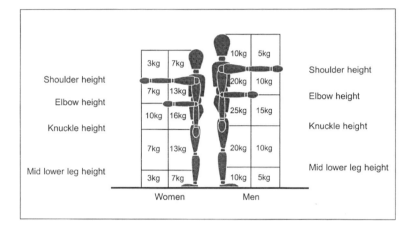

- Each box in the diagram above shows guideline weights for lifting and lowering.

- Observe the activity and compare to the diagram. If the lifter's hands enter more than one box during the operation, use the smallest weight. Use an in-between weight if the hands are close to a boundary between boxes. If the operation must take place with the hands beyond the boxes, make a more detailed assessment.

- The weights assume that the load is readily grasped with both hands.

- The operation takes place in reasonable working conditions with the lifter in a stable body position.

- Any operation involving more than twice the guideline weights should be rigorously assessed - even for very fit, well-trained individuals working under favourable conditions.

- There is no such thing as a completely 'safe' manual handling operation. But working within the guidelines will cut the risk and reduce the need for a more detailed assessment.

An extract from "Getting to grips with manual handling", a publication by the UK Health & Safety Executive.

2.4.7 Provide counterweights sized to fit the associated cradles. Weights shall be fabricated from either cut steel weighing approximately 3,120 kg/m³ or, at the Tenderer's option, cast iron weighing approximately 7,200 kg/m³. Counterweights shall be finished with smooth edges free from burrs. Chamfer one corner of each weight at 45° to allow ease of loading. **Each counterweight shall not exceed 12 kg net weight.** Cast iron counterweights shall have cast into them the initials of the Arts Centre; cut steel weights shall have the initials stamped on them.

An extract from the counterweight flying specification for Stratford Circus.

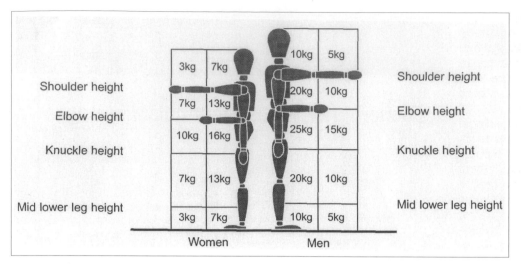

	3kg	7kg	10kg	5kg	Shoulder height
Shoulder height			20kg	10kg	
	7kg	13kg			Elbow height
Elbow height			25kg	15kg	
	10kg	16kg			Knuckle height
Knuckle height					
	7kg	13kg	20kg	10kg	
Mid lower leg height					Mid lower leg height
	3kg	7kg	10kg	5kg	
	Women		Men		

For Imperial units multiply kg by 2.2 to obtain the load in lbs.

me to the HSE guide for employers on manual handling, and I'd just like to spend a minute talking through this diagram with you.

Each of the zones indicated in front of the man and the woman figures standing there are supposed to represent the maximum weight that you should consider lifting in that area. Now it has to be said that the HSE have done brilliant work with this, because these are guidelines for risk assessment. It doesn't mean that you're not allowed to lift more than 5 kg (11 lbs) off the floor if you're a bloke; what it means is that if you do you should assess the risk, because there is a likelihood that in time you'll hurt yourself. It does, however, seem quite stringent, doesn't it? In celebration of the football match on Saturday I picked up a crate of Stella Artois and carried it out into the garden and put it down by the barbecue. Now in doing that I had exceeded, pretty much, the guidelines there, but it was a one-off. Meanwhile, my two-year-old son, who happened to be sitting on the floor and weighs 15 kg (33 lbs) was picked up by my wife to get him out of the way of the bottles. She far exceeded the guidelines there. So in everyday life we are all going well past these guidelines all the time, probably without even thinking about it. The laptop bag that I carried here today weighs 7½ kg (16½ lbs), so just picking that up off the floor probably beats most of this.

So what does that mean in terms of the rules that can be applied in addition to that diagram? We've already considered the zones that the lifters' hands pass through; when you're picking something up, you should adopt the lowest weight of the zone that you're passing through. So if you're picking up something up off the ground to put it above your head, you should adopt

the lowest figure which you can see at the top of the female diagram is 3 kg (6½ lbs) at full reach. So it doesn't matter that you're carrying it mostly at the 10 kg (22 lbs) zone, which is where most of us carry things; if you've got to go through any of those other zones, that's the weight that you should adopt.

There are additional constraints. If the lifter twists to the side more than 45°, reduce that weight by 10%, and by 20% if you twist more than 90°. Now just remember Richard Brett loading that cradle on the video. The guideline weights are also for infrequent operations, so if you're doing whatever you're doing 5–8 times a minute, knock a third off it, if you're doing it 12 times a minute, knock 80% off it. Now, lots of you have loaded counterweight cradles. I reckon I can get a weight into a cradle at least once every 5 seconds. I know there are some technicians who can do 2 weights every 5 seconds. So we might need to apply that.

The other thing is that the operation should not be biased to one gender. So if you're designing a counterweight system, you need to assume that there will be a woman operative. I was embarrassed myself at Newham because Charlie, the flyman, is a woman! How does that mass pan out in terms of counterweights? Let's assume a 10 kg (22 lbs) counterweight and a female operative. We need to reduce that to 7 kg as all the counterweights pass through the woman's mid lower leg to knuckle zone, so that's our maximum for there. Reduce that by a further 20% because we need to twist over 90° if the fly floor and loading gallery are set out as in the video, and we need to reduce that by a further 80% for the frequency of the operation. What does that give us? An allowable counterweight of 1.1 kg (2½ lbs), which would take 227 loading operations to load fully a 250 kg cradle. Eeeek!

Now, in fact, you could call this evaluation the beginning of a risk assessment in response to the guidelines. "Let's look at the diagram," I thought. Well, most loading is done by men. There are some women who are stronger than men; it tends to be the strongest person on the crew that does the loading. I thought we could safely adopt lifting 10 kg (22 lbs) between mid lower leg to knuckle zone. The twisting; well, what if you move the weights before you put them into the cradle? What if you actually just drag them backwards one by one, then kneel on the floor and use your arms to put them into the cradle? I thought we might get away with just – let's be generous – a 10% reduction for 45° twisting. What about the frequency? This was where I started on the maths! If there are 30 × 250 kg counterweight sets with a diversified load of 50% across the system (in other words, when a show is loaded in, not all the counterweight cradles are fully loaded – the chances are you're probably using only 50% of the capacity of the whole system), that would equate to 30 × 250 × 50% = 3,750 kg (8,250 lbs) or 375 × 10 kg (22 lb) counterweights to be loaded. While these operations are intensive, they're carried out perhaps only once a week. Averaging those across a 39-hour week of the person who did the loading comes in at 9 operations an hour. The man from Newham Council wasn't very impressed with that, but he was sufficiently bamboozled to refer the matter to their higher authority, the HSE Food and Entertainment Field Operations Directorate, as they are called. That was last year, and you will forgive me for not having chased them very hard for not having yet responded!

There are plenty of people here at Conference who may suggest some solutions. We're hoping to get into a discussion later and we await hearing what you think the alternative options might be. Thank you very much. Ω

Photos: courtesy the crew at Theatre Royal Norwich

Counterweight loading and flying operations at Theatre Royal Norwich: note the safe loading gallery and the additional rope lock on the near set.

A summary of the maths and conclusions as presented by Andy Hayles.

THE CONCLUSIONS

•The Diagram
  Most loading is done by men – 10 kg between mid lower leg to knuckle zone.

•Twisting
  If operator moves weights (without twisting) closer to cradle for loading, then the second operation twisting is less than 90 degrees, attracting only a 10% reduction (1 kg).

•Frequency
  If there are 30 number 250 kg counterweight sets with a diversified loading of 50% across the installation, this equates to 3,750 kg or 375 number 10 kg counterweights; or 375 loading operations.
  While these operations are intensive, they are carried out perhaps once a week. Averaging 375 operations across a 39 hour week equates to 9 operations an hour, well under the 12 operations a minute barrier.

THE MATHEMATICS

• Assume 10 kg counterweight and a female operative.

• Reduce to 7 kg as all counterweights pass through the mid lower leg to knuckle zone.

• Reduce by 20% (1.4 kg) for twisting over 90 degrees.

• Reduce by 80% (4.5 kg) for frequency of operation.

• **Allowable Counterweight = 1.1 kg.**

• 227 operations are required to fully load a 250 kg cradle.

THE RULES

If the lifter's hands enter more than one box, use the smallest weight.

If the lifter twists to the side more than 45 degrees, reduce the weight by 10%, and by 20% if the lifter twists beyond 90 degrees.

Guideline weights are for infrequent operations. Reduce weight by 30% for 5 to 8 operations a minute, and by 80% where the operation is repeated more than 12 times a minute.

Operation should not be biased to one gender.

Jonathan Johnson is President of the British Association of Spinal Surgeons and Honorary Consultant Orthopaedic Surgeon at King Edward VII's Hospital for Officers. Since May 1992 he has been Consultant Spinal Surgeon at the Royal National Orthopaedic Hospital Trust, London and Stanmore, Essex. He has taken time to observe counterweight loading and other operations in the theatre in order to be able to provide guidance on the matter of body strain.

Second speaker: Jonathan Johnson

Thank you for asking me to speak to this specialist audience. Basically, I am going to talk, from an orthopaedic surgeon's point of view, about occupational biomechanics, go on to say something about back pain and occupation, and then finally discuss how much of the risk of low back pain is preventable and refer to some recent voluntary ergonomic guidelines to target back pain and other musculoskeletal disorders.

Occupational bio-mechanics

There is a close relationship between work and low back pain disability. There are various possible injury mechanisms and the three models usually quoted are:

1) single overloads
2) repetitive loading
3) static loading.

Direct Trauma (extrinsic overload), such as a fall or a blow on the back, is actually an uncommon cause of low back pain in industry. On the other hand, overexertion is quite common and single injuries are probably less frequent than repetitive. Repetitive loading gives fatigue of tissues.

Fatigue in metal is believed to occur through crack propagation, and we have all learnt something about this recently from failures in the railroad. Cracks propagate until failure occurs. However, in biological tissue cracks can heal so that overexertion is influenced by age, fatigue, etc, and the load level at which an injury may occur is individual. This can vary widely over a wide range.

What are the tissues involved?

1) The disc – degenerative changes can be accentuated by loading.
2) Vertebral bodies – you can get trabecular micro fractures and these have been observed but are relatively rare except in osteoporotic patients.
3) Muscle strains.

The difficulty is in knowing the precise pathology. Low back strain and 'muscle injuries' are seldom explored surgically and we therefore do not know the exact pathology. However, experimental studies suggest that the myo-tendinous junction is affected. The other suggestion is that lumbosacral strain is a ligamentous problem.

Bio-mechanics of posture

The upright standing position is very stable and requires little muscle activity to maintain (Figures 1 & 2).

Bending forwards or sideways requires muscle forces to counterbalance the moment created. These forces are supplied by the trunk muscles, (Figure 3), and bending forwards is illustrated. The situation is much more complex when asymmetry is involved; in these situations there is a forward bending movement but there is also combined lateral bending and sometimes twisting. This causes unequal stress concentrations. Twisting is resisted in the spine by the facet joints and these may therefore be stressed. The disc is also more sensitive to rotational strain.

Manual lifting and loading

Four factors are important in manual lifting:

1) The posture of the subject when the lift is performed.
2) The weight of the object and the location of the object relative to the body.
3) The origin and end point of the manoeuvre.
4) The speed at which the object is being moved.

There are obviously other factors such as the bulk and size of the object and the ease of lifting. For example, position and grip are important. And two other points:

Posture: Given the same weight, large internal forces and moments are created in, for example, maintaining a forward bending posture. In addition, forces and moments are created by the weight of the object being handled and by the location of the object relative to the spine (Figures 4 & 5).

Symmetrical lifting, that is holding the load with both hands in front of the body, is the most common method of manual handling. As already stated, stress concentration can occur from asymmetric lifting manoeuvres and these, therefore, should be avoided if possible. In addition, the arm and shoulder are not designed or developed well enough to permit lifting heavy weights in an asymmetric fashion. Lifting from the floor by bending the knees and keeping the back straight, ie from a squatting position, moves the load closer to the body but this requires

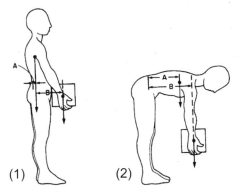

Figure 1: During bending forward, the centre of gravity of the trunk moves forward relative to the lumbar spine. Therefore the moment arm (A) increases. Assume A to be 2 cms during standing and 22 cms during bending. The weight of the upper body is estimated to be 450 N. The forward bending moment resulting from the posture of the trunk is 9 Nm in upright standing (1) and 99 Nm during bending (2). To this trunk moment has to be added the moment created by the weight of the box (say, 100 N) and its moment arm B (18 cms when standing upright and 31 cms during bending). The moment attributable to the external load changes only slightly, from 18 Nm (1) to 31 Nm (2).

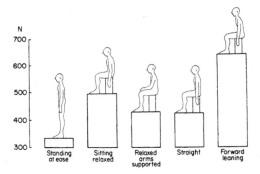

Figure 2: The load on the L3 disc in unsupported sitting is higher than the load during standing.

that the object fits between the legs. If the object is too large to be brought between the legs, then the squat-lifting method is actually more stressful than the stoop-lifting method.

Back pain and occupation

Complex forces act on the lumbar disc during rotational movements and lifting weights while in the stooping position, and the difficulties of measuring the real pressure when someone is doing heavy manual work are very considerable. Radiological films are of little help.

Chaffin & Co. workers have evolved a technique for calculating what they call lifting strength ratios (LSR) based on each weight lifted in the job and the predicted lifting strength of men in various postures. They have shown that back pain has a high instance amongst those who are required to lift weights in manual materials handling, which makes maximum demands in terms of lifting strength. They have also stressed the importance of load position in relation to the weight bearing axis of the body.

Occupational trauma

Various painful conditions of the back have been associated with particular activities. However, others can result from over-indulgence in hobbies or sports after prolonged periods of inactivity. It is easy to postulate that prolonged heavy manual work may encourage the development of degenerative changes in the discs and the joints. However, while some of these are the process of ageing, there are other predisposing factors like genetics. It has been shown, however, that berry pickers who stoop have significantly more back pain than those such as aubergine pickers who stand. Sitting and driving have also been shown to cause, and to increase, instances of back pain amongst workers.

From bottom left:
Figure 3: Intra-abdominal pressure supports the extensor mechanism,
Figure 4: Lifting a box which will not fit between the knees; the bent-knee method (B) produces a greater moment than the bent-back method (A) because of the longer moment arm, and
Figure 5: limits on lifting.

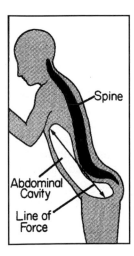

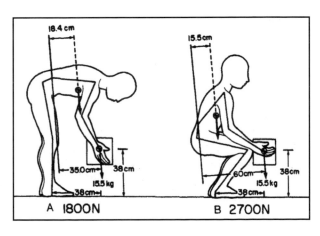

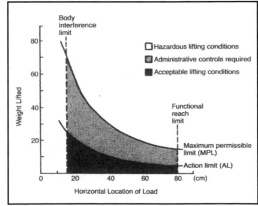

Types of work and back pain

Various surveys suggest that men whose jobs make the greatest demand on the lower back in terms of muscular effort have a similarly high prevalence of disc disease. On the other hand, those in sedentary occupations also tend to have a higher prevalence of all types of back pain than those whose jobs involve standing or walking about.

Prevention and control of back pain

Many studies suggest that back pain is occupationally linked. It seems logical, therefore, to consider how the onset may be prevented or delayed. Should workers in particular industries be screened with X-rays and similar to exclude obvious disorders like spondylolisthesis before being allowed to take a particular post? Unfortunately, routine examinations of the back, particularly movement of the lumbar spine, may be useful in assessing clinical progress in patients with symptoms, but it seems to have a disappointingly low sensitivity and specificity as a predictor of future episodes in those who are otherwise healthy. There have been suggestions that people with small spinal canals are more likely to suffer from problems than those with wider canals but this has not really been proven.

Maximum loads

Regulations about weight-lifting are often rather indecisive but basically centre around the hypothesis that no-one should be required to handle a load of such weight that is likely to cause injury. However, specific injuries do have quite well defined limits and there is general agreement with the suggested maxima of **25 kilograms** for a compact load for young people and an arbitrary maximum of **58 kilograms** overall. In America in 1967 the International Labour Conference suggested **55 kilograms** for adult men.

In 1981 the National Institute of Occupational Health and Safety (NIOHS) published guidelines suggesting limits on lifting based on:

1) the horizontal location of the load in front of the body at the start of the lift
2) the vertical location of the load at the origin of the lift
3) the vertical displacement of the load during the lift
4) the frequency of the operation.

In addition, the weight of the object is always considered. They worked out a maximum permissible limit and produced a suitable graph. These are obviously not perfect and cover only symmetric lifting but they are better than some of what we have had in the past.

Pulling and pushing is also an important material-handling task. While only about 20% of overexertion injuries have been associated with these activities, they do seem to happen less than when lifting.

In the UK, recent attempts to draw up guidelines or even introduce regulations on weight-lifting have led to a certain amount of resistance by employers on the grounds that the current evidence, though indicative of relative risk, does not have precision in respect of defining it.

As far as the theatrical profession is concerned, physical effort, especially when sustained for long periods or carried out in awkward stooping postures, does appear to result in significantly higher proportions of disc disease. Furthermore, there is often a high amount of sickness absence associated with these conditions.

One of the difficulties about theoretical and practical teaching is that there may be failure to take into account the awkward posture and weight distribution facing the individual which I think applies to the particular technique of loading and unloading counterweights in the theatre profession.

Again in the United States, the Occupational Health and Safety Administration (OHSA) propose a new ergonomic standard for industry and promise to prevent hundreds of thousands of work-related musculoskeletal injuries each year. They published their suggestions in 2000 and claimed that they thought they could prevent three million work-related musculoskeletal disorders over a 10 year period; that is, about 300,000 per year (at present, about 600,000 people are injured severely enough to require time off work). This would save nine billion dollars on average per year. This would require participation by employers, managers, leaders and employees in reporting hazard information. There would also need to be a full programme of job hazard analysis and control, which could lead to examination of problem jobs, staff training and the management of musculoskeletal disorders.

This was followed this year by the National Academy of Sciences report on musculoskeletal disorders in the workplace. They reviewed all the studies on ergonomic interventions to prevent low back pain. They noted that scientific studies have not yet even determined the anatomic sources of most low back pain and the aetiology of back pain remains obscure despite the best guesses and inferences of prominent researchers. They accept there probably is a causal pathway between workplace exposures and low back pain disorders. The programme that was going to be adopted during the Clinton administration was rejected last year but it now looks as though there are going to be some voluntary guidelines based on the OHSA report.

Conclusions

In conclusion, it makes sense to have some sort of maximum weight that should be lifted but we do need more evidence-based medicine to tell us whether this will significantly reduce the amount of time lost with back pain. There are many issues we could discuss such as whether people trained to do lifting and doing a job regularly have fewer problems than somebody who is doing it only occasionally, and how this corresponds with suggested weights lifted in laboratories for research. As far as your profession is concerned, there has been very little work done on pulling weights on ropes and such other hauling processes. Thank you. Ω

References:

Figure 1 is from Andersson, G.B.J., Örtengren, R., Herberts, P.: Quantitative electromyographic studies of back muscle activity related to posture and loading. Orthop. Clin. North Am. 8:85-96, 1977.

Figure 2 is from Andersson, G.B.J., Örtengren, R., Nachemson, A., Elfstrom G.: Lumbar disc pressure and myoelectric back muscle activity during sitting. The Scand. J. Rehab. Med. 6:104-114, 1974.

Figure 3: Redrawn after Troup, J.D.G., and Edwards, F.C.: Manual Handling. A Review Paper, London, Her Majesty's Stationery Office, 1985.

Figure 4 is reprinted from 11E Transactions 6:105–113, 1974. Copyright Institute of Industrial Engineers, 25 Technology Park/ Atlanta, Norcross, Georgia 30092.

Figure 5 is From Posner, I., White, A., Edwards, W., Wilson, C.: A biomechanical analysis of the clinical stability of the lumbar and lumbosacral spine. Published in Spine 7:374–389, 1982.

All these illustrations are from a chapter called Occupational Biomechanics by Gunnar B.J. Andersson in The Lumbar Spine, edited by James N. Weinstein and Sam W. Wiesel, The International Society for the Study of the Lumbar Spine, 1990, published by W.B. Saunders Company, Philadelphia, PA 19106

Third speaker: Louis Janssen

We heard earlier a little bit about the background to counterweight operations here in the UK. We have gone down the same road a little way; a couple of years ago a risk assessment was done by the Safety Inspectorate and that has led us in a certain direction. But before that I need to tell you something about the Dutch theatre system. All the theatres in our country except a few are road houses, and these road houses take in productions, many of which are one-night stands. So a production gets in at 10 o'clock in the morning, it will set up during the day, and hopefully be ready at 5 o'clock. We have something to eat, do the show in the evening and get out in the night. The day after, a new production gets in. So that means loading and unloading on a daily basis. This causes us to have to shift a lot of counterweights and, I have to tell you, we have only single-purchase flying systems. We don't have double-purchase systems, so all the figures I give you are on single-purchase systems. For a double-purchase system the figures are higher.

$$\text{NIOSH formula}$$
$$RWL = 23 \times Hf \times Vf \times D \times Af \times Tf \times Cf$$

There is a method used to measure physical strain called NIOSH which is internationally accepted. I think that this formula represents the diagram with the boxes which Andy showed us. With this formula you can calculate a recommended weight level and, if you put all the correct parameters into the formula, the maximum weight you can lift is 23 kg (50 lbs). So we rounded that up a little bit to 25 kg (55 lbs) in The Netherlands, but that is basically the maximum you can lift, and then only under ideal circumstances.

What was very common in The Netherlands was that the operators had a counterweight table so they didn't need to go onto their knees to pick up the counterweights from the floor. The weights are on the table on the same level as the cradle, so at least you don't have to go up and down all the time; you move so you only have to twist to one side. Doing the calculations for working without a table shows that the maximum counterweight can only be 2 kg (4½ lbs), but with a table it can be 5 kg (11 lbs). In practice, under the new law which was developed 6 kg (13 lbs) is allowed as a maximum weight. In The Netherlands a full

Louis Janssen has some 30 years' theatrical experience working in many theatres in The Netherlands and has been involved in renovations, planning and feasibility studies. He was the Technical Director of *Toneelgroep Amsterdam* for 11 years before becoming a full time consultant. He is a Board member of the Dutch Theater Technology Association and of the Dutch technical theatre magazine, and is active within OISTAT. He is the present bearer of the 'Frits van den Haspel' Award, a prestigious award in the field of theatre technology in The Netherlands.

Photo: Frits van den Haspel

A counterweight table in Stadsschouwburg Amsterdam. These are used in The Netherlands to reduce the strain of loading and unloading counterweights.

Force required to get
a single-purchase
fly bar moving:

Empty bar -150N-300N
Bar + 72kg -250N-400N
Bar + 126kg -450N-800N

counterweight was always 12 kg, and half a weight was 6 kg, so we have now standardised on this 6 kg (13 lb) weight.

Another element which we haven't heard too much about is the force required to move a flying set. In the video we saw the flymen moving the flies very easily but I can imagine that if they had a fully-loaded set they would look a little bit different, maybe a little bit red from the effort! There are considerable forces necessary to get a flying set moving on a single-purchase system: for an empty bar, 150–300 Newtons (34–68 lbf), for a bar loaded with 72 kg (160 lbs) on it, 250–400 N (56–90 lbf), and for a bar loaded with 126 kg (275 lbs), 450–800 N (100–180 lbf).

These figures also depend on the state of the installation; you can have one manufacturer who is better than another and one theatre that's doing more maintenance of the installation, so there are differences caused by that.

The Safety Inspectorate did this risk assessment on manual counterweight flying systems in The Netherlands back in 1998. They decided that the work we are doing is not good for our bodies. So they developed, together with the people in the theatres, a standard, and it's a very simple standard. It's half – it depends on the typeface – but it's half a page of A4. And it's called **Norm 2**. It's a standard for mechanising flying systems in theatres. I say 'Standard for Mechanising Flying Systems' – maybe that's wrong, because the only thing this **Norm 2** does is to abolish *manual* counterweight systems to a certain degree, and I will show you to what degree.

The goal of the standard is to organise the work in the workplace in such a way that physical strain will not endanger the health and safety of the employees. The standard allows for a maximum installation of only 20 counterweighted fly bars. The maximum weight per bar may not exceed 75 kg (165 lbs). The type of construction of the counterweight cradle does not permit a weight of more than 75 kg (165 lbs) to be put in. As these are all single-purchase sets we have the same weight on each side of

the system, and this means that the counterweight cradle is shortened so that if you put 75 kg on it, it's full. The maximum weight of a counterweight may not exceed 6 kg. And the use of a counterweight table is obligatory.

The use of auxiliary motors on manual flybars is permitted provided that the auxiliary motor overhauls the arbor and the employee who operates the flying system is trained sufficiently. The Commission for Safety, Health and Wellbeing in the Theatre will, in cooperation with some training institutes, develop standards of education, and the aim is to develop training for flying operators. The training will conclude with a certificate; this training obligation is applicable both for the operation of manual counterweight systems and for mechanised flying systems.

Then there was the whole standards timetable, which is that these written rules have to be implemented before January 1st 2004. This term can be extended for a maximum of three years until, at the latest, January 1st 2007, under the condition that before July 1st 2001 a plan of approach is submitted to the Safety Inspectorate in which it is clear that a decision is taken about adaptation of a flying system and that the financing is secured. A request for a subsidy is not sufficient, and an agreement has to be made with the supplier about the period in which the change and modifications will take place. The safety inspector will judge the plan and will inform the theatre if the submitted plan complies with the governing conditions. Theatres that had a hybrid manual/electric flying system on January 1st 2000 are allowed to submit a proposal in which their own specific situation is acknowledged in respect of the time for implementation. The inspector will take into account the actual setup of the system when judging the alternative proposal.

About eight to ten years ago a Dutch manufacturer made a hybrid system; he took a manual system and added a motor to it. You could then use the motor to lower the bar. You then had to put counterweights into the cradle and when it was in balance you could work manually. That helps, but shifting the weights still has to be done. The Inspectorate allows a little bit more time for these theatres, because of all the money they have invested; they get some time to get some benefit. The Safety Inspectorate will consult with the

Norm 2
Standard for mechanising flying systems in theatres
Goal

To organise the work and the workplace in such a way that physical strain will not endanger the health and safety of the employees.

Standard

- A maximum of 20 manual counterweighted fly bars is allowed, the maximum weight may not exceed 75 kg per bar; the type of construction of the counterweight cradle does not permit a weight of more than 75 kg.
- The maximum weight per counterweight may not exceed 6 kg; the use of counterweight tables is obligatory.
- The use of auxiliary motors on manual fly bars is permitted provided that the auxiliary motor seizes upon the arbor and the requirements below this point are fulfilled.
- The employee who operates the flying system will be trained sufficiently. The commission for safety, health and well being in the theater will, in cooperation with some training institutes develop standards of education. The aim is to develop a training for flying operators. The training will conclude with a certificate. The training obligation is applicable both for the operation of manual counterweight systems and for mechanised flying systems.

Timetable

- The above written rules have to be implemented before January 1st 2004
- This term can be extended with a maximum of three years until at the latest January 1st 2007, under the condition that before July 1st 2001 a plan of approach is submitted to the safety inspection, in which it is clear that a decision is taken about adaptation of the flying system, the financing is secured (a subsidy request is not sufficient) and an agreement is made with the supplier about the period in which the adaptation will take place.
- The safety inspector will judge the plan of approach and will inform the theatre if the submitted plan complies with the governing conditions.
- Theatres that had a 'manual/electric' flying system on January 1st 2000 are allowed to submit a proposal in which their own specific situation is acknowledged, with respect to the time of implementation. The inspector will take into account the actual setup of the system when judging the alternative proposal.

Consultation

- The safety inspection will consult together with the commission for safety, health and well being in the theatre about the best way to enforce the standard.

Commission for Safety, Health and Wellbeing in the Theatre about the best way to enforce the standard.

Where are we now? After this summer – and there are no real figures available, but this is my observation – after this summer of 2002, about 70% of the theatres are ready. We will have a mechanised flying system in these theatres. Next year, about 25% will change, so it will be a busy year, and then there are about 5% of the theatres, maybe a little bit less even than that, who have applied for extension of the period, so they will change between 2004 and 2007. And that's it. Thank you. Ω

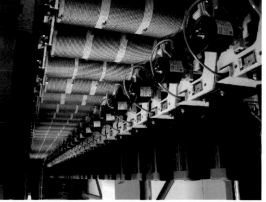

The grid and hoist installation during commissioning in the Rotterdam Schouwburg Theatre in August 1999. Hoists and control by Stage Technologies.

Photos: Techplan

Questions and discussion

Question from the floor

How many theatres are there in Holland?

Louis Janssen, Speaker

Between 150 and 200. It depends on what you describe as a theatre – it's about 150. Theatres in The Netherlands are owned by the cities, so all the theatres – no, not all, most of the theatres – are municipal theatres, so they are funded by cities, whereas the theatre companies that tour around, the software, is funded by the state government. So in this case the state government said you have to abolish the manual systems and the cities have to pay for that.

Another question from the floor

Can you explain about the risk assessment protocol in Holland whereby they could justify coercing people into large amounts of expense to eliminate such a risk? If this process was risk-assessed in the UK, because it's not liable to produce a fatal accident or a severe injury, you probably could justify not taking as radical an action as they have in Holland. This would be as a result of taking account of the economic side of the risk assessment.

Paul Edwards, Chairman

Can I chip in before you answer that one? In this country I think we'd have to identify the risk as leading to possible permanent disability, and so it's still fairly high level on the risk-assessment bit. *Fairly* high level, but …

Louis Janssen, Speaker

I don't know if I completely understood the question; are you saying that with a motorised system you have a higher risk?

Same questioner

No, I'm saying that there is considerable expense involved in changing over these systems. When the risk was being quantified as being a risk which had to be eliminated, or had to be eliminated as much as possible, I was wondering how these costs were accounted for in this risk assessment.

Louis Janssen, Speaker

Yes, well there were rows about this, of course, by the theatre organisations; the managing directors of theatres made a lot of fuss about it, but it was just that the authorities said, "How much money is your health worth?" It was proven that it was not healthy, so then the inspectors said, "This way of working is not healthy." They didn't tell us how to solve the problem – that's another issue. They only said, "This is not healthy; make it healthy," and that's all. But making it healthy is contradictory to making theatre. I mean, you can add a motor which makes a lot of noise and has one speed, but then I don't know if you can make proper theatre with that. So that was the problem and that's something we are struggling with a lot, but we cannot choose this any more. How can we, with low cost, have a system which makes good theatre possible?

Dave Ludlam, Barbican Centre

Of that 70% that you've suggested are sorted out this summer, how many theatres have taken the passive option of just limiting their loadings? Or have they all got mechanisation of some sort?

Louis Janssen, Speaker

It's only a very few theatres who have limited their options, very small theatres who say, "Okay, I take out 20 of the 40 sets, so I work with only 20 sets and I limit them to 75 kg." It depends on their programme. These are generally school theatres and that kind of building in very small communities. Under the touring conditions in The Netherlands, if you want to receive a touring company, you have to comply.

Dave Ludlam, Barbican Centre

And are most of the motorised solutions fixed-speed?

Louis Janssen, Speaker

No, the solutions for mechanising the flying systems are generally computer-controlled, with variable speed.

Paul Edwards, Chairman

And that reference takes us back to one of the Conference presentations earlier on today.

Ms Kiem-Lian The, Toornend & Partners

I'd like to react to a question raised earlier. Dutch law actually requires employers to do everything within their means to reduce physical strain, and this applies to theatre as well as many other sectors. And they actually calculated that changing these 100 or so theatres to a power-assisted system would cost Dfl 250 million (£80m, US$132m €113m), an investment which is indeed quite sizeable. There is, however, a small measure of subsidies available that the theatres can request, and this covers about 1%, I think, of the actual investment. So it is expensive for everyone.

Paul Edwards, Chairman

But time will tell what the benefit is – we've got an idea of cost, but time will tell what the benefit will be.

Ms Kiem-Lian The, Toornend & Partners

Well, the benefit is really the weak point, as far as we see it within this Norm. It's not really a Norm that tells you what you should do. It only says ... it kind of restricts the use ... it's not even outlawed, you can use it, at least, if you conform to these restrictions that were mentioned earlier, but it leaves 1,001 possibilities for any new system within a theatre. So we fear that it will only increase the diversity of systems used and therefore may be even opening the door to different kinds of hazards within a theatre.

Paul Edwards, Chairman

Yes. It is important to watch for any secondary hazards.

American member of audience

The number 75 kg (165 lbs) sticks in my mind, and I would like to address a comment to you, Mr Johnson. Just how much risk are we at when we're moving 75 kg? The only reason I'm throwing that number around is, if I remember correctly, New York City School is designed to a standard of 350 kg (770 lbs) for a counterweighted pipe, and I believe one of the consultants was talking about theatres that he's just done in California where he had 3,000 lbs (1,360 kg) as a payload on a pipe. So if you wouldn't mind addressing that question of 75 kg, and in the practical world what kind of strain is that putting on an individual?

Jonathan Johnson, Speaker

The maximum recommended load that you should lift is, I think I said, between 55 and 58 kg (120–128 lbs). I assume when you're saying 75 kg you're talking about a counterbalance system, so that the actual load on your back is nothing like that – I don't know what the exact load is. We've been given a figure in Newtons required to move a counterweight set of about 300 or 400 N (68–90 lbf); I don't know how that compares with lifting a 1 kg (2¼ lb) weight. But obviously you want to get things down to a minimum.

The other thing I mentioned is whether we should be screening people. We don't really know what the effects of reducing these loads are going to be in Holland, and it might be just as cost-effective to pre-screen people going into the job. What was tried here in the UK, when we had compiled some data and still had some coal mines, was looking at potential miners when they started in this job and assessing them. You can do simple tests on assessing the size of their spinal canal, whether they've got any obvious conditions like spondylolisthesis, which can be inherited; I mean obvious things you can see on a straightforward X-ray, to try and screen out people who you think would be at risk of damaging their backs. Maybe that would be just as cost-effective as trying to reduce a counterweight load from 12 kg to 10 kg (26 to 22 lbs).

Paul Edwards, Chairman

A potentially interesting matter on discrimination law coming up there!

Ian Albery, Sadler's Wells Theatre

I've got an interesting story, perhaps, in the sense that at Sadler's Wells Theatre we went entirely to a power-flying system. It's exceptionally good, but the systems were, when we first investigated them, not of the quality that we wanted. We wanted extreme silence but the motors had to be within the stagehouse (fly tower). I thought of an idea, which was adopted, of having electric motors and hydraulic brakes. Brilliant! – it's the most silent flying system, probably, in the world, and the Royal Opera House followed it about a year later, putting in a similar hydraulic braking system. But the risk, I think, in some senses has increased, because while we have no back strain we now have a system that moves so silently that nobody onstage can sense it. With any hemp system – either single-purchase or double-purchase counterweight system – anybody on stage who has experience can actually hear that slight rumble, that movement. But now the actual spotting of every super-silent power-flying set in operation is absolutely crucial, because you can kill somebody, I reckon, a lot easier now than we could previously. With power-flying systems there's also the other aspect of damage. They can fly, now, at such high speeds and with such loads that you can rip a set apart in absolutely no time because you don't have the sensitivity of a manual-flying system. I know that we have all these user health and safety assessments and so on, but I think sometimes if you do things only for health and safety reasons and you don't have other good and valid reasons, you can end up actually with a greater risk which has to be managed. That's obviously what management is about, it's about managing risk – but I do think you're trading one risk, possibly, for a whole range of other risks.

Paul Edwards, Chairman

It's true; we have to come to some kind of a balancing assessment where we look at the cost-benefit. And the motorised systems, they have their problems, but equally a good motorised system with a decent braking system will stop far faster than a man on a rope haul could stop a system – far faster.

Ian Albery, Sadler's Wells Theatre

There are other interesting comparisons in theatres. Here in the UK we can use power-flying at up to 2.4 metres/second (8 feet/second). In certain European countries it's limited to 1.2 metres/second (4 feet/second). Speed is important for doing very fast transformation scenes, particularly in dance. Having a front gauze flying out at very high speeds is a very attractive artistic thing to be able to do, but you're actually enabling far higher speeds, and using far greater weights, and therefore genuinely increasing risk which has to be managed.

Louis Janssen, Speaker

That's another risk assessment to do, of course. If you buy a power-flying system, you do a new risk assessment on that. We don't have rules for the maximum speed in our country, but it's common practice that the maximum speed is around 1.8 metres/second; and in some larger houses they want to go to 2 metres/second (6'-6"/second). And another thing we have is that above a certain weight on the bar, we will decrease the speed. So, for example, above 250 kg (550 lbs) the speed will go

down from the maximum of 1.8 metres to 1.2 or 1 metre/second.

Paul Edwards, Chairman

A point that's worth making about the silence of the systems is that silence can't always be necessary! I defy anybody to hear a system rumbling during *Miss Saigon*, *Phantom of the Opera*, or any of the big musicals – there are rarely any quiet moments.

Question from the floor

Have there been any attempts in Holland to try to keep counterweight systems and to change the handling systems, for example, making the counterweight with water, you fill it up and then pour it out; were there any discussions about this?

Louis Janssen, Speaker

No. The shifting of the weights is the biggest and best identified problem, but the other problem is pulling the rope with a completely twisted back. Everybody knows if you pull a set you want to see what's happening on stage behind you. If you have a set with 250 kg (550 lbs) on it, you really need a lot of force to get that moving or to stop it. So that's the other element in the whole story. But no, we didn't look at water systems.

Andy Hayles, Speaker

It would seem, Louis, that the Dutch have gone from manual systems pretty directly to power-flying, and there doesn't seem to have been much work done on a form of happy medium.

Louis Janssen, Speaker

No, but that's up to every client. I mean each theatre could go along that road because the law doesn't prohibit them from doing that. They can do it.

Andy Hayles, Speaker

The 75 kg which is allowed is nothing, is it? It's a very small load. I mean, the point about the water, and other people have mentioned lead shot, and hoppers, and dragging – ways of getting weight into the cradle that wouldn't involve manual handling. It's not something that …

Paul Edwards, Chairman

Linking cradles to use two bars together is another solution which is quite common.

Andy Hayles, Speaker

I don't know if anyone here has come across any cunning means of getting weight into the cradle that doesn't involve moving weights manually. (*Pause*) That'll be a 'No', then!

Paul Edwards, Chairman

Quite a resounding one! Deafening!

David Campbell, Victorian Arts Centre, Melbourne

I'd like to follow on from what Ian Albery was saying. Our State Theatre has got 112 lines of power-flying and the Playhouse Theatre has got 70 counterweight sets, mostly single-purchase, but some double-purchase. I'd certainly make a comment about the need to be aware of the transfer of risk. We've recently had a lot of risk assessments done on the power-flying in the State Theatre that's been operating for 15 years now and the risks involved are probably as great, if not more, with the power-flying system as they are with counterweights. They're just different risks.

But other things have gone up; the power system has actually increased the labour costs for the hirers because we've now pretty well got a minimum of two fly people on every show even though with the counterweight system we'd often have only one flyman. Some of the reasons are the ones that Ian cited earlier in regard to being able to see your load because you can't feel it any more. So we've often got a flyman on the OP (non-working) gallery as well as the operator on the prompt side gallery, and there's quite often other spotters involved if the show's a bit more complex. We often do an individual risk assessment for each production that's coming in, and if an opera or ballet has particularly complex flying they may require even more flymen, who are often there only in an observation capacity.

That's looking at it holistically. Certainly the aspect of the 75 kg (165 lbs) maximum cradle capacity is one that needs to be looked at, because you can injure yourself very badly with 75 kg and yet operate safely with 1,000 kg (2,200 lbs).

Andy Hayles, Speaker

I have a quick question for those of you who are lucky enough to have a power-flying system. How do you deal with things like putting stage weights on the backs of braces? How do you deal with unloading things from lorries that are irregularly loaded? I think that's the real worry, and it is the bigger picture about what we're expected to do in theatre; it is dangerous work. The construction industry is changing. It's now possible to build different kinds of blockwork wall depending on whether you need one operative or two operatives to put the block into place to cement it. And we're all aware, obviously, of the risk assessments we have to do to mark scenery coming out of the back of the trucks and to carry around risk assessments with our shows, but it is overall a huge issue and certainly bigger even than just the flying.

Paul Edwards, Chairman

In fairness, a counter-argument to that has to be that if we're offloading whatever, there's a whole team of us doing it, and so we're sharing the load and we're not doing repetitive loading. As you suggested, on a show we could easily be loading up 350 weights, so there we have got the repetitive action coming into it. That actually flags up something interesting; Andy described earlier about trying to hoodwink the local authority with this idea of spreading the loading over a week, you know, the average over a week, and not in any actual get-in that I've ever seen!

Chris Baldwin, Theatre Consultant

The figures that we've talked about so far apply to lifting objects; that's all very clear. Does this same information transfer to the very different task of pulling downwards when flying using hemps? There must be quite a lot of different things happening to the spine. What sort of limits and recommendations are coming out in respect of that? Has any research been done? I can't find very much in the ABTT publications.

Jonathan Johnson, Speaker

I think you're right. There has been a certain amount of work done on pulling and pushing, but not very much, and not the sort of pulling that is involved in this particular work – it's mainly been about pushing forwards and backwards as opposed to pulling up and down. So I think the answer is you're right; there's very little information. All we know is you are in a standing position, you need much muscle activity and you're using your arms more than your back. Now the problem about that is, of course, that in the human the way we've evolved is that the arms and shoulders are not actually made for carrying or pulling very big weights in that they're not very well developed. That in theory should be a problem, but as far as I know, looking through the literature before this talk I found very little actually on that sort of action.

Paul Edwards, Chairman

Again, the Manual Handling Regulations of course talk about manual handling operations, the use of physical force to move an object. It doesn't say 'lifting and carrying', but really the Regulations do apply. What's lacking is good guidance on them, as you quite rightly say – not enough study, not enough guidance.

Alan Cohen, Stage Engineer and Independent Technical Consultant

I've spent nearly 40 years being involved in manual counterweight systems, single- and double-purchase. A couple of points come to mind. I wouldn't think that a javelin thrower would start throwing the javelin without a lot of careful training and without wearing the necessary support, so perhaps our flymen should be given – or maybe they undertake themselves – the necessary training, and perhaps someone develops the necessary body belt specially for this twisting action, but I don't think anyone's given this any consideration.

But going right away from the theatre, there are other fields where far more injuries are being generated, like repetitive strain injury to wrists, and millions of people who sit at keyboards in front of monitors who are starting to suffer deteriorating eyesight from glare; there are other fields such as the construction industry where I'm sure a lot of operatives, the labourers, are not given any training and willingly still carry over-heavy loads. We are a relatively small and specialised industry. I'm not saying we shouldn't be looking at ways of improving our flying systems, and the weight table on the loading gallery is an obvious one, but we must get it in proportion.

And the other point, which hasn't come up in the session so far, is that once you've got a relatively heavy load, say as much as 300 kg (660 lbs), on a bar, say a

Frenchman – and we use far more steel in scenery today than we ever did before – once that's moving you have a different set of conditions in trying to retard it, because once that scenery is going out and the cradle's going down, you've got to stop the rope in an unnatural position. Perhaps we should be looking at a redesigned rope lock or another device which will help with the control of all this.

Ian Albery, Sadler's Wells Theatre

I think we're all actually missing the point that the reasons for putting in power-operated flying systems with sophisticated control are artistic. In dance we use flying very much as part of the balletic or dance experience of the evening. So what impelled us at the Wells to put in a power-flying system was nothing to do with Health and Safety, but it was because artistically we could get better control to serve the choreographer, the designer and the director. It's rather like saying we should have stayed with master dimmers of the old variety of the 1930s – which might also have had a repetitive strain aspect to them – as against computerised lighting control systems.

Paul Edwards, Chairman

But if you can call it Health and Safety, it comes out of a different budget – that's very useful!

Ian Albery, Sadler's Wells Theatre

I like that!

Paul Edwards, Chairman

Here is a point, a small point. I don't know if Jonathan will agree with me here. Who here is a sports person, does sports – running, whatever it is? Now, would you dream of leaping into your sports activity without doing a bit of warm-up and possibly taking a bit of care afterwards? You wouldn't normally, would you? And yet we ask our crews who are doing all this physical work just to leap straight into it without any warm-up or preparation. Are there additional loads on the body, additional problems if they don't do warm-up? I mean, could we quantify whether such preparation would significantly reduce risk?

Response from the floor

In the last six months I have got all my crew to start warming up before they move scenery. All the actors do a warm-up, the crew now do a warm-up, and my number of injuries has gone down by 100%.

Paul Edwards, Chairman

What more can we say? You see a lot of Japanese firms who have everybody doing warm-up exercises at the start of the day. Why not? It seems a good idea. Unfortunately our idea of warm-up exercises for many flymen is for them to do a bit of weight-lifting!

Dave Roxburgh, Welsh College of Music and Drama

I've trained kids how to fly and I'm absolutely horrified. I'm horrified at the concept of getting rid of counterweight flying. I can't believe it – I'm absolutely shocked! Yes, there's a risk factor, yes, there are weights, and yes, warm-ups; safe working practice is everything here. Surely, if you have a code of safe working practice, people are trained to do that and there's a risk management on top of that; isn't that enough? Yes, power-flying for certain situations, but I just can't believe that we could consider going down that road in this country.

Paul Edwards, Chairman

We've got a problem in that we'd have to reduce the standard weights with the current systems that we've got set up. The reach is so far, and the distance that they have to lift through is so far, that it's difficult to come up with a modified system where you can say, "That would be safe." That's the problem. We can redesign the cradles perhaps so they're right in front of you. And there are other issues that we didn't even touch on here because we were looking at strain; for example, dropping weights, and should the bottom of the counterweight installation be caged in? There are a number of systems where the bottom of the counterweight system is not protected. So there are these other issues as well. If we could design a better system, then perhaps we could defend it. It's difficult to defend what we've got at the moment.

Audience reaction

Why not have machines loading cradles?

Paul Edwards, Chairman

There we are, a good solution. Why can't we have machines loading cradles? Has anyone heard about a water-filled counterweight system? I don't know why that didn't take off – was it just that it was slow to fill? Sounds like a sensible way of tackling it.

David Adams, Chairman ABTT Safety Committee

It seems to me even if you sort out the entire counterweight cradle problem, and in theory provide an infinitely variable motor, that is one with infinite torque ability, this would allow you to get rid of that element. So long as you operate in a mode which involves doing something physical there, looking over your back, it has got to be dangerous. Actually if you look at the positioning of the flyman and what he's doing, I think you've got to say that's it's an unsafe situation. And we've got to cure it.

Paul Edwards, Chairman

We've already got the idea of the Australian model; we were talking about needing two people, or three additional spotters and so on. The average fly gallery we're talking about is about 1–1.5 metres (3'-3"–5'-0") wide, so I'm effectively standing and hauling here, and looking at something moving over a rail down there. I can't see why we don't have the same number of spotters now. We don't, actually, use them normally, do we? We have markers on the hauling lines and we go by those, far more than we look at the moving scenery.

Andy Hayles and others

You've got the feel factor in the ropes, haven't you? There's the feeling you get when a set gets caught up or whatever, which counts for a lot. If you're dropping in a piece, you feel it if it hits anything and you can stop. I've hit people with the conduit bar in the bottom of the cloths, but I know that I've done it!

Paul Edwards, Chairman

You know once you've hit them. But if you were standing at the rail, you would see far better, you could see if you're going to hit somebody. There's no reason why we can't have a walkabout remote control, none at all. I'm actually tending to be more in favour of the idea of going away from counterweights because of the many problems with them, but I don't say that this would rule out the problems entirely.

Andy Hayles, Speaker

I just wanted to try and put Dave Roxburgh's mind at rest. Refer to the HSE booklet 'Getting to grips with manual handling' that I mentioned earlier. I think you are saying that we mustn't exceed the guidelines for lifting weights. But it says no, the risk assessment guidelines are *not* safe limits for lifting, but work outside these guidelines is *more likely to increase the risk of injury*, and so you should examine it closely for possible improvements. It's not saying you can't, it's just saying be careful.

Peter Dean, Guildhall School of Music and Drama

I'm just want to come back to Dave Roxburgh, really. I'm horrified, in a slightly different way, that we've been using counterweights for however many years. We've all been working in the theatre and we've not really assessed the risk to the level that we're now being asked to, and we've potentially been doing some very unsafe practices without really thinking about them. This is clear because the earlier show of hands indicated how many people do this work, and how often.

Paul Edwards, Chairman

What makes me chuckle is that I often hear – because I go around running Health and Safety training all the time, especially for theatre – and I often hear, "… these new regs that have come in…" What new regulations? – They've been applicable for 10 years! We've been doing training on this subject, but we've obviously not been addressing the main issues.

Jonathan Johnson, Speaker

It would appear to me that nobody in this industry knows the exact size of the problem, and one of the American ergonomic views was that there should be some sort of logging of incidents so that we can all report into somewhere centrally. We've done that in the UK with rugby; spinal injuries in rugby, or rugby injuries generally, are reported to the Rugby Football Union, and we now have a much better idea of the incidence of serious injuries on the rugby field, which we didn't know five or ten years ago. Therefore, before changing all the rules maybe we should just try and find out what the actual incidence of injuries from these systems in the theatre really are.

Paul Edwards, Chairman

Okay, well that's about it. Thank you very much to our speakers, and thank you very much for your participation. Ω

Overhead Suspensions

Chairman: George Ellerington, Senior Consultant, Theatre Projects Consultants
Speakers: Martin Honeywill, Automation Director, Unusual Rigging
           Maurycy Sowka, Managing Director of ASM Steuerungstechnik GmbH
           Dr Fred Maeder, Technical Director, Waagner-Biro Stage Systems

Introduction: George Ellerington

This session is about overhead suspensions and it follows on quite well from the previous session in this room, which was on the strain of using manual counterweight systems. We're going to look at hoisting equipment, which provides one possible alternative to the problems with counterweights that were highlighted earlier. We're not particularly going to focus on control systems for power-flying systems, or on standards, because these are covered in other sessions; we're going to look more at the actual machinery that's used for hoisting and flying in the theatre.

As a consultant I've looked forward to the day when we can go out and buy proven off-the-shelf products suitable for use in the theatre. I have to say they have been a long time coming, but it seems now that more and more manufacturers are developing products that are suitable for use in the theatre, and we shall see some examples of these in this session.

We need hoists that can perform many different requirements in the theatre. We need hoists that can lift and dead hang loads like lighting and scenery and masking, but we need hoists that may be used during the performance for special effects, for instance, or to move scenery. We need single-point hoists that can be used on their own or in different groups; we need multi-line hoists for moving flying bars. We need hoists that are portable and flexible and which can be reconfigured by users, but we also need hoists for permanent installations and for specific purposes. And when selecting hoists we need to consider noise, speed, lifting capacity and safety, which is becoming an increasing priority. We need hoists that are reliable, are easy to use, and most important we need hoists that we can afford!

There are various companies that have been developing products specially for us and the three gentlemen on the panel have each got different solutions to the various problems of hoisting in theatres. First we have Martin Honeywill from Unusual Rigging – he's going to talk about chain hoists specifically – then Maurycy Sowka from a company called ASM, who market their products through Gerriets among others, and he's going to talk about the products they have, including a steel-band point hoist. Last but not least, we have Dr Fred Maeder who is from Waagner-Biro, and he is going to tell us about the sophisticated power-flying hoists that they have been developing over the last year or two.

So without further ado I will ask Martin to kick off for us.

First Speaker: Martin Honeywill

What I'm going to be talking about is not specifically a fixed chain hoist, but I'll be looking at generic control systems for chain hoists, and what some of us think we currently use chain hoists for, and describing some of the more innovative uses of chain hoists. I hope to get you thinking about where chain hoists could be applicable. They do have disadvantages, but they also have advantages, and we'll try and cover some of those in this talk. I'm going to try and keep my discussion as general as possible. A chain hoist is a chain hoist. Some manufacturers will have advantages in their products in terms of size, speed, lifting capacity or whatever but, if we try and keep the approach fairly generic, you can apply a lot of what I'm going to say to many different chain-hoist systems.

Martin Honeywill is Senior Automation Engineer/Designer at Unusual Rigging Ltd, the largest and longest established rigging company in the UK, where he has worked since 1992. Prior to joining Unusual he began by designing DMX lighting desks and dimmers for companies like Green Ginger and ADB. Martin has a degree in Electronics and Computer Science.

A typical complex rig of trussing and chain hoists with which Unusual are used to coping: this is for "Beauty and the Beast" at Liverpool Empire.

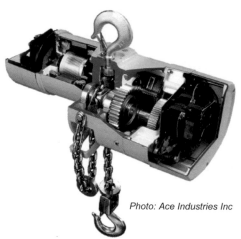

Photo: Ace Industries Inc

A cut-away view of one of the many different types of chain hoist available.

Most people see the traditional uses for chain hoists as more of a back-room function. They are used for storage, temporary handling and temporary lifting of equipment. And in our business specifically, being a rigging company, we use them for construction of temporary structures and actually building temporary environments. I'm going to start by talking about some of the situations where we've used chain hoists for permanent installations.

First, I want to give you a very quick overview of what a chain hoist is. I am sure that most of you know what we're talking about, but basically a chain hoist consists of a motor, which is either single-braked, or double-braked as may be required in some situations. We then have some form of slipping clutch or clutching device which will then drive through the gearbox onto the load wheel. There are many variations on this theme; for example, in the Verlinde V104 hoists where the motor rotor also forms part of the brake assembly, but otherwise that's generally the idea of what we're referring to when we talk about chain hoists.

Some of the disadvantages with chain hoists include their being fixed-speed devices, or maybe a dual-speed device with a dual-speed motor. In their traditional sense they've got no positional feedback, and they can be deemed as being noisy. Some people think of them as oily; but a lot these sort of things have changed with more modern technology.

Let's consider some of the advantages of chain hoists: they're compact, they're robust, they're rugged, and very easy to set up as a temporary piece of equipment. They're very cheap when compared to other sorts of lifting equipment. This is because the chain hoist is designed as a piece of industrial equipment; they're built in very high volumes and you've got the advantages of scale in terms of bringing the costs down. The chain itself is actually a very durable medium; it can be in some situations a lot more durable than steel wire-rope. Also generally you have a built-in clutch with a chain hoist, which is an automatic device to stop you overloading it; you can't pick up a load that's greater than the chain hoist is rated to lift.

An unusually-suspended BMW for a corporate gig at the Millbrook Concept Centre.

The basic control systems that are often used with chain hoists give direct control of just the motors, and all the control equipment is elsewhere, often down on the ground away from the chain hoists themselves. When using three-phase chain-hoist motors, altering the phase sequence simply allows the chain hoist to either raise or lower and that is easily controlled remotely.

You then can have chain hoists which have got a degree of local control built into them; where they've built the contactors and the control system actually into the chain hoist. This has some advantages; it's generally easier to make chain hoists that have built-in control equipment comply with various standards like VGB 70; these units can incorporate limits which are fitted to the chain hoist mechanism and so on.

We've also got available simple variable-speed control systems, some built by third parties and some actually built by the chain-hoist manufacturers themselves, often with a very basic variable-speed pendant control which can be used remotely.

Photos: Unusual

When we require more advanced control systems, we have to start incorporating more features into the chain hoists. We can incorporate positional feedback by putting some type of position encoder in the chain hoist. At first, this was some sort of link-counting device, often put outside the chain hoist. These weren't very accurate and were also susceptible to damage. Then people started to incorporate some form of pulse counter actually built into the chain hoist mechanism; this still not being particularly accurate nor particularly robust. More modern chain hoists can incorporate small robust quadrature encoders that actually provide both positional and directional information and output a high number of pulses. It is possible to output a large number of pulses per millimetre on a chain hoist, so you can actually get quite a high-resolution feedback.

Some chain-hoist systems actually incorporate load cells, either into the fixing point of the chain hoist or into the hook assembly on the chain hoist, to provide feedback information on the load. These are very useful temporary rigging installations when you're actually using chain hoists as part of the short-term fixtures and fittings of a building, or if you're building a temporary structure and you want to make sure you're not overloading specific points.

We've been working on developments using intelligent encoders, as have, I'm sure, many other people in the industry. This increases the intelligence in the chain hoist from the point of view of its knowing its position. There are encoders now which are powered from the supply that's going to the chain hoist, so the encoder itself has effectively got an absolute encoder within it. Such a unit knows exactly where it is; it doesn't need to be interfaced to any other piece of equipment to actually store its own position. Once you've got this degree of intelligence in the chain hoist, you can start to do other sorts of things. You can interface with the load cell also, you can gather together the information that you want to glean from the chain hoist on a data bus, and you can log this information. This can lead to creating extensive duty-cycle data so that if you're hiring chain hoists out you can actually get real information back from the units as to how long and what they have been used for.

You can also have radio-control systems. These are generally based on crane-control technology which leads us to another way of looking at whether chain hoists can fulfil your requirements. You often see a chain hoist hanging at the back of the theatre with its controller hanging down to one side and the chain hanging down with it. But you can also use a tracking chain hoist on a trolley, or on a beam trolley, and with such a chain hoist you can have quite a sophisticated control system handling its lateral movement, as well as its raise and lower functions.

Such a control can include a number of requirements that lifting equipment has to meet. I'm sure my colleagues, who are going to follow me, will probably be able to give you far more information on VGB 70 than I can, but I can give you a brief synopsis of some of its requirements. Basically the fixing points put in for chain hoists must have a safety factor of 10:1; it requires hoists to be de-rated by a factor of 0.5, so a one-tonne chain hoist would become a half-tonne chain hoist. Safety features include the requirement for a fail-safe system, which is interpreted as needing a double braking system. There is a requirement for dual limit switches – the normal top and bottom limit switches and also ultimate top and bottom limit switches – which are fed back into the control system. Although not specifically mentioned, people often build in, as part of these safety features, overload detection and slack-chain detection, sometimes done with limit switches, sometimes done with load cells. Another feature that I should mention with VGB 70 is the fact that it's an overall accident-prevention standard, and part of its remit is basically talking about common-sense operation of equipment. And so the operator's skill and competence need to be taken into account.

I would now like to run through a couple of examples of some of the jobs that we've done, just to highlight some of the different uses that chain hoists have been put to.

The first is the Royal Albert Hall where we put in a control system for the temporary rigging of the basic house winching system. The temporary rigging points were there, and the client wanted to select points dynamically, group hoists together and move items up and down, and also integrate the existing load-cell into the system. This typifies what I was saying about temporary installations of a semi-permanent nature; this one was in there for a year.

Unusual Rigging were Gold Sponsors of the Theatre Engineering and Architecture Conference 2002

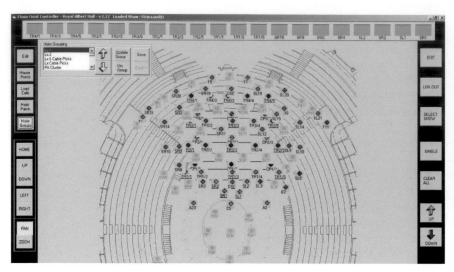

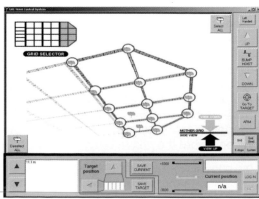

Left: the control-system display for the chain hoists over the stage end of the Royal Albert Hall, and right: the rigging and the access bridge for "Kiss Me Kate" at the Victoria Palace.

As an example of a number of chain hoists that were actually moved during the show, we put in a chain-hoist system where we were actually moving all the sails at the back that enclosed a central performance area; all the blue screens were moved up and down by chain hoists. And here's a good example of an installation where some of the drawbacks of the chain hoists weren't in fact an issue. Noise didn't matter; as there was a big show going on, with fireworks, sound, lights and everything, so the noise that these screens made just motoring down slowly wasn't a problem.

A job that we've finished very recently is the system that we've put into Earl's Court. It's a permanent installation in the roof, and allows us to fly things, and effectively to bring the roof down to ground level to allow shows to be rigged in a much easier way, in line with Health and Safety regulations. With this facility, additional suspension points can be put in, shows can be rigged and the hoist platforms can be taken back out again, up to show height. Part of the reason I am mentioning this installation is that its performance surprised me when we put the system together. Part of our client's requirements was that there should be no

deviation from point to point of more than 10 cm (4") , and we were very sceptical about whether we'd actually be able to achieve that. The height that the majority of the grids have to fly to is just over 25 metres (82'-0"). We found that we can actually fly a grid in to the floor and back out again and have a safety trip level set; the basic reason why this had a control system associated with it was to ensure that all the chain hoists moved at precisely the same time. If one hoist stopped, or moved out of level with the others, then the whole system would stop and could be re-levelled. And we found we were indeed getting less than 10 cm (4") deviation between the chain hoists at maximum travel. So there's another successful use to which chain hoists have been put.

In summary I'd just like to say that you shouldn't overlook chain hoists when you're considering specific requirements. In a sense, a chain hoist is a rough and ready point hoist; that's one way of looking at it. You can sometimes find that they are a nice, easy, cheap, cost-effective solution for some problems – not all – but they do overcome a large number of problems. Thank you very much. Ω

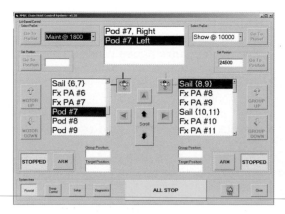

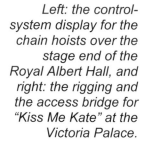

Special hoist control panels developed by Unusual Rigging for, left: the London Dome and right: Earls Court, London.

Photos: Unusual

Second speaker: Maurycy Sowka

Mr Sowka began by expressing his gratitude for the invitation to speak about new developments in stage and hoist technology, especially the steel-band hoist systems developed by his company ASM Steuerungstechnik GmbH. He pointed out that all their products comply with BGV C1—the highest German safety standard.

ASM produces innovative steel band hoists and super-silent chain hoists as well as the complete appropriate range of hoist control systems. The focus of the presentation is on two brand-new products, the SPC Point Hoist and the Flying Bar Systems PR 300 and PR 500. The company ASM itself was founded in 1988 and is located in a little town called Bad Wuennenberg-Haaren, approximately 25 km, or some 15 miles, to the south of Paderborn, right in the middle of Germany. ASM employs a skilled staff with comprehensive managerial and engineering experience. They cover the total range of drive technology and control systems for stage applications.

Regarding the steel-band products, the ASM products are specially and, if needed, individually designed to meet any specification in stage technology. ASM has a many different products in the ranges. For example a number of point hoists for different applications, as well as flying bar systems, a special lighting hoist, a curtain hoist and a media hoist. The steel-band system is a ASM patent.

Major and decisive advantages of all of the products include their silence, very long lifetime (greater than 10 years), high reliability, a very compact construction and no lengthening of the steel band in use.

As an example, the **P250JR Point Hoist** is a special hoist for TV studios and smaller theatre applications. Its speed can be up to 16 metres/min (52'-6"/min), and its load capacity to 300 kg (660 lbs). The control system is integrated into the hoist and this hoist can be provided with both variable-speed and computer-control devices.

The **Stage Hoist** is a very silent and fast point hoist for mobile applications. The maximum speed is 1.2 m/sec (4 ft/sec) and the maximum load capacity is 250 kg (550 lbs). This hoist can be provided as self-mounting, which makes the installation very easy.

The **Curtain Hoist** has been assembled in a television studio, where it hoists curtains or screens up and down fixed to a track system. Steel-band technology has also been used to create a special **Media Hoist** for lifting and carrying video or data projectors or lighting equipment.

A number of well-known institutions in the theatre, television and event industry have chosen ASM products for good reasons. Thus, the company has been part of a number of challenging projects; the Thalia Theatre in Hamburg, and the Volkswagen Arena in Braunschweig, many TV studios and other venues. At the Thalia Theatre, ASM installed a steel band lighting hoist with a load capacity of 2 tons and a variable speed of up to 0.5 m/sec (18"/sec), fully computer-controlled and with a cable management system integrated into the truss system. Since the start of ASM´s production of steel band hoists, more than 1,000 systems have been produced.

The brand-new **SPC Steel Band Point Hoist** is specially designed for mobile stage applications. It can be integrated into a truss systems and can also be used as a flexible hoist on a walking grid in a theatre. This very silent hoist uses just a single steel band. Its load capacity is 250 kg (550 lbs),

Maurycy Sowka is General Manager of ASM-Steuerungstechnik, a specialist design and manufacturing company which produces point- and chain-hoist systems. His company has developed the steel-band hoist which has been installed in many TV studios and some theatres. Maurycy is very experienced in the design, development and fabrication of new and innovative point-hoist systems for theatres and studios, particularly in regard to safety and performance.

Photos: ASM-Steuerungstechnik

Left: a Steel Band Stage Hoist; centre: a P250 JR Steel Band Hoist, and right: a Steel Band Media Hoist, providing accurate repositioning as the steel bands do not stretch.

Steel Band Curtain Hoist installed in a television studio

its maximum speed 1,2 m/sec (4 ft/sec), the noise level below 48 dbA. The SPC point hoist has a drop of up to 30 m (100 ft) and a compact size. It is powered by a highly efficient servo motor system which allows a very high duty cycle.

The introduction of the patented ASM **Flying Bar** system has attracted a lot of interest worldwide. There are two types, referred to by their maximum load capacity of 300 kg (660 lbs) and duty cycle of 60%, or 500 kg (1,100 lbs) and 100% respectively. All the mechanical elements are integrated into an aluminium-truss system. When assembled into a fly tower there are no horizontal forces or loads, only point loads on the load-bearing supports in the walls of the stage.

The ASM Flying Bar systems can be installed very easily, because they are pre-assembled in the factory. The special construction allows a silent and smooth operation for a very long lifetime. Although the standard maximum speed is 1.2 metres/sec (4 ft/sec), ASM is able to provide a higher maximum speed of 2 m/sec (6'-6"/ sec) on request.

It is possible to install a walking grid directly onto the Flying Bar modules, giving a dual use for the truss system. With this facility, maintenance, special applications, modifications and so on become very easy. For instance, a number of additional mobile SPC Point Hoists can be placed and used on such a grid in accordance with the needs of the show design.

The module of the PR 300 and PR 500 Flying Bars consists of a housing for the motor and the control system, which is fixed to a truss. All the other mechanics are integrated into, and protected by, the truss construction. Installation in a theatre building, equipped with only the necessary load-bearing supports, is very simple. The truss construction spans the width of the fly tower. The first two PR Flying Bar modules are installed, one with its housing on the left, one with the housing on the right. The two modules are followed by the next one and so on. The number of modules can be varied depending on the individual needs of the theatre.

Additionally, diagonal movements are also possible. The Flying Bar systems allow an angle of up to a maximum of ±10°, the SPC Hoist even a maximum of ±45°.

In summary, the decisive advantages of the **Steel Band PR Flying Bar System** include:

- the aluminium truss construction
- dual use for a walking grid
- the modular design
- pre-assembly at ASM
- easy installation and maintenance
- flexibility
- possibility of diagonal movements
- silent, smooth, fast and reliable operation.

Steel Band Lighting Hoist at the Thalia Theatre and the SPC Steel Band Point Hoist.

Photos: ASM-Steuerungstechnik

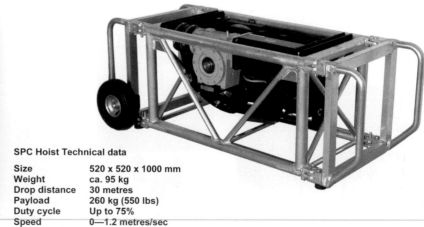

SPC Hoist Technical data

Size	520 x 520 x 1000 mm
Weight	ca. 95 kg
Drop distance	30 metres
Payload	260 kg (550 lbs)
Duty cycle	Up to 75%
Speed	0—1.2 metres/sec
Noise level	< 48 dBA

Principle of Flying Bar System

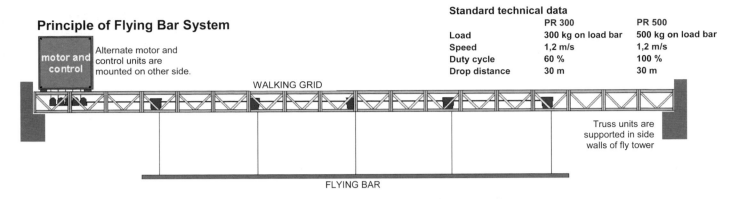

Standard technical data		
	PR 300	PR 500
Load	300 kg on load bar	500 kg on load bar
Speed	1,2 m/s	1,2 m/s
Duty cycle	60 %	100 %
Drop distance	30 m	30 m

motor and control

Alternate motor and control units are mounted on other side.

WALKING GRID

Truss units are supported in side walls of fly tower

FLYING BAR

Photos: Techplan

If required, all these machines can be provided with suitable control systems made by ASM.

ASM also have **Chain Point Hoists** in their product range. Naturally these comply with the highest German safety standards (BGV C1 and VGB 70). The ASM Chain Hoists operate very silently, and their standard speed maximum is 7 m/min (23 ft/min), but a maximum speed of 30 m/min (100 ft/min) has already been achieved. The load capacity goes up to 1,000 kg. The P 500 K hoist is specially designed for fixed applications, such as in arenas. The DUO 1000 is a very new and innovative point hoist for mobile applications, its housing being made of a special heavy-duty rubber material.

And to control the movements of all the above-mentioned products, ASM also provides control systems suitable for the most complex applications. First, there is the CANcon Point Hoist Control, based on CAN network technology, followed by a brand new development, the GENESIS Motor Control. Further, ASM offers a new lightwave-transmission based system, the ASM Stage Control Pro System. Ω

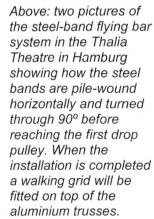

Above: two pictures of the steel-band flying bar system in the Thalia Theatre in Hamburg showing how the steel bands are pile-wound horizontally and turned through 90° before reaching the first drop pulley. When the installation is completed a walking grid will be fitted on top of the aluminium trusses.

Right: the P500K and left: the DUO 1000 chain hoist with its housing made of heavy-duty rubber material.

Third speaker: Dr Fred Maeder

Dr Fred Maeder is a Technical Director with Waagner-Biro Stage Systems Germany with special responsibilities for the operations in the UK. He has a First Degree in Automation and a Doctorate in Control and Systems Engineering. He started his industrial career at Krupp Industries GmbH and became Director of the Antenna Engineering Division. He then worked in Pittsburgh as Product Manager for Antennae, Stage Technology, Mechanical Car Parking and Bridge Building and, when his interests in stage equipment won, he became Manager of STATEC Stage Technology, moving shortly afterwards to set up the Duisburg office of Waagner-Biro.

Dr Maeder introduced the content of his presentation:

1. Types of winches for the upper stage machinery.
2. Technical customer requirements for the winches.
3. Safety technical requirements and components for the winches.
4. Selective criteria for the most important components.
5. The attachment of components to the winches.
6. Noise level requirements for winches.
7. Development of super-silent components.
8. Noise measurements with the new winches.
9. Final reflection and prospects for the future.

1. Types of winches for the upper stage machinery

Picture 1 shows the classical design of a winch with horizontal cable drum. A standard angular gear (for example a worm gear or bevel gear) is screwed tightly onto a machine frame structure and the drum is inserted into one side. The opposite side of the drum will be supported by a simple bearing. The electric motor with the double brake and the encoder will be fitted onto the gearbox.

The brakes can also be positioned between the gearbox and the motor. Nevertheless, this method requires a large adapter for the motor.

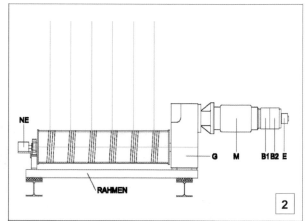

Advantages: simple, reasonably priced standard elements as in catalogues.

Disadvantages: without machining of the base frame structure, there will be additional load placed on the bearings at the output shaft of the gearbox. Bevel gears are relatively noisy and pure worm gears have a bad efficiency rate (less than 0.5). Integration of a load sensor is difficult.

Picture 2 shows the use of a classic two-step helical gear. Since the centre distances between the axis of the input and output shaft is normally too small, the motor must be mounted on the opposite side to the drum. As a consequence this leads to a relatively long machine structure and complicates accessibility to the winches. Normally both shafts of a standard gearbox do not protrude on both sides through the housing, therefore the ultimate limit switch box must be located on the opposite end of the drum.

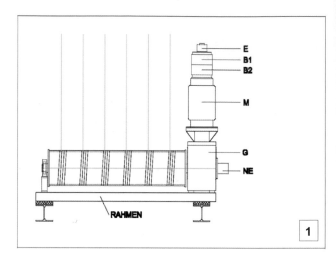

Advantages: simple, reasonably priced standard elements as in catalogues, helical gears in quality version are quiet.

Disadvantages: long structure, additional load placed on the bearings at the output shaft of the gearbox as shown in picture 1, limit switch lies on the other side, integration of a load sensor is complicated.

Picture 3 shows the use of a special narrow gearbox with extended shaft centres, so that the motor can be located parallel above the drum. This leads to a very compact machine structure. The brakes can be fitted tight onto the opposite side of the gearbox. The second bearing plate will be screwed tightly to the gearbox with metal rods. Consequently the complete winch becomes a rigid frame structure and a separate basic steel frame becomes superfluous.

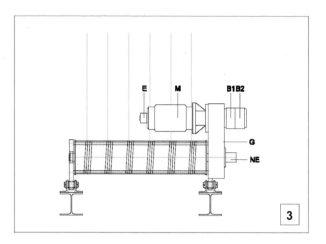

Advantages: compact machine structure, specialised gearboxes of high quality are silent, and the motor can be removed without the need of holding the load.

Disadvantages: Special gearboxes are more expensive, additional load placed on the bearings is still possible due to bending of the drum at very high radial loads, integration of a load sensor is complicated. The layout of the winch with the motor directly above the drum can in some cases restrict the routing of the wire-ropes from the drum.

Picture 4 shows a layout which mostly eliminates the previously described disadvantages. Two nearly identical bearing plates, which are held in position by metal rods, support the drum. A hollow shaft gearbox will be mounted onto the extended shaft of the drum eliminating the additional load placed on the bearings at the output shaft of the gearbox. The gearbox will be fixed to the bearing plate via a torque arm, into which a load sensor can be integrated easily. In the case of a bending drum no forced loads work on the bearings of

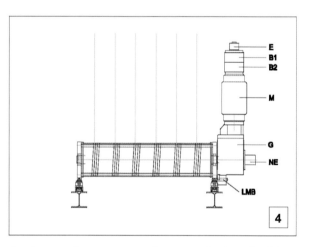

the output shaft of the gearbox. The desired angular gear can be manufactured with a optimum combination of a worm and helical gear extremely silent and with a relatively high efficiency rate (more than 80%). All the electro-mechanical components can be installed onto the same side of the winch for good accessibility.

Advantages: compact and force free optimum machine structure, special gearboxes of high quality are extremely silent, the motor position does not interfere with the running of the wire-ropes, a load sensor can be integrated easily.

Disadvantages: special gearboxes are more expensive than standard components as found in catalogues.

The Waagner Biro Stage Systems Group were the Platinum Sponsors of the Theatre Engineering and Architecture Conference 2002

Picture 5 shows, just for the record, a layout with a planetary gear, as a so called 'pot gear' within the drum. I personally started 15 years ago with this solution; it was supposed to be called the 'whispering winch®'. But it turned out to be a flop. The planetary gear is by nature very loud and cannot be manufactured to a high quality. Hard coupling it to the drum made the noise-emission levels even higher. This type of a 'silent' winch has been changed into a 2,000 watt vacuum cleaner.

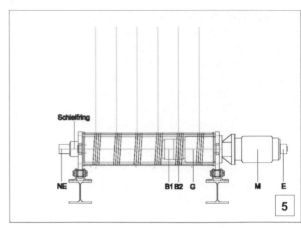

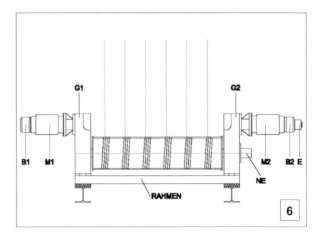

whispering winch® trade mark of Statec Bühnentechnik GmbH

Advantages: none
Disadvantages: many
Net result: not recommended!

Picture 6 shows a symmetrical layout with 2 gearboxes, motors and brakes each. This winch was shown at Showtech in Berlin 2001. The manufacturer advertised with the slogan of 'double safety' by the means of use of double components. While double brakes are necessary, it does not need two gearboxes in order to achieve double safety; one gearbox with a 2:1 factor is sufficient. Even though I do not know the initial criteria, I dare to say that this type of winch cannot be economical.

The installation of vertical winches in the "Theater an der Wien" in Vienna.

Picture 7 Just for reasons of completeness I want to show the principals of a vertical winch. This very narrow winch was developed to be installed in exchange for the old manual counterweight hoists in those shafts at the side walls of the stage tower. This winch consists of a vertically-standing steel tube on which the drum is supported by bearings at the top and bottom. The gearbox is mounted onto it and is held in position via a load sensor as a torque arm. The diverter pulleys are installed into a vertically movable carriage that moves parallel to the running wire-ropes. The motion of the carriage is achieved by an extension of the drum shaft machined to form a lead-screw with the same pitch as the drum grooves. With the wire-ropes turned through 90°, the fleet angles to the winding drum are therefore constantly normal to the drum grooves.

Photo: Waagner-Biro

2. Technical customers' requirements for the winches

The motor room and installation conditions play a major role. Wherever possible the winches with horizontal drums should be installed in two rows next to each other. See **Pictures 8 and 9**: view from the top and longitudinal section through the stage tower. The desired distance between the battens therefore determines the centre distance between the winches. For a long time in countries speaking the German language this distance was 250 mm (10") Consequently the manufactures of winches decided to fix the system width of the winches to just under 500 mm (19").

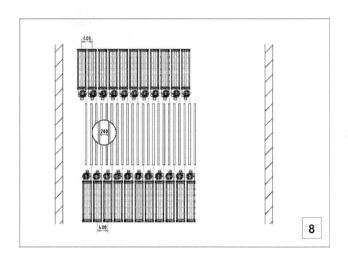

I remember very well a day approximately 10 years ago, when Richard Brett, the stage engineering consultant, visited us and persuaded us to take the 'international measurement' of 200 mm (8") distance between the battens into consideration when developing new winches. So, we developed winches just under 400 mm (16") in width. This new development was just finished when we received the invitation for tenders for the Royal Opera House in London written by Clive Odom and the same Richard Brett. We were very surprised to read the demand for 150 mm (6") distance between the battens, which now meant that winches of 300 mm (12") overall width were now necessary!

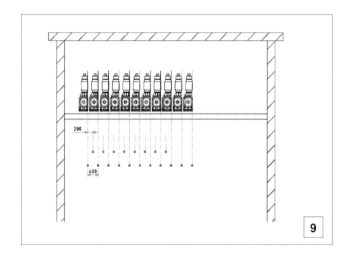

Some further requirements appearing in the specifications of customers are compiled in **Table 10**. Beyond this the following is desired:

- a local control panel on the winch for easy maintenance and service,
- an auxiliary drive in case of failure of drive components,
- appropriate and fast accessibility to the winch, preferably without sound-absorbing enclosures.

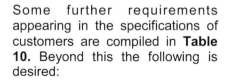

Maximum payload	300 up to 1000 kg
Maximum lifting speed	0.3 up to 2.4 m/s
Alternative load / speed	Up to 500 kg at 1.2 m/s Up to 250 kg at 2.4 m/s
Maximum travel range	10 up to 35 metres
Control speed range	$\geq 1000 : 1$
Maximum acceleration	≤ 3 m/s² = 30% load
Positioning accuracy	± 1 mm
Accuracy of synchronized moves	± 1 mm in normal operation ± 20 mm in emergency stop
Noise pressure level	≤ 35 dB(A) in 1st row of auditorium

3. Safety technical requirements and components

A compilation of safety technical requirements according to German standards and those of other European countries is shown in **Table 11**:

DIN 56921-11 for Across Stage Battens
DIN 56925 for Point Hoists

I am here considering only the electro-mechanical parts of the winch, not the control systems as these would be too much for this session. This table also gives an overview of the variety of sensors, from which a fault-finding system can be monitored. These control signals can initiate the stop of the particular winch or the group of drives involved.

Design all supporting elements	For double nominal load
Design wearing parts (as wire-ropes)	For 10 times of nominal load
Wire-ropes retained in grooves with slack-wire	Fixed cross groove protection
With guided loads	Slack wire-rope detection
Emergency stop distance < 0. 5	2 independent brakes
Main switch for each drive	Maintenance switch
Limitation of travel range	Mechanical limit switches (although electronic limit switches are acceptable)
Protection against failures of limit switches	Forced action ultimate limit switches
Protection against overload	Load measuring device with power cut off
Protection against overspeed	Speed detection with power cut off

11

4. Selection criteria for the most important components

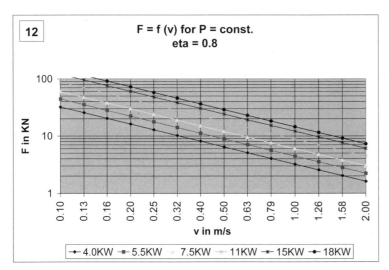

12

F = f (v) for P = const.
eta = 0.8

F in KN

v in m/s

-•- 4.0KW -■- 5.5KW   7.5KW -*- 11KW -*- 15KW -•- 18KW

These are:

Selection of the motor: F = f(v), P = const. **Diagram 12**

Selection of gearbox and drum diameter: **Table 13**

Selection of gear ratio: see $n_{Mot} = f(v)$ **Diagram 14**

Selection of brake torque: normally it is not sufficient to determine this by taking the motor torque and increasing this by a standard dynamic factor of 1.3 to 1.5. To be more precise, the necessary brake torque is a direct consequence of the permitted stopping distance during downward travel. This should amount to less than 0.5 metres (19") according to the recommendation of the DTHG during the eighties.

13 Selection of gearbox and drum

Drum diameter	Drum circumference	F_{max} in kN for gearbox torque in Nm		
mm	metres	1,500	3,000	6,000
230	0.723	6.5	13.0	26.1
270	0.848	5.6	11.1	22.2
318	1.000	4.7	9.4	18.9
350	1.100	4.3	8.6	17.1

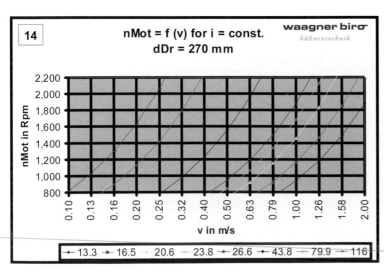

14

nMot = f (v) for i = const.
dDr = 270 mm

waagner biro
bühnentechnik

nMot in Rpm

v in m/s

-+- 13.3 -*- 16.5   20.6 -*- 23.8 -*- 26.6 -•- 43.8 -+- 79.9 -*- 116

The stopping distance is affected by:
- the total mass hanging on the wire-ropes
- the sum of all inertias (motor, brake, gears, drum)
- the gear ratio of the gearbox
- the rate of efficiency of the gearbox
- and above all the reaction time of the brake.

As a result, brake torques can amount up to the double the value of the motor torque.

At the same time the deceleration of the hanging payload has to be observed. According to experts it should not exceed more than 5 m/sec² (16'-5"/sec²), in order not to have excessive loads working on the connecting parts to the pieces of scenery. **Table 15** shows the calculated results of two examples. At the present time there is an increase in cases of higher speeds of approximately 1.8 m/sec (6 ft/sec). At these speeds the requirement of stopping within 0.5 metre (19") cannot be met. In this case the necessary brake torque would lead to dangerous deceleration phases. It is agreed with the experts in Germany that the maximum permissible stopping distance will be raised to 0.8 metres (2'-7").

Total stop distances after power failure				
Parameter	Example 1	Example 2	Example 3	Unit
Lifting speed max.	1.200	1.800	1.800	m/s
Gearbox ratio	20.610	16.480	1.000	--
Brake torque static	52.839	66.081	1,217.137	Nm
Brake torque dynamic	100.000	132.000	2,000.000	Nm
Reaction time of brake t1	0.120	0.120	0.250	s
Acceleration during t1	4.497	5.412	7.699	m/s²
End speed after t1	1.740	2.449	3.725	m/s
Deceleration after t1	4.014	5.399	4.952	m/s²
Travel distance during t1	0.176	0.255	0.691	m
Travel distance after t1	0.377	0.556	1.400	m
Total braking distance	0.553	0.811	2.091	m

15

waagner biro
bühnentechnik

5. The attachment of components to the winch

It should be the aim to avoid toothed belts for driving the tachometers, encoders and limit switches as shown in **Picture 16**. Toothed belts, which drive safety relevant sensors, have to be monitored, which calls for further expenditures. One should try to connect all required components directly at the appropriate positions and onto revolving shaft ends. The highest aim should read: 'reduction and simplifying of elements'. **Picture 17** shows an example of a better installation of the necessary components.

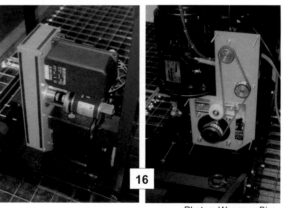

16

Direct connection of sensor mechanism

17

Photos: Waagner-Biro

6. Noise-level requirements for winches

The main demand reads: sound pressure level to be < 35 dB(A) in the first spectator row or on the stage at all operating conditions.

Since the stage tower with its equipment is responsible for an absorption of 20–30 dB(A), all machines situated on the open grid must have a sound pressure level of less than 55 dB(A) at a distance of 1 metre (3'-3"). Furthermore they have to be installed in a manner that oscillations and vibrations are avoided as far as possible with regard to the steel structure of the tower. Otherwise the winches have to be sound isolated by the disliked and expensive secondary measures.

The aim of constructing a winch with a noise output of 50 dB(A) or less is extremely difficult to achieve. Every moving part of the winch has to be manufactured to be as noise-free as possible.

7. Development of super silent components

We have arranged for a manufacturer to develop a super-silent motor for us, which can be delivered in three sizes. We have also found a gearbox manufacturer who was willing to carry out special developments. The technically optimum result for noise was achieved by a compromise between a worm gear with a low gear ratio and a high efficiency rate combined with a second high-quality helical gear for generating the required output torque. Finally we have found a manufacturer who developed an electro-magnetic double brake that almost completely avoids the usual 'clacking' sound when the brake engages or releases.

8. Noise measurements with the new winches

Picture 18 shows the layout of the prototype of the gearbox and motor in the sound laboratory. The possibility existed to load the drive via a jointed shaft to a braking machine located outside the laboratory room. The sound-pressure levels at a distance of 1 metre (3'-3") from the drive for diverse operating conditions are shown in **Diagram 19**. The parallel columns give the results of independent tests, one performed by the motor manufacturer and the other one by an acoustic expert team.

Photo: Waagner-Biro

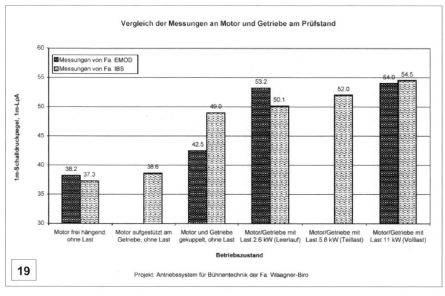

At this point I would like to allow myself the remark that expensive hydraulic drives will become extinct in upper stage machinery because of the current large development of very silent electro-mechanical drives.

The third-octave band in **Diagram 20** shows the well-known 'mountain range' over frequency. In the FFT-spectrum shown in **Diagram 21,** all tooth frequencies and their harmonics can be found.

We had special problems in analysing the frequency peaks which could not be assigned to a harmonic tooth frequency, see **Diagram 22**. By pure coincidence, we discovered the origin was from within the motor which we had not taken into consideration due to it's small contribution to the noise. The peaks originate from the relatively strong magnetic saturation of the motors, that have been designed for stage machinery and therefore short operating periods. When reducing the voltage at the motor, the resonating areas disappear completely. Unfortunately these frequencies make up approximately 3 dB(A) of the total sound level of the complete winch.

We have tried to sound-technically isolate the stimulating magnetic frequencies of the motor from the winch, for which further tests have been carried out in a sound laboratory, see **Picture 23**.

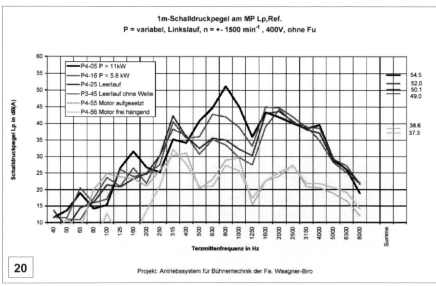

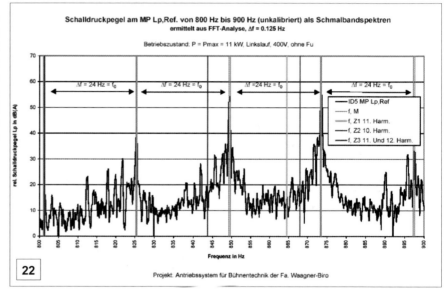

Photo: Waagner-Biro

The sound power levels of all single components are shown in **Diagram 24**. One can see that the drum, which does not cause any noise by itself, contributes to a relatively high proportion to the noise emission. Nevertheless it was unsatisfactory that all the tests performed on a completely assembled winch have only been carried out in a condition without any loads being carried.

For these reasons Waagner-Biro decided last year to build a test tower of 20 metres (65 ft) in height at their daughter company BATIK. The winches for testing and evaluation can easily be installed on a test bed, wire-ropes can be installed and the winch can be loaded with variable weights in the tower, **Picture 25**. This test facility is unique up to now as far as we know.

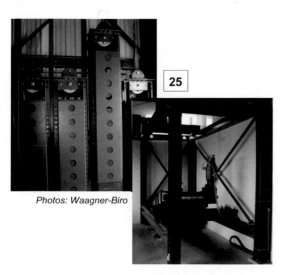

Photos: Waagner-Biro

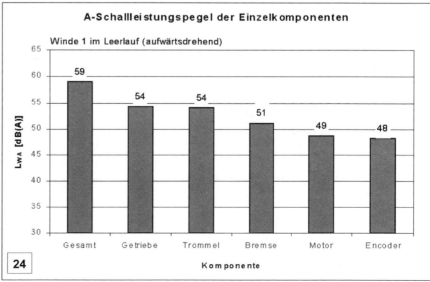

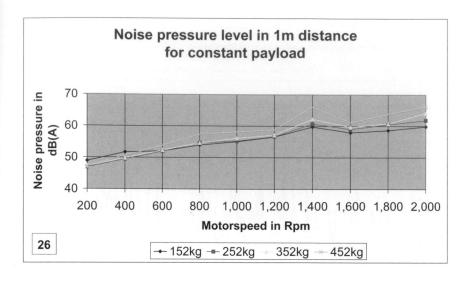

Noise pressure level in 1m distance for constant payload

(Diagram 26: Noise pressure in dB(A) vs Motorspeed in Rpm; legend: 152kg, 252kg, 352kg, 452kg)

26

The first test results of a winch running with different loads over a wide speed range are shown in **Diagram 26**. The phenomenon of the high level around the 1,400-rpm mark has not yet been analysed. Presumably the settings of the electronic drives in the vicinity of this synchronised speed, 1,400 rpm, play an important role.

9. Final reflection and prospects for the future

Winches without a gearbox are already slowly establishing themselves, due to good technical reasons, in the design of personal elevators. Waagner-Biro has shown such a trial winch with a multi-pole motor last year at the fair in Hannover and at Showtech in Berlin, see **Picture 27**.

Provisional tests have shown that such winches can reduce noise emission significantly. However the necessary motors, which are still have to be finally developed, are likely to be comparatively expensive.

The question of the safety brake has to be examined closely. After a broad survey of established brake manufacturers, it has to be said that at this time no double brake exists with the following necessary specifications:

- an outer diameter smaller than 400 mm,
- a dynamic brake torque of 2,000 Nm,
- a reaction time of less than 250 ms.

With this data the braking distance of a 680 kg (1,500 lb) payload winch with a speed of 1.8 ms/sec (6 ft/sec) takes over two metres (6'-6") to stop. This is shown on Example 3 in **Table 15**.

Diagrams 28 and 29 show the speed and stopping distance related to the braking time. As long as the braking distances after an electrical power failure amount to 2 metres or more, the use of this new technology will not be feasible for some time due to safety reasons. Thank you. Ω

Right: Trial winch with multi-pole motor and no gearbox on show in Berlin.

27

Photo: Waagner-Biro

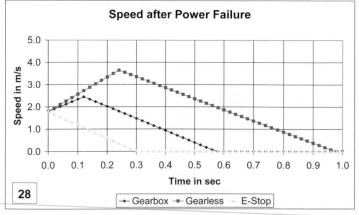

Speed after Power Failure

(Diagram 28: Speed in m/s vs Time in sec; legend: Gearbox, Gearless, E-Stop)

28

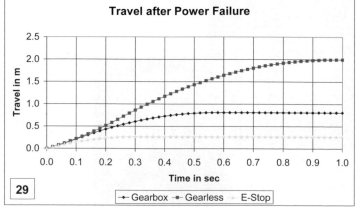

Travel after Power Failure

(Diagram 29: Travel in m vs Time in sec; legend: Gearbox, Gearless, E-Stop)

29

Questions and discussion

Alan Russell, Theatre Projects Consultants

Dr Maeder, in your last example would not some regenerative braking from the inverter drive be useful to slow down your motor? With the latest motor drives you can get 100% regenerative torque, that is braking torque, when you stop a motor.

Fred Maeder, Speaker

That is right. We always consult our safety people when we do acceptance tests, and they always say, "Please, I want to see if the brake can stop the load in any case; maybe you have a drive failure, so that it cannot power the motor, then you have to stop with the brake."

Alan Russell, Theatre Projects Consultants

I understand, but I believe that these new inverters will work with a power failure because the power is generated by the power already in the hoist. So as it slows down it produces electrical power that drives the inverter.

Fred Maeder, Speaker

You are right, but for example when the output of the torque signal coming from the computerfails, it stops the output current of the motor, of the drive, and you have no current to brake it down. So it can happen.

Ian Napier, Centre Stage Engineering

I see that your double brake is only at one end of the system. You don't protect failure of the gearbox, and also, does a double brake have double electrical circuits?

Fred Maeder, Speaker

Yes, of course, I didn't mention any control system. But we do have double brakes and we also have double circuits for those.

Ian Napier, Centre Stage Engineering

What happens if there's a failure of the gearbox?

Fred Maeder, Speaker

The gearbox should not break, because we size it to carry double the maximum load. That is always accepted. Every load-carrying element between the scenery batten and the brake has to be designed for a double load, and designed so that normally for a double load these parts will not fail. We only apply 50% of that design load at any time during normal operations.

Simon Smith, The Wyllyotts Theatre, Potters Bar

What's the optimum or maximum drop on a steel band hoist?

Maurycy Sowka, Speaker

It depends on the type, but up to 40 or 50 metres (130 to 165 feet) is no problem because the steel band is very thin, 0.4 mm or 0.5 mm (0.02"), so a machine only gets a little bit bigger when we make a longer drop.

David Ludlam, Barbican Theatre

In the UK certainly we're used to normal wire ropes, and we understand the inspection regime for them in terms of looking for loose strands and core extrusion and similar indications of damage. How do you inspect these steel bands? What do you need to inspect them?

Maurycy Sowka, Speaker

The production of the steel band is controlled by an electronic control, and then we have in the factory the possibility of quality control by eye, which is okay. In the smallest steel-band hoist we have 20 times security on the steel band, and now we have a great many machines without one damaged steel band.

David Ludlam, Barbican Theatre

So what you're saying is that in service inspections it's sufficient to make a visual inspection and that this would be adequate, all you need?

Maurycy Sowka, Speaker

To service the bands, it's only necessary to look to see if the steel band is okay. Provided you don't twist them together they won't get damaged. It's a special stainless steel; it's not hard, it's spring steel, but it's very flexible.

William Conner, Schuler & Shook

Dr Maeder, in your first couple of illustrations you showed a scheme with two motors and separate brakes. In the United States we have actually quite a few machines using that scheme. The brake and the gearbox are sized for the full load and only the motor is sized for half the load, so you can basically remove one whole end of it, plus they're positioned on opposite ends of the shaft, so that seems like a lot of redundancy. Would you like to comment?

Fred Maeder, Speaker

The question is for what load you have the gearbox designed; for the nominal load which you're hanging on the drum? Not the double one?

William Conner, Schuler & Shook

Sized for a full load, with a safety factor.

Fred Maeder, Speaker

Oh, with a safety factor. Then there's no reason to have the double gearboxes; that makes the hoist more expensive. I don't see any reason for that. You're saying that you can reduce the size of the motor? But a double motor costs normally less than two single motors with half power. That also makes no sense.

William Conner, Schuler & Shook

The benefit is the separation of the brakes, eliminating a single point of failure.

Fred Maeder, Speaker

Let me clarify this. You have on each side only one brake. Each motor has one brake only, so then it is clear you have to have the gearbox designed for the full load. That's clear, and you have the single brake on each side. It is possible but it's more expensive than a single gearbox.

George Ellerington, Chairman

We have to end there. I'd just like to say thank you to you all for what has been a very interesting presentation. Ω

Stage Control Systems

Chairman: Alan Russell, Director, Theatre Projects Consultants
Speakers: Guy Voncken, Guddland digital, Waagner Biro Group
               Mark Ager, Managing Director, Stage Technologies Ltd
               Ted Fregon, Chief Executive Officer, Bytecraft Automation Pty Ltd
               Günter Anderlohr, Chief Engineer, Stage Controls, Rexroth Bosch

First speaker: Guy Voncken

Guddland digital has been a company in the Waagner Biro Group since the beginning of this year. I would like to present to you our CAT 100R, which is our mobile control system for stage machinery. And maybe it's not completely true that I will talk about the future of our ideas, but I will talk about what we have now, and so the future is already here, I hope.

I will divide this presentation into four parts: first I will talk to you about the CAT 100R from the outside, that is from the operator's point of view. Then we will have a short look at the safety technology that we have built into the CAT 100R, and after that we will see what the operating system, Linux, has to do with our wireless control desk. And at the end we will briefly talk about the feedback we have received from the operators and talk as well about the future.

This is a new wireless control desk for motion control, for operating all types of stage machinery. As well as bringing these pictures of the new device, it is so portable that I have brought one with me in my luggage, so I am able to show you the real thing. Please feel free after this Conference session to come and have a look at our new device, to touch it and to feel it. In this way you will find out what it could offer you for operating your machinery.

Let me give you some technical data for the CAT 100R; we built inside the device a TFT LCD screen with 800 × 600 pixel elements to which we have added a resistive touch screen. The dimensions of the device are 36 × 25 × 5.5 cms thick (1'-2" × 10" × 2.2" thick) which are more or less comparable to those of an A4 size notebook, and so are the weight at 3.5 kg (7.7 lbs) and the battery lifetime of 3 hours – which is a bit more than the battery lifetime of, let's say, the stand-alone operation of my notebook computer.

The wireless data transmission is done via the DECT protocol; maybe some of you are familiar with this protocol as it is used in lots of cordless home telephones, for instance the Siemens cordless home telephones, and many other manufacturers are working with DECT protocol in the 1·8 GHz range.

You can use the CAT 100R within a distance of 50m to the central radio station. In our tests we found that the distances up to 300 metres (1,000 ft) are well possible; we carried out these tests in a free field, so there were no steel structures or anything. Of course in the theatre we have to take into account all these structures and decorations. We guarantee an operational range of 50 metres (164 ft), which should be enough even for very large stages.

Other features include an external battery charger, so the battery is easily chargeable without opening some part of the device. There is another possibility for charging the battery, simply including the charger inside

Guy Voncken studied automation and electronics at the University of Nancy in France, where he obtained the *Maitrise* degree. He has worked since 1990 at Guddland digital, where he was leading software development for production and quality control until 2000. He is now responsible for Graphical User Interface programs and ergonomics in the CAT development division.

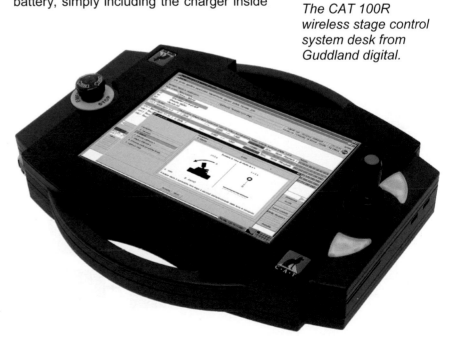

The CAT 100R wireless stage control system desk from Guddland digital.

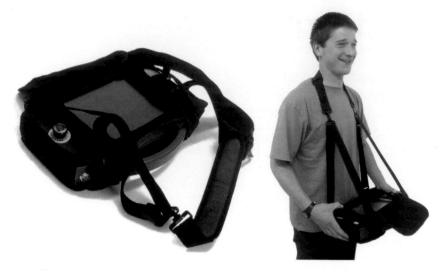

Demonstrating the CAT 100R in its halter case.

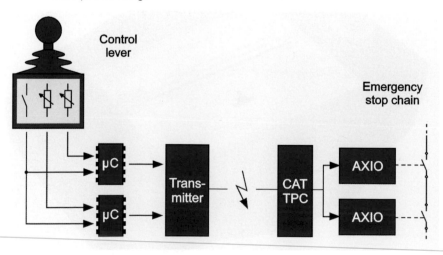

The duplication of the control signals and their processing.

right-handed device, thanks to the symmetrical design. So you can take it and operate it from either side, and there is a facility for turning the screen display around while doing this.

Now let's have a short look at the safety technology of the CAT 100R. At first sight it might seem criminal to control something safety-critical like stage machinery, something which can be very dangerous, with something so unreliable as a wireless data link. So how can we ensure that this really works? And I would like to tell you immediately, we are not criminals; so just let me explain how we do it and how we can ensure the safety of machinery operated by the CAT 100R.

the device. In that case you connect the operating cable to the plug mounted on the unit. It is important to understand that the same desk exists in another version; the CAT 100 (without the R at the end which stands for radio transmission). And the CAT 100 works like a normal mobile desk, still very light and portable, but useable only with the cable, which can be up to 20 metres (65 ft) long.

Getting access to control machinery using the desk is achieved with the help of a chip card. If you do not have a chip card, which is a personal chip card with your data loaded onto it, you cannot move the stage machinery. I think this is an important aspect of safety. Of course there are other systems which work with a password and so on, but we thought that this method was the easiest one. And at the same time the card is used for switching on the CAT 100R.

And the last feature, which I like most, even though I'm right-handed, is that you can use CAT 100R as a left-handed or

When talking about safety there are mainly two things which are very important. The first one is the control of the data, so that the control of the motion required is transmitted without any fault to the axis controllers on the fixed installation. How do we do this? We simply read the control signal from the position of the potentiometers, by two independent micro-controllers, which then both send data packets via the transmitter to the fixed installation where both data packets are forwarded to both of these axis controllers. I think there's no need to mention that of course we have two axis controllers per machine, because otherwise the whole system would not comply to the *Anforderungsklasse 5,* Qualification Class 5 of the German DIN Standard.

Now what are the axis controllers, our AXIOs, what are they doing with these data packets? They are comparing the two data packets they receive, and they are comparing their reactions with the next steps they would take for controlling the motor of the machinery. Only if everything is exactly the same – that is the contents of the data packet and the next steps they would take for controlling the motors – only in that case does everything continue to run. If something goes wrong in the transmission, both AXIOs have the possibility to open the emergency stop chain and so the motors will stop immediately.

Another thing which is important is what happens if the operator forgets that he is controlling some stage machinery and takes the radio desk and runs outside in the street and along the sidewalk with it? As it is so light, you really can forget that you have it in your hand! We have to guarantee in that case, and also in the situation where the data transmission, the radio link, would be upset, that the affected radio link is detected without fault or delay and that the axis controllers will immediately open the emergency stop chain. This works in the following way: the axis controllers not only compare the data contents which they receive, but they expect these packets of data to arrive at regular intervals. This means if there are some data packets missing for a certain time, the axis controllers will immediately say, "One moment, there is something going wrong; I do not receive any more data packets," and they will open the emergency stop circuit. In a similar way, we are transmitting the signal from the dead-man's button; if this isn't received because nobody's pushing the dead-man's button, nothing will happen, simply all the data packets will be stopped. We do this by switching off the power to the transmitter, so we can be 100% sure there are no more data packets sent, and again the axis controllers, after a short time-out, will stop the whole system.

This would be enough for the German DIN standard, but in order to be a little bit better than required we do not want AXIOs controllers to wait for this time-out before stopping all the machines. We therefore quickly transmit a last data packet to the axis controllers which has, as its content, the signal that the emergency-stop button has been pushed, and then we cut off the power of the transmitter. This is in order to decrease the reaction time of the axis controller when somebody pushes the emergency stop button.

With this technology that I have just explained, the TÜV (German Insurance Certification Body) agrees that our CAT 100R corresponds to the German DIN standard 19250, *Anforderungsklasse* 5. I noted in another presentation, by Ted Fregon of Bytecraft, that there's a certain problem in translating some German words. I translate this as Qualification Class. Those of you who are German will surely know that *Anforderungsklasse*, with that magic 5, defines the classification which is required.

Now we will briefly talk about Linux and what this operating system has to do with our CAT 100R. There are some keywords that you hear nearly every day which are very often used in other contexts, other than in relation to a stage control system like our CAT 100R. They are: *Reliability; Safety; Source Code Availability; Fast and Professional Help*. Let me give you some examples. If we are talking about *Reliability* and *Safety*, it is possible you heard these key words very often in connection with big web applications, web servers, protection against unauthorised access, and similar. Officially, we are doing another job here with the CAT 100R, so these two words cover important features for us like being able at any moment to switch off the CAT 100R without doing a formal shutdown. Why should we have to explain the need to shut down first? Because otherwise there will be no file allocation table on the hard disk or flash disk or … but there is no need with Linux. Simply take batteries off the device, reconnect and switch it on again and it will start as normal. No checking disks, booting up and all that.

The next point, that you have also surely heard very often, is *Source Code Availability*. It is mentioned very often in the context, "Oh yes but, well, if I really have a mistake somewhere in the software, I can debug it myself; I can correct the software myself." Again I have to say that we never have had to do it with Linux; it would be – with any operating system – a nightmare to search for the corresponding code or line somewhere deep in the last C file.

So this has a completely opposite meaning for us; for instance, we do not debug the software because up until now it hasn't been necessary. But we are able to change the software, to adapt the software to our special needs, and in this respect I can give you the example of simply turning the screen contents around. We took the corresponding part of the X-windows programme (the graphical display software of Linux) and changed it, and we also did a small amount of translation inside. We were able to do this very easily and very quickly, without special drivers or other features, and without contacting outside firms to write us a special driver programme.

Our CAT 100R system has been installed since March 2002 in the Volksbühne in Berlin. It is being installed right now at this moment in the City Theatre of the city of Luxembourg and also in the National Theatre in Helsinki. Helsinki is actually an installation of CAT 100s, the wired units, not the radio system at the moment. I am

The Linux penguin takes on the CAT!

A further addition to the CAT range of control desks: the CAT 180.

very proud to tell you that the feedback we have received so far from the Volksbühne in Berlin is very good: that the people there appreciate the features of the CAT 100R really a lot; they told us that the CAT 100R has allowed them to change their way of working on the stage, and that it makes the work on stage very much easier. It is so easy to set up the decoration while standing just in front of it, not some 10 or 20m away as in many installations with fixed control positions. You can really have a very close look at your scenery while it is moving; it's just not somebody with the microphone telling you, "One more millimetre – stop! – backward!" and so on. They also tell us it's getting safer, as they take the device to the place where they can have the best view onto the moving stage machinery. We are waiting for the feedback from the other two theatres as soon as they are fully installed and operating.

Now a quick look at the next things to come; I am proud to introduce a new member of the family of CAT desks. This is our new CAT 180, which is also a mobile desk, but of course it is mobile, not portable. It has a big screen of 500 mm (18") diagonal, four control levels and many compatible features which I will be happy to explain to you separately if you are interested in the possibilities of our CAT system. Many thanks. Ω

Second speaker: Mark Ager

Rather than talk about a specific product, I thought I should just give a bit of history, a bit of a look into the future as well, and give an overall idea of what we do and what we're aiming for. I'll also talk a bit about standardisation, custom design or product development.

When I first started in the industry about 15 years ago – hmmm, longer than that; the grey hairs are showing! – basically all stage control systems were custom products. The specifier, either the user or their consultant, wrote a long specification and a manufacturer would come up with a price and, if successful, supply the installation. Ideally, this has the advantage that it gives the customer exactly what he specifies. And, as the installation was always engineered to a specific need, whatever the theatre wanted, that was what we supplied. There was obviously a lot of involvement and discussion between the user and the supplier, and consequently the user got a whole lot of custom-made equipment.

There were a number of disadvantages with that way of working. There was a long delivery time – first of all the user needs to work out what the hell they want; secondly there are large engineering resources, time and costs required, and then the time necessary for hardware engineering and the writing of software, etc. But the bigger crunch comes later, because supporting such systems becomes very much harder in future years. I was actually working for a period supporting a system where the manufacturing company had gone bust! But even where the company doesn't go into liquidation you can end up with a system five or six years after handover about which the engineers, even if they're still with that company, will have forgotten everything. It was a custom-built specific project and they have moved on to greater things.

It is also, from the consultant's or user's point of view, very difficult to assess the capabilities of the supplier. We all tell you we can do absolutely everything, and I'm sure you always believe us, but to make that judgement without seeing whether or not a company can actually supply the right equipment, working fully and on time for a particular project is almost impossible.

With a product-based approach, one of the big advantages for you as purchasers is that you can go and try a similar system to that which you want to buy. A second thing is that you can see the desks that both we and our competitors make. There is no way that anyone wants to pay for the development of one of these current desks for a single venue – the costs would be far too high. There is also the issue of upgradeability of systems; as new software is written for other venues, that software can be fed back into previous users' systems. Then there is the commonality of parts: at the moment we've got about five shows running in the West End of London. Obviously they each need to run every night. If each of these was a custom desk, each theatre would need to hold a spare desk and all the other special parts, or they are in difficulty if anything goes wrong. As it is, we've got five Acrobat desks on five shows and we have another couple in the office. So we keep the spares for these theatres rather than each of them having to hold the spares themselves.

There is also the benefit of enhanced support; this has helped both us and the end users because we have quite a lot of people around who know our systems – not only engineers for the engineering problems, but operators who have used the desks in terms of plotting and operating them – these people provide support, not only in the early years, where everyone is switched on and knows exactly what the project's about, but also in the later years when you still need to know how the system works and how it was engineered.

Because there is a standard product, there's a commonality of systems, and there's much more availability of trained operators. We are sending operators to places like the Royal Opera House and to other venues both in Europe and in the States to provide trained help to new users. That's a huge advantage over a unique system where when you first turn it on everybody has got to learn anew.

Because these systems are part of a product-based approach, it's much easier to expand the system. So you don't get the problem of, "You said in your specification it was to control 52 axes and we've built it for 52 axes." It's much easier for us as suppliers to be flexible; for instance, we've just done a job where we installed 55 axes

Product Based Approach - Advantages

- See system working before making purchase decision
- Development costs shared among venues = more features
- Upgradeability of systems
- Shared user experiences
- Commonality of parts = reduced spares holding
- Enhanced support
- Availability of trained operators
- Expandability
- Greater innovation

and recently expanded it by adding another 50 axes. All the client had to do was buy the winches and the control systems for those axes. The control desks, all the file servers and the remainder of the installation stayed as they were in the initial installation.

Another thing, as you might have sensed already, is that there is a push for greater innovation. The various stage control system manufacturers are obviously all competing against each other; we need to produce desks that outshine our competitors'. Rather than the user having to specify at the time, and writing *these are additional features that maybe you can provide* which is going to put the cost up, we're already out there doing a lot of development and paying for it ourselves.

A short background to Stage Technologies. We started about eight years ago and one of our guiding aims was to set up a product-based automation company. We started primarily in the West End and that was part of the reason, at least, for us going for our product-based approach. We had to have very fast delivery times. In terms of fixed installations, most theatre projects are nine months, possibly a year, and sometimes longer. In terms of West End shows, we could very easily get an order and eight weeks later have to have something working on stage. So if you haven't got something on the shelf, or at least know what you're going to build in those eight weeks, you're unable to deliver. And for a long time in the West End that's exactly what had been happening – people had been delivering late, simply because they didn't have the component parts built.

STAGE
TECHNOLOGIES

Stage Technologies were Gold Sponsors of the Theatre Engineering and Architecture Conference 2002.

Mark Ager is a founder member and Managing Director of Stage Technologies, a major supplier of automation equipment for theatre. The company has installed automation systems in many theatres including the Royal Opera House, Lyric Opera of Chicago, Rotterdam Schouwburg, Göteborg Stadtsteater and the Royal Exchange Theatre. On leaving university, Mark spent 6 years working for the Royal Shakespeare Company, running a large power flying system. He then worked on design of automation system in the packaging and printing industries, before returning to the theatre.

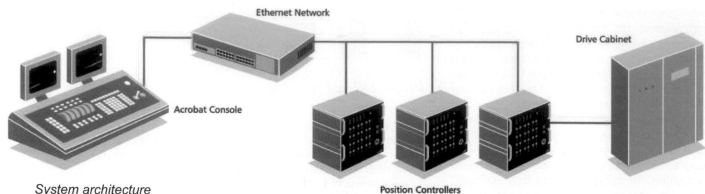

System architecture for single-user system for "My Fair Lady" in the Theatre Royal in Drury Lane.

The diagram above gives an idea of the architecture we use; this is an example of a show-based automation system. The front end is an Acrobat console which basically allows the operator to operate 5 or 6 separate groups of motors, and to plot simple or complex cues, etc. The desk talks via an Ethernet network to the control racks which each contain 24 axes of control. Here they are hooked up to a drive cabinet; alternatively they can be connected to DC servo motors which tend to be our standard motor of choice. They can also control AC motors, AC servos, hydraulics, converters for small power axes and similar outputs. So whatever these

drives are, and very often on West End shows there'll be a huge variety of drives, it's the same 24-axis Maxis rack being instructed by the same standard-product Acrobat.

When we took on the installation in the Royal Opera House a couple of years ago the requirement was not for a single control desk. What is happening increasingly in a number of theatres is that multiple control positions are required to talk to the system, and this specification led to the development of the Nomad control desk. This installation includes the same back-end Maxis racks interfacing with the drives. In fact, the Opera House crew could pull out the Nomad system and plug in an Acrobat into this system and it would control it without difficulty; it would work quite easily with these racks.

The Acrobat was designed as a fixed desk, single-user, single-operator, for use on shows. Then we have the Nomad, a

The architecture of the multi-desk system in the Royal Opera House indicating the relative levels of the installations.

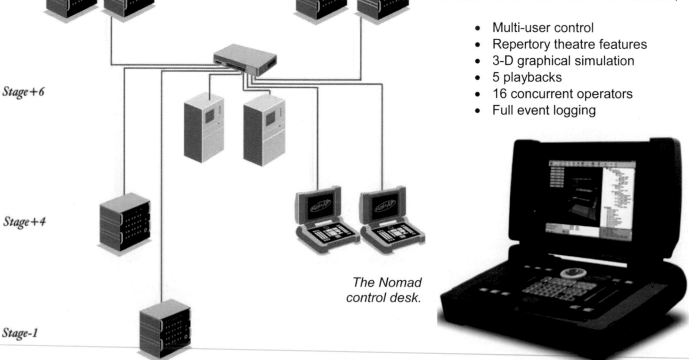

- Multi-user control
- Repertory theatre features
- 3-D graphical simulation
- 5 playbacks
- 16 concurrent operators
- Full event logging

The Nomad control desk.

portable, multi-user desk, designed more for repertoire houses, with features for rigging, controlling and management of the house. As part of this development we created our Solo hand-held controller, a small portable unit, designed as a rigger's control; it's not radio linked – it has a cable coming out of it – but with similar features, very light and easy to use.

So here we can see the advantages of a product-based approach. You've got here the ability to choose either an Acrobat desk with a Solo, or Nomads with a Solo, or indeed Nomads and Acrobats if you could find a particular use for these together; and all these units talking to the Maxis racks.

Instead of always using these 24-axis racks which, although they're very capable, do have a cost overhead, a big innovation for us over the last year has been in two new developments, both designed to keep costs down. The first is a Maxis TC (TC stands for Twin Channel) designed for those axes where you don't need full synchronisation or complex mapping; things like chain hoists, small inverters or simple curtain tracks, this

kind of equipment. A Maxis TC runs these, but it also runs them very economically – far cheaper than hooking in the 24 axis Maxis MX racks. And the other innovation, which is going to be increasingly common over the next few years, is integrating the control functions in the drive. So we now have Maxis ID (Integrated Drive) which integrates the motion control element within the drives. All the positioning and processing sits within the drive unit, linked via network backup to either the Nomad or Acrobat controls.

And what we're doing now is combining these various technologies on different projects. An example is the project in Gothenburg Stadttheater, which combines all these technologies in one venue. Here we have four Nomads, a Solo control desk, and then 70-odd positioning servo drives accessed via a gateway. However there are also racks of Maxis ID positioning controllers which have been put in to control existing under-stage axes. The theatre has a 1920s drum revolve with about five axes on it, and that's connected into the control system. We also have a little Maxis TC system controlling three chain hoists, which travel back and forth providing an economic solution for these extra items.

All the axes look exactly the same to the user so, from the operational point of view, we can send people from the Royal Opera House out to train people on site, and they will not need to know anything new or special about how the system works. In

Left: the ACROBAT control desk and above: the SOLO riggers' control which connects to the standard control points and can be used to set deads, trim heights, and for axis diagnostics.

The installation in Gothenburg: the flying hoists are controlled by the positioning servo drives (top right); the understage equipment by the drive cabinet (bottom right) and the chain hoists by the Maxis TC (top left).

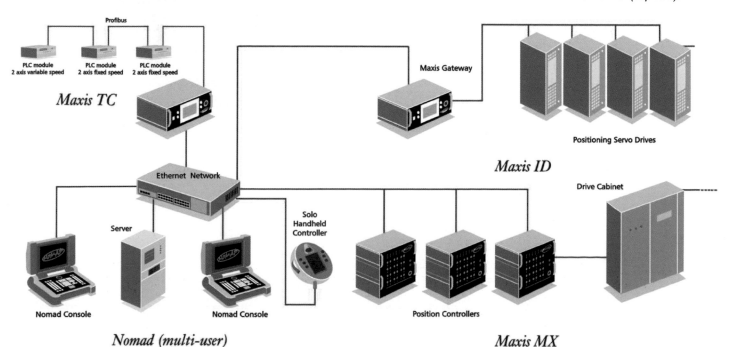

terms of positioning servos or the Maxis TC they all look exactly the same as previously to the user.

I mentioned innovation so I thought I'd finish by just talking about one of our innovations, which some of you might have seen in earlier incarnations. This is 'Pathway'. Pathway started as a two-dimensional system for plotting the flying of people who were suspended between two hoists in the Millennium Dome and who travelled up to 200 metres in big circles. We then expanded that system to allow three dimensions for *The Witches of Eastwick* which was staged a couple of years ago but sadly failed as a show. We have recently developed the three-dimensional plotting from *Witches* into allowing the plotting of six-dimensional curves, ie: a point in space and all the angles that it can have, for the show *Chitty Chitty Bang Bang*. Basically the stage engineering mechanics allow the car to move in six dimensions on the arm and then there's a gimbal that provides an additional three degrees of freedom. All this mechanical engineering was actually done by another of the companies supporting the Conference, Delstar Engineering, and we provided the control for all these motions.

I will try to explain the kind of plotting capability that we have with Pathway. On a 3-D view of the stage we can see a curve and we can adjust this curve. You have a number of 'draggers' which you can use, so it's a bit like dragging a 2-D curve in a drawing package except this is now a three-dimensional curve which allows us to plot in space. On a second screen we can define the angles that the car takes as it goes along the path. We did a lot of this,

because one of the things we've been focusing on is simulation so that you can avoid the huge costs of trying the whole thing out on stage first. For this project, we actually simulated the car and simulated its moves before the thing was built, to give the design team an idea of what they were going to see. You can look at the car from any point in the auditorium, and as many sightlines in West End theatres are appalling, this was particularly useful. You need to check that you can see the main effect of the show from most of the audience positions otherwise they'll complain about their £50 tickets! So a lot of work was done simulating the car before we got to the theatre and then, on stage, actually modifying it and running it several times, before finally putting the playback into action with the machinery on the stage.

To conclude on this product-based approach, Pathway was an innovation that's come about over the last two or three years. At the same time it is able to be applied back to all the systems we've put in to date (other than the TC systems, which don't allow these facilities). We've currently got about 1800 axes in 35 venues; all of them could take the Pathway software and use it for point hoists or other pieces of the machinery as may be required by a particular production. Ω

A drawing of the mechanics of the flying car in "Chitty Chitty Bang Bang" and the 'Pathway' simulation developed by Stage Technologies for programming multi-dimensional motion.

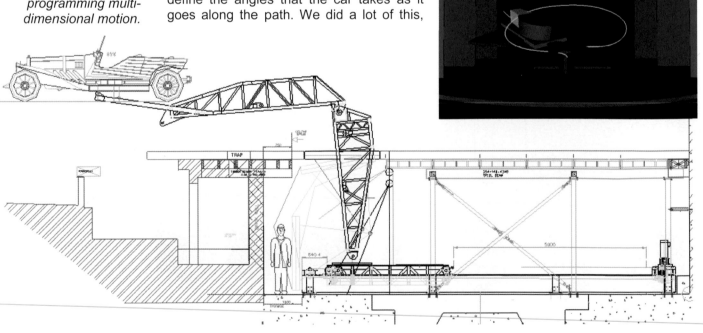

Third speaker: Ted Fregon

Anyone who heard my previous presentation might remember my description of some of the acronyms used in our business and in software engineering. One of them is SOUP, which is Software Of Uncertain Pedigree. I'm using Windows XP which is supposed to be perfect, but I have just had to reboot my computer!

At Bytecraft one of the biggest projects that we have at the moment is in the National Grand Theatre (NGT) of China in Beijing, and I thought that a description of that project, which is pretty amazing, would give an insight into the current state of the stage control system art in Asian theatres. It is important to note that there are actually three theatres in the Beijing NGT project and we are providing the systems in the Opera Theatre, in conjunction with Mitsubishi Heavy Industries.

I don't know if anyone here has been to Beijing, but I made my first visit about two weeks ago and I was absolutely amazed; the place is huge. In an aerial photograph of Beijing it is possible to identify the Forbidden City and Tiananmen Square, and now the new opera theatre can also be seen. Unlike the Great Wall of China, which the Chinese *claim* is visible from the moon, I think this building actually may well be; it's quite immense.

It's being designed by a French architect, Paul Andreu from Aeroports de Paris. Its structure is in the form of a huge titanium dome, surrounded by a moat. It is near the Great Hall of the People, which can also be identified. The theatre audiences enter via a tunnel which goes underneath the moat which surrounds the building. The moat is glass-bottomed so that they can see out and we can see in.

Inside there are three performance spaces. The photograph of the model shows the Opera Theatre – it's in the same orientation as the previous picture – and the Drama Theatre that SBS Dresden and Rexroth Bosch are working on together, and finally the Concert Hall.

The cross-section through the opera theatre shows that the roof structure is actually completely independent of the buildings that are inside, so in fact what we've got is three quite independent and very large performance buildings all covered by this immense titanium done. I can't wait to see it finished!

Ted Fregon is Chief Executive Officer of Bytecraft Automation Pty Ltd, a privately owned and operated company which he co-founded in 1984 and which is the only company specialising in both lighting and automation control system solutions. Ted has formal qualifications in electronics engineering and more than 20 years in stage machinery and stage lighting control system design and development. He has a particular interest in international codes and regulations.

Aerial view of central Beijing with the major landmarks identified, right: an impression of the completed China National Grand Theatre with the model below.

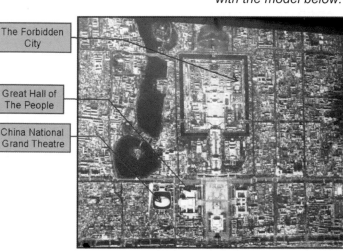

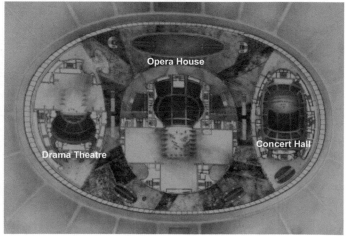

Drama Theatre

Concert Hall

Opera House

Photos: Bytecraft

China National Grand Theatre: the actual construction on site in May 2002.

The stage level plan of the Opera House showing the six lines of wagons, side and main stage elevators, and the revolve wagon in the rear stage.

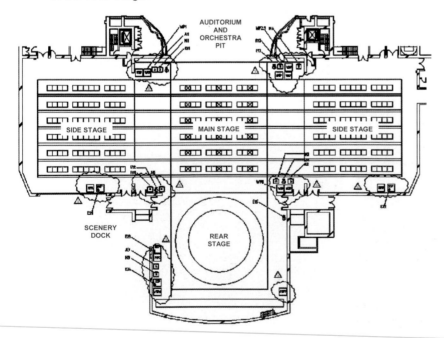

The quality of the workmanship, the precision of the work, the cleanliness of the site and the site organisation really leaves one speechless; I've never seen the equal of it anywhere in the world. It's quite outstanding! The whole site was cleared and new concrete poured before they started to do this construction. There's no dirt anywhere – it's like a factory floor, the whole site. And it's being built very quickly.

The important features in the Opera Theatre are that there are six main stage elevators and the corresponding side stage elevators, and a wagon with a large revolve in the rear stage.

We are preparing documentation and drawings that show the location of all our equipment throughout the venue. Actually, one of the difficulties we've had on this project is that we have to produce all our documentation in Chinese and English, with some in Japanese, so every drawing has multiple layers with the various languages on. We have to produce some drawings in Japanese because we're a sub-contractor to Mitsubishi, and, as we want to be able to read all the drawings ourselves, we put English on most of them.

The equipment list of the overstage machinery shows that there are, in summary, some 235 axes overstage. When we build our systems, we break our equipment down into what we call linear axes and binary axes – I think this is similar

Machine	Description	Quantity	Drive Quantity	Linear Wincon Qty	Binary Wincon Qty	Axis Type	Wincon type	Drive
OH2.1	Safety Curtain	1	1			Major	PLC ONLY	Inverter
OH2.2	Side Stage Acoustic Door	2	2			Major	PLC ONLY	Inverter
OH2.3	Rear Stage Acoustic Door	1	1			Major	PLC ONLY	Inverter
OH2.4	Portal Towers	2	2		0.5	Major	Binary	Inverter
OH2.5.1	Portal Lighting Bridge	1	1		0.25	Major	Binary	Inverter
OH2.5.2	Teaser	1	1		0.25	Major	Binary	Inverter
OH2.6.1	House Curtain Greece Type	1	1	1		Major	Linear	Vector Inverter
OH2.6.2	House Curtain German Type	1	1	1		Major	Linear	Vector Inverter
OH2.6.3	House Curtain Italy Type	1	2	2		Major	Linear	Vector Inverter
OH2.7	Scene Change Curtain	5	5	5		Major	Linear	Vector Inverter
OH2.8	Cyclorama Bar	2	2	2		Major	Linear	Vector Inverter
OH2.9	Lighting Bridge	4	4		1	Major	Binary	Inverter
OH2.10.1	Cyclorama Lighting Bridge	1	1		0.25	Major	Binary	Inverter
OH2.10.2	Mechanical Access Device	2	2	2		Major	PLC ONLY	MCC
OH2.11.1	Side Lighting Ladder - Horozontal Moving	10	10		2.5	Major	Binary	Inverter
OH2.11.2	Side Lighting Ladder - Vertical Moving	10	10		2.5	Major	Binary	Inverter
OH2.13	Powered Flying Bar	62	62	62		Major	Linear	Vector Inverter
OH2.14	Side Powered Flying Bar	4	4	4		Major	Linear	Vector Inverter
OH2.15	Tracked Point Hoist (13x6)	78	78	78		Major	Linear	Vector Inverter
OH2.16.1	Free Single Point Hoist	24	24	24		Major	Linear	Vector Inverter
OH2.16.2	Free Single Point Hoist	8	8	8		Major	Linear	Vector Inverter
OH2.19	Rear Stage Powered Flying Bar	12	12		3	Major	Binary	Inverter
OH2.20.1	Flying Mechanism Vertical	1	1	1		Major	Linear	Vector Inverter
OH2.20.2	Flying Mechanism Horozontal	1	1	1		Major	Linear	Vector Inverter
				191	10.25			

Control Legend.

- Linear Wincon Only
- Binary Wincon Only
- Linear Wincon / PLC
- Binary Wincon / PLC
- PLC only control
- MCC control

Overstage machinery: 235 machines; 216 axes; 66 battens; 110 point hoists.

Machine	Description	Quantity	Drive Quantity	Linear Wincon Qty	Binary Wincon Qty	Axis Type	Wincon type	Drive
	UNDERSTAGE							
OH1.1.1	Orchestra Pit Elevator	1	1	1		Major	Linear	Vector Inverter
OH1.1.2	Electric Conductor Elevator	1	1			Major	PLC ONLY	Inverter
OH1.2.1	Orchestra Pit Elevator	1	1	1		Major	Linear	Vector Inverter
OH1.3.1	Forestage Compensator Lift	1	2		0.25	Major	Binary	Inverter
OH1.3.2	Forestage Compensator Lift Raking	1	2		0.25	Major	Binary	Inverter
OH1.4.1	Main Stage Elevator	6	6	6		Major	Linear	Vector Inverter
OH1.4.2	Main Stage Elevator Raking	6	12		1.5	Major	Binary	Inverter
OH1.4.3	Main Stage Elevator trap opening devices	18	36		4.5	Major	Binary	MCC
OH1.4.4	Main Stage Elevator Net & Fence 1	12	24		3	MINOR	Binary	Inverter
OH1.4.4	Main Stage Elevator Net & Fence 2	12	24		3	MINOR	Binary	Inverter
OH1.4.5	Main Stage Elevator Interlock Door	1	1			Major	PLC ONLY	Inverter
OH1.4.6	Main Stage Elevator lock device	12	12		3	MINOR	Binary	MCC
OH1.5	Side Compensator Lift	12	24		3	Major	Binary	Inverter
OH1.6.1	Side Stage Wagon	12	12	12		Major	Linear	Vector Inverter
OH1.6.2	Side Stage Wagon Lock Device	24	24		6	MINOR	Binary	MCC
OH1.6.3	Side Stage Wagon Connecting Device	12	12		3	MINOR	Binary	MCC
OH1.7	Side Stage Compensator Lift	12	24		3	Major	Binary	Inverter
OH1.8	Rear Stage Compensator Lift	1	2		1	Major	Binary	Inverter
OH1.9.1	Revolving Wagon	1	4	2		Major	Linear	Vector Inverter
OH1.9.2	Outer Revolving Ring	1	4	1		Major	Linear	Vector Inverter
OH1.9.3	Inner turn table	1	4	1		Major	Linear	Vector Inverter
OH1.9.4	Revolving Wagon Lock Device	2	2		0.5	MINOR	Binary	MCC
OH1.10	Revolving Wagon Compensator Lift	6	12		1.5	Major	Binary	Inverter
OH1.11.1	Lift for Soft Scenery Storage	1	1			Major	PLC ONLY	Inverter
OH1.11.2	Automatic Storage Rack	1	2			Major	PLC ONLY	MCC
OH1.11.3	Automatic Storage Connecting Device	2	4			MINOR	PLC ONLY	MCC
OH1.12	Seating Wagon	1				MINOR		
OH1.13.1	Under Rear Stage wagon 1	1	4	1		Major	Linear	Vector Inverter
OH1.13.2	Ballet Stage Floor Raking	1	2		0.25	Major	Binary	Inverter
OH1.14.1	Under Rear Stage wagon 2	1				Major		
OH1.14.2	Under Rear Stage wagon 2 Deck Slide	1	1		0.25	MINOR	Binary	MCC
OH1.15.1	Trap Lift 1	2	2			Major	PLC ONLY	Inverter
OH1.15.2	Trap Lift 2	2	2			Major	PLC ONLY	Inverter
OH1.16	Powered Protecting Door	24	24		6	Major	Binary	MCC
				25	40			

Control Legend.

- Linear Wincon Only
- Binary Wincon Only
- Linear Wincon / PLC
- Binary Wincon / PLC
- PLC only control
- MCC control

Understage machinery: 65 axes; 6 main stage elevators with raking; 12 side stage wagons; revolve wagon with concentric revolve; 2 rear wagons with ballet floor and raking.

to what Mark was talking about with his different types of Maxis cards – so a linear axis is a full-function position controller whereas a binary axis still has some position control and provides multiple axes on a card, but it doesn't provide a closed-loop position control.

The drawings on the next page give a good idea of the extent of the stage engineering. The understage section shows the complex elevator systems in the forestage and orchestra pit. In addition to the main stage elevators and the cloth store upstage, there is actually another stage wagon in under the rear stage which is used for ballet

Sections of the Opera House in the China National Grand Theatre.

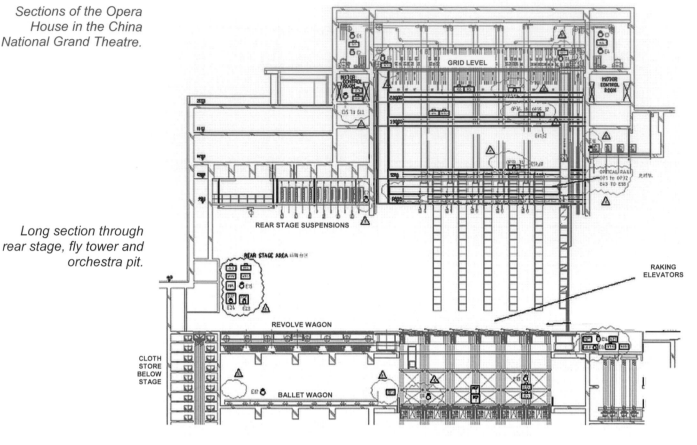

Long section through rear stage, fly tower and orchestra pit.

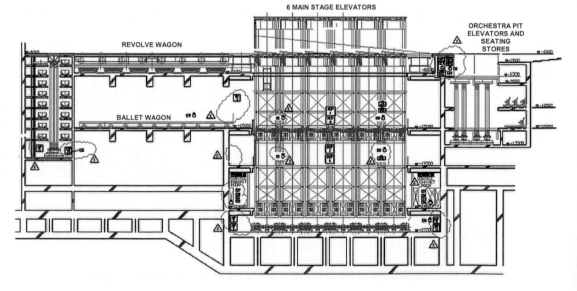

Long section through understage showing ballet wagon store, main stage elevators raised and the orchestra pit.

performances. The understage machinery requires a further 65 axes, so the total, including sundry controls, is 413 axes in the overall system.

The way that our system architecture works is shown in the diagram on the next page. Essentially the main computer system provides all the motion control and includes both redundancy and a supervisory processor. This whole system is actually built to conform to IEC 61508 SIL 3. SIL 3 is the highest Safety Integrity Level function that's within our system, so that's why it incorporates the additional supervisory processors.

The main console incorporates both the overstage and understage axis control blocks. This console equipment includes a

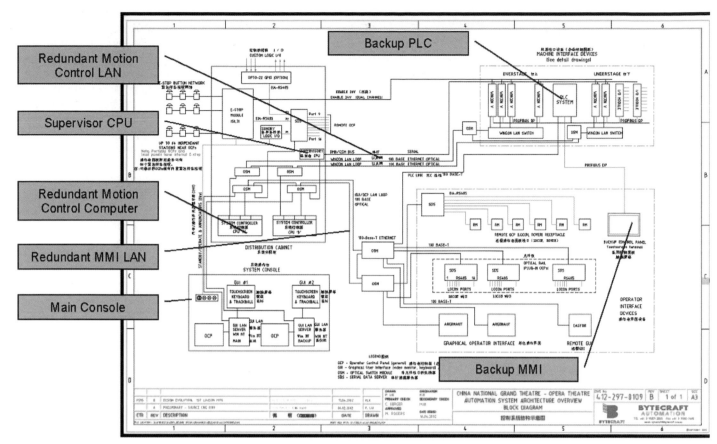

Above: the main control system architecture.

Programmable Logic Control (PLC) as well. This is a very large PLC – it's a Siemens S7 which has more than 6,500 points on it! One of the reasons we integrate a PLC into our equipment now is to include the interlocking functions. In the *Theatres on the Bay* in Singapore, which we're just completing, we don't have a PLC for this, and the entire PLC logic, which includes the interlocks on gates, equipment positions, traces, etc, we did within our own State control system. In Beijing we're actually providing a large PLC to do all the interlocking (a) because of the extent of it and (b) because of the risk class. By using the S7 PLC we achieve the security that is appropriate. There is also an Ethernet connection from the PLC back into the console, so we can display all the information required about everything that's going on.

The PLC also provides a backup. It's a third level of backup, because there are several levels of backup in this system; there's obviously redundancy in the main control system, and we have several layers of redundancy, but if all else were to fail there's also the PLC system.

One of the significant parts of the understage control system includes the integration of the PLC and the Profibus

network with the WINCONs, which is our terminology for an axis controller. This architecture enables the State control system to acquire information from all 6,500 points of the PLC I/O.

The diagram of a typical axis represents all the machinery associated with one axis in order to achieve this security level. It includes an axis control card which is a dual channel controller providing the two independent processors necessary to provide the required security level. There is a vector inverter; we've also got dual encoders, an incremental and an absolute encoder, dual brakes, dual controls, and we've got a dual-channel emergency-stop system – it's quite complex.

We're preparing construction drawings which model all of the cabling routing through the building in 3-D. There is a lot of cable to go into this building. These special drawings can actually be rotated in our design labs, which make them very useful in practice. Different colours are used to represent each of the many different types of cable including, for example, an optical-fibre backbone and RS 485 wiring linking various bits of equipment and so on.

The MMI (Man/Machine Interface) screens on the console give complete views of the

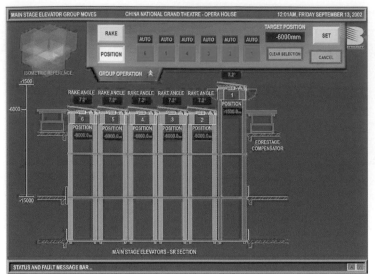

Above: a typical graphical user interface (GUI).

machinery which are animated, of course, so that when the machinery is moving you can see, for example, on the understage installation how the stage rake is changing, and you can select the rake you require and so on. We also include a 3D model of the stage in the corner of the screen which highlights the part of the stage that you're actually looking at. The graphics can show on the whole screen a model of the stage installations which can be rotated so as to be viewed from the most satisfactory angle. This will form part of the user interface of the system when it's complete. Thank you very much for your attention. Ω

Typical overstage machine to IEC 61508 SIL 3.

Dual Channel Axis Controller

Safety Telegrams

E/Stop Control Bus

PLC Ethernet

PROFI Bus

Safety Telegrams

Machine Control Network: understage.

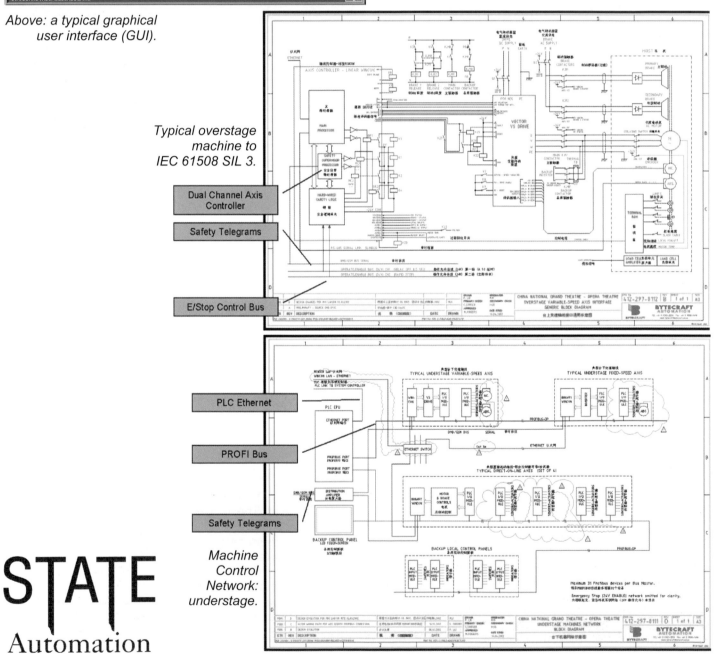

STATE
Automation

Fourth speaker: Günter Anderlohr

To start my talk I would like to put forward a claim: we cannot consider control desk design and safety equipment separately. I would like to explain this statement with my first point, the influence of safety equipment on desk design. Secondly, I will speak about European requirements on safety equipment under generic standard IEC 61508, thirdly, some new requirements on the performance of control systems, and finally about a new generation of desks.

We cannot consider desk design and safety equipment separately. I would like to illustrate this point with a brief review that shows how safety equipment has influenced our desk design over the last two decades. In 1984 we developed a desk with a PC and a monitor, but we could not pursue this development for two reasons – the first reason concerns the safety equipment, the so-called 'Echo' principle, which could not be implemented properly, and secondly the acceptance of desks with video monitors, in Germany at least, was by no means overwhelming, only about 50%.

That led us to develop our VTB 1000 system with front-panel modules. What safety philosophy is behind this? First there is a failsafe movement command entry – I will explain later – and second the so-called Echo principle. The diagrams below and on the next page show how it works. The problem occurs if we put any values for position and velocity and so on which do not correspond with the actual values which are in the axis controller. And this led us to a construction incorporating two separate ways; one for the data input, and the other for the data output for the display. And how about using the PC, and how to include this Echo principle? Of course you can implement the proper software which does the same job as we did with the front-panel technology, but you cannot do this in two separate ways. Nevertheless, we abandoned our front-panel system. The reason was the effect on our security position.

I will never forget the discussion of safety equipment some 14 years ago: "You may have the safest system in the world, but nobody will be interested in it if it cannot do everything they want it to do." And the reaction of another associate was, "If you make things too complicated, we will have to look for another partner." This could not be clearer, I think. It means the user is interested in having a control system that is easy to handle but that also has sophisticated features. And some security is regarded as important, everybody claims it as the highest priority as long as the price and the features of the system are not affected.

We started the development of a new form of desk in 1992, the VTB 2000 SC, in which we departed from the Echo principle, but we always retained a failsafe command entry; this is still fulfilled 100% as before. In the following diagrams I will show what *failsafe command entry* actually means.

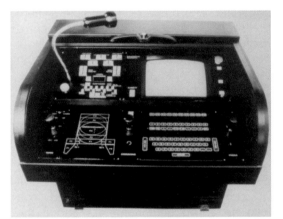

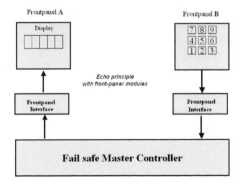

Günter Anderlohr. After training in Industrial Electronics, Günter worked for AEG-Telefunken at Konstanz as a development engineer and then at the European Centre of Research at Grenoble, before joining Rexroth at Lohr am Main. Here he was an engineer in the Control Systems Department and in 1987 became Chief Engineer for the Electronic Group working on Stage Control Systems where he has been responsible for a considerable number of installations in theatres throughout Europe.

Top: control desk with PC and monitor 1984; middle: control desk with front-panel modules 1986, and bottom: Echo principle with front-panel modules.

Left top: Bosch Rexroth Group VTB 2000 SC control desk from 1992. Diagrams from top: (1) Echo principle with only one PC; (2) simple control without safety equipment; (3) control system with dual command input; (4) control system with dual command input and redundant controllers; and (5) Control System SYB2000 SCII

You can implement this system with any type of controller, with no problem. The question is, however, whether the safety is adequate. The answer on a simple system is *'No'*, because in the event of a malfunction by any electronic component no hazardous condition is allowed. And in this case a simple error in the entry of the signal can appear without pressing the button. This is a simple error, but it is not allowed. So we go further and create a system with two complementary signals. The controller is only okay to run when it receives two signals, one in the high position, the other low, and in this event it will continue, otherwise it won't start. You also have two potentiometers and if the calculator has two different values the system will activate an emergency stop.

But does this provide adequate safety? The answer is *'Yes'*, if these underlying controllers – the master controller, bus coupler and axis controller – cannot create any hazardous condition by any malfunction. This is what a redundant controller system has to provide and this is what we heard about earlier; the *Anforderungsklasse* 5 requirement for two channels and two controllers.

The lower diagram on this page is our actual system in our new unit. You will see we have a PC, we have controller A and controller B, we also have redundant complementary signal inputs and we have a classical emergency-off control without any calculator or processor. It provides safety in all eventualities.

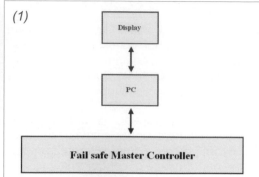

(1)

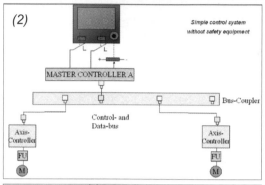

(2)

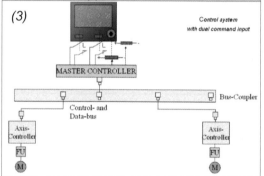

(3)

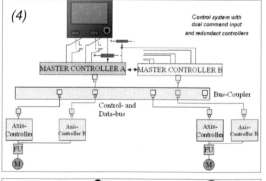

(4)

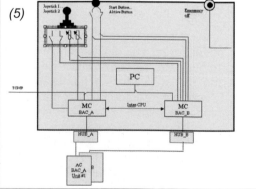

(5)

Rexroth
Bosch Group

Now I come to the second point; the new requirements in safety equipment under generic standard IEC 61508. I will show you only the most important things because I am persuaded that we have to take account of these standards in the next years. Perhaps it will change a lot of our development. There are seven parts, and part 6 is only there to explain parts 2 and 3, so you can see that it is not so easy to handle! I've been told that in Germany this standard is due to replace the current DIN V 0801 by 2004. What will happen in Germany in 2004 when our national application standard DIN 56925 relating to stage technology must be replaced by a revised edition? It is my dream not to create a new German national standard, but to actually produce a European standard for stage technologies, which is long overdue. But this is only a dream, I know. There is no money to create a technical committee in Brussels.

I want to show you some typical characteristics from this standard which are not implemented in our existing DIN V 19 250 and DIN V 0801. The first is the keyword 'safety lifecycle'. And the first objective of this lifecycle concept is to achieve an adequate level of functional safety throughout the life of the system. It covers from the beginning, Phase 1, Concept, to Phase 16, Decommissioning. And there is a difference; this standard not only considers the safety of electronic parts but of the complete installation as a whole system.

> *Part 1: General requirements.*
> *Part 2: Requirements for electrical / electronic / programmable electronic safety-related systems.*
> *Part 3: Software requirements.*
> *Part 4: Definitions and abbreviations.*
> *Part 5: Examples of methods for the determination of safety integrity levels.*
> *Part 6: Guidelines on the application of parts 2 and 3.*
> *Part 7: Overview of techniques and measures.*

The 7 parts of the IEC 61508 Standard.

It covers the electronic safety-related systems and also the other technology, all forming one block; the total combination of safety-related systems and the non-safety-related systems are together in one system. The concept for the safety-related systems must consider the non-safety-related systems, because it says that any error could be a demand for action by the safety-related system. It sounds a little bit complicated, but this part is interesting.

It also requires an assessment of the probability of failures, which is not included in the current regulations. The mean time between failures is a new validation of system safety and really imposes on the engineering quality and the ability of the manufacturing companies. There are concepts and possibilities for calculating the probability – 10^{-6} for a Level 1 system, and 10^{-9} for Level 4 – of a dangerous failure occurring per year.

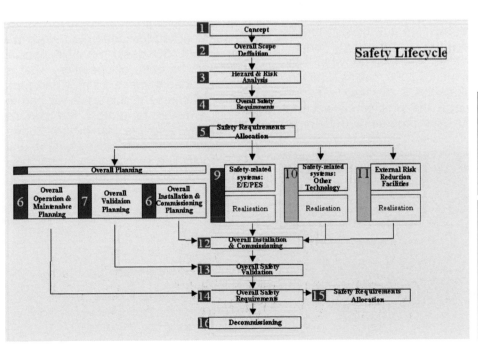

The complete safety lifecycle concept of IEC 61508 and, right: a rough comparison between standards.

Safety Integrity Level SIL	DEMAND MODE OF OPERATION	CONTINUOUS/HIGH DEMAND MODE OF OPERATION
	(Probability of failure to perform its design function on demand)	(Probability of a dangerous failure per year)
4	>=10^{-5} bis <10^{-4}	>=10^{-9} bis <10^{-8}
3	>=10^{-4} bis <10^{-3}	>=10^{-8} bis <10^{-7}
2	>=10^{-3} bis <10^{-2}	>=10^{-7} bis <10^{-6}
1	>=10^{-2} bis <10^{-1}	>=10^{-6} bis <10^{-5}

Kategorie nach EN 954_1	Anforderungsklasse nach DIN V 19260	Safety Integrity Level nach IEC 61508
B	1	-
2	2/3	1
3	4	2
4	5/6	3
-	7/8	4

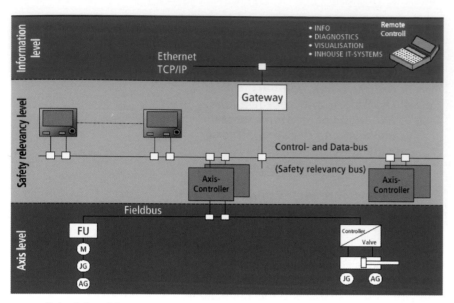

Principle of the new generation of control units from Bosch Rexroth.

Looking at the comparison with the existing security levels it would be not so easy to make the transition from AK5 to Safety Integrity Level 3 (SIL3).

If you take account of the history of the lifecycle, you have to do any re-engineering with all the documents from a system always running. I think for everybody that it's best to consider starting work with this IEC 61508 as soon as possible.

I go now to point no 3. We finished a project recently in the National Theatre in Budapest* where as part of the testing and commissioning we moved up to 90 axes in one cue. With this performance you can make the different scene changes very rapidly and in just a few seconds they have a complete scenery change. So here are new requirements; we are thinking that 90 axes simultaneously is not so bad, you can do a lot of things with this, but what if the client demanded 200 axes moving together? Okay, this is possible: why not? But, as always, the problem is security, because you have programmed 10 or 20

Prototype hand-held control and the SC desk.

milliseconds to monitor all the different parameters and to compare these in the calculator. To allow the ever-growing groups to be monitored within 10 milliseconds will require greater and greater capacities from the computers and faster and faster data-buses. Our system SYB 2000 is based on the Ethernet; in 1987 we made this Ethernet real-time capable with a special protocol, and in 1997 we improved our system further by the development of a protocol which is capable of handling up to 255 participants. Now the fast 100 MHz Ethernet has made the feasibility of a group of 200 axes moving simultaneously a more realistic proposition.

Point 4: we are considering a new generation of control units. We have a prototype for a new hand-held unit. We want to achieve this in both a wired and a wireless unit, because we think it should really be like a hand aid; you can put it in your pocket and while you cannot do everything with it, you can do the most necessary operations, and you always have it with you, this is the idea.

Then there are the methods of accessing the data; it must be easy to get access to all the data, not only from the remote control but also from a single desk. And we think we should be able to get on the data even off the frequency converters for the drives, the parameters of the digital amplifier, all using a remote terminal thousands of kilometres away.

With this development we are able to fulfil these demands and also provide state of the art controls with 4 or 5 playbacks as are usually asked for today. And when we designed our SC desk, we paid special attention to the ease of operation. That is why we decided to make a single-part work surface. Of course in this case we had to develop a cover to protect the surface mechanically. And the last picture shows the desk with the cover closed over it, and now I would like to close my speech by saying thank you for listening; thank you very much. Ω

*Pictures of the Budapest installations referred to are on page ET 7-20

Questions and discussion

Don MacLean, Cirque du Soleil

The adoption of DMX512 communications protocol for lighting systems was very helpful in terms of establishing a community standard and allowing interchange of systems, but also helped bring this equipment into more common use throughout both large and small theatres and the inter-operability of systems. Where do you feel the idea of a standard communications protocol for our flying systems, that is show-control systems, is going? We've heard now about a number of different protocols used and I'd like a response from each company, if you would.

Ted Fregon, Speaker

We've been using Ethernet as our underlying protocol ever since we started in this business in the '80s. One of the things that has interested me was when the lighting community started to work on the ACN protocol, and the work of ESTA in the United States. We therefore joined the committee of ESTA, hoping that we could probably persuade the committee to include motion control within that scope. That seemed to be unsuccessful, and I think that if you look at the progress of ESTA in producing the ACN protocol, to my knowledge it's nowhere near complete yet, and that's only for lighting control. Motion control is much more complex; there are many more issues. There are a number of proprietary issues involved as well, so I think a it's a lovely dream, a wonderful dream, especially for the customers, but I fear it's a long way off.

Alan Russell, Chairman

What we want is a standard protocol for our stage control systems, just like DMX is for lighting.

Günter Anderlohr, Speaker

As long as I've worked in stage machinery, I've always been envious of the lighting systems people. They can always do what they want to do, because there are no safety implications behind their controls.

Mark Ager, Speaker

I think it's partly an economic argument. I don't know how many thousands of lighting desks there are around in the world. At the moment we ship, maybe, tens of desks per year. There's a huge investment in that desk which is potentially supported by the other equipment – the computers, the drives, the mechanics. So from our point of view as suppliers it isn't worth our while to put the effort into getting a common standard because if we sold just the desk there's nothing else there.

The other side of this is, at the moment, users are just beginning to accept the fact that they might buy the mechanics and the electrical systems from different suppliers. There's been, I think, traditionally in stage control systems, an assumption, certainly in this country, that such installations won't necessarily work. Customers still want to buy the whole system from one supplier so they've got one firm to go back to if there are difficulties. They're now beginning to accept they can buy electrical and mechanical systems separately. To then split down the electrical system of these installations into separate suppliers of control, processing and drives is not really going to work anyway. I think perhaps it's the clients and consultants who need to drive this one.

Guy Voncken, Speaker

Well, it seems I will have the final word on this, but I do not really have anything new to add to it. I just want to remind you of the following; when you think about coupling several devices, it's always the interface which is the problem. Just look at the problem that have had here with our various laptops when trying to connect them to this data projector. It did not always work; nobody knows why. Just imagine this happening with something safety critical like stage machinery. As long as it is only some DMX for controlling spotlights, there is really no problem. But I would not feel comfortable with connecting our CAT 100R, for instance, or some other part of our control system, to some other contractor's machinery where I do not know if these interfaces will really, really work as they were specified.

Louis Janssen, HWP TheaterAdvies BV

Can we take this one a little bit further? I understand why you don't want to hook up your control desk physically to another drive or mechanical system. But what about exchanging the data? That's another level.

Ted Fregon, Bytecraft; speaker

Actually, I'm happy to expand a little bit more on that because, in the case of the system I was describing for Beijing, we've actually adopted the Profibus protocol. I'm not sure what the right terminology is, but when you use Profibus and you want to connect to a particular machine like a variable-speed drive or similar, there's a file that comes along with it that describes what all the bits do so that two devices from different manufacturers can talk to each other. And to that extent we have adopted Profibus as a standard protocol. But when it comes to connecting our axis controllers to another motion-control base, that is to a different main, central computer, that's the area that – and here I agree with all the other speakers – would be fraught with danger.

Mark Ager, Speaker

I think you're talking here about taking a show from one venue to another venue and setting it up to be the same show. I don't think the users have got used to that idea. For part of my talk I was going to explain that we've done two theatres, the Theatre de la Monnaie in Brussels and the Lyric Opera in Chicago, that both share the same productions; they have absolutely the facilities necessary to copy between the shows. It's the same system, but they still don't do it. I don't think users have caught up with the potential benefit, and they don't ask for it. If we had this requirement, if there were operas moving between our installations and, say, a Bytecraft system, and the users started asking for this facility, I think then it would get driven, but I guess nobody's calling for it yet.

Guy Voncken, Speaker

I don't completely agree on this, because I have experienced many times people asking us, "We are a theatre that is often inviting guest players to come here, why do we always have to get printouts and then have to type in the data again and again?" I think there is a need for it. But on the other hand I have to be honest; I think there is really little pressure on any of us. The driving force is simply missing, as we are not really obliged to do it, and so nothing happens. Unfortunately the customer is in a bad situation in that he has not really the ability to press for such a standard. But I really feel the need for this. One thing I must remind you about is that there was a German group, from the DTHG, a similar body to the ABTT in the United Kingdom, which wanted to establish such a standard, but they failed.

Günter Anderlohr, Speaker

I want to say that I think you have to put this question to the consultants, too, because their specifications are so different. As equipment suppliers, we do what the consultants and what the customers want. If you always demand the thing that you want, I think after some years everybody will have it. But specifications are always different. There's no system in it, I think.

Alan Russell, Chairman

My suggestion is that you guys do a reverse takeover, and use your technology to control moving lights. You can then generate a common protocol for all stage controls … Let's thank our panel! Ω

The stage floor in the National Theatre in Budapest where Bosch Rexroth operated 90 axes simultaneously during commissioning.

Photos: Bosch Rexroth

Changeable auditorium techniques

Chairman: Jason Barnes, Production Manager, Cottesloe Theatre, Royal National Theatre
Speakers: Professor Julian Herrey, Venue Consultant, Berlin
           Stuart Wilson, Technical Manager, Waagner-Biro Stage Systems (UK)
           Robert Heimbach, President, Gala Systems Inc.
           Jason Barnes, Production Manager, Cottesloe Theatre, Royal National Theatre

First speaker: Julian Herrey

Are you sitting comfortably? Then I will begin! Adequate conditions for the audience at an event include being able to see the entire viewing area and sitting in a comfortable chair. Yet the state of the art seems to be large 'multi-purpose' halls with flat floors, more or less flimsy stacking chairs, and mediocre sightlines with disagreeably high rostrum stages.

Spectators seem to accept the inadequacies of this type of facility, but in order to compete with increasingly sophisticated home multimedia experiences, vendors of live events will have to offer more comfort and excellence when providing the real thing. The days when meeting participants will put up with sitting on simple ballroom chairs in the 23rd row without an auditorium rake are numbered.

A typical multipurpose hall (COEX Seoul)

Viewing requirements

The spectator should experience a complete view of the presentation area. Depending on the nature of the activity, view requirements will vary. The spectator should be able to see ballet dancers, basketball players, and other athletes from the feet up, and speakers or musicians, from the waist up at least. On the other hand, basketball players will be playing on a surface at ground level, ballet dancers on a stage between 80 and 110 cm (2'-8" and 3'-7") high, musicians between floor level (chamber music) and 150 cm (4'-11") (rock

concerts), and lecturers between 20 and 80 cm (8" and 2'-8"). The playing area will vary in depth too. Ideally, the viewer should be able to see over the heads of the rows in front. This means that a line drawn from the eyes of the spectator to the lowest point of the viewing area would have to be at least 10 cm (4") above the eyes of the onlooker one row further forward. Events without a raised play area, or with a deep auditorium, will need a steeper rake than for a high stage or a limited number of rows. In larger halls excessively steep tiering rakes will be undesirable too, as the dimensions of the scene are dwarfed by the seating.

Spectator well-being

The issue in point is spectator well-being. He or she may not correlate specific factors with a particular impression of unease, but in the end the seating configuration and comfort may have a profound influence on event appreciation. These often subliminal environmental factors are subconsciously compared with a variety of standard experiences: the reclining seats in an aeroplane, on a train, or in an automobile, the easy chair in the living room and the executive chair, perhaps, as positive examples with pleasant associations; and cafeteria chairs, kitchen chairs, bar stools, and stadium bleacher seats at the other extreme. Wobbly chairs may suggest impermanence or even dilapidation; hard seats with little or no upholstery represent

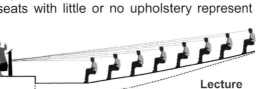

Lecture

Performance

Professor Julian Herrey is the former Technical Manager of the International Congress Centre Berlin and Professor of Theatre and Event Engineering at the Berlin University of Applied Sciences. He is now acting as a consultant on venue planning and operations, and has been reviewing seating schemes for Gala Systems Inc.

A clear illustration of the difference between lecture hall and performance space sightlines.

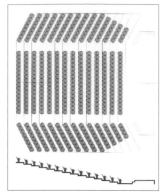

Basic automated seating configuration

economy or frugality; comfortable, firm chairs with ample upholstery, opulent comfort, ample legroom and space demonstrate premium treatment. Similarly, the order and appearance of the total seating configuration may be significant: straight rows appear anonymous and authoritarian; angled and curved seating are more communicative, implying character and individuality; flat auditorium rakes suggest communal, collective; steeper rakes connotes intimate, individual surroundings. The successful venue requires a suitable ambience.

A well-designed auditorium is the necessary path to appropriate spectator comfort. Fixed tiered seating will generally be the result, but this makes a hall untenable for other types of events and thus restricts use frequency. Installing temporary tiered seating in a level hall is a lengthy and usually prohibitively expensive operation.

The solution would be to push a button and quickly transform the flat empty floor of the multi-purpose hall into stepped tiers containing comfortable theatre-style premium seats. The hall would be readily transformed from a meeting to a banquet space, to breakout sessions or a theatre, an exhibition, or even to a tiered banquet hall for entertainment or presentations during a served dinner. Thus the rake should be variable to accommodate all sightline requirements; for maximum flexibility it should also be possible to use the stepped floor without any seats. It will not be possible or reasonable to pre-set all these configurations, but the most difficult one (between a level empty floor and tiered row seating with good comfortable chairs) would be a minimum.

Above and below: diagrams of the ultimately flexible venue.

Presently available systems

This is not a utopian dream but can be readily realised using one of a variety of systems presently available on the market. The features of individual seating systems vary significantly, not only in flexibility but also in expense. When considering costs, the major factors will be the price of the seating machinery, building costs for peripheral ancillary space required, and storage space for the chairs when not in use.

Telescopic seating unit

Telescopic seating units

The most widely used system, made by many manufacturers all over the world, and the least expensive, is the telescoping seating unit.

The tiering consists of consoles attached via struts and brackets to a base which rests on the flat floor of the hall. The cost will be about US$750 (£450, €640) per seat (not including the chair itself). Although it is possible to fold somewhat upholstered theatre style chairs in the small recesses available, a slight odour of basketball court bleachers cannot be completely eliminated. The tiering rake generally cannot be adjusted although an interesting variant using two rows per tier permits a shallower and a steeper sightline depending on

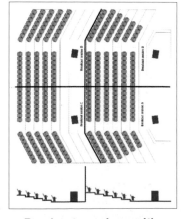

Breakout sessions with moveable partition walls

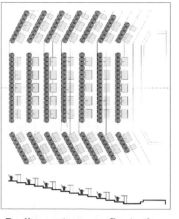

Parliamentary configuration with working tables

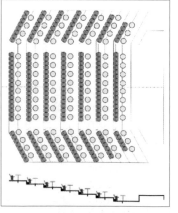

Supper club with cocktail tables

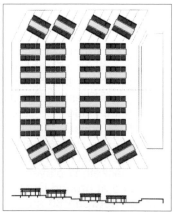

Tiered banquet with stage show

Telescopic (retractable) seating unit by Kotobuki in open and closed formats.

Photos: Kotobuki Seating

whether the two rows or just one row of seating per tier is extended. So far as flexibility and well-being are concerned, the telescoping system has further drawbacks: the folding chairs are not as stable and comfortable as fixed theatre-style seating, and the tiered floor generally cannot be used for other purposes without the chairs.

Seating on wagons

Moveable seating wagons

A second, commonly employed flexible seating system consists of moveable units or wagons containing fixed tiered seating which are moved into position in a level hall. The units are usually tailor-made locally for a specific architectural configuration. They range from wagons with three or four tiered rows of seats up to hundreds of seats on top of a large hinged ceiling that can be tilted down into position. These systems manage only one fixed tiering rake but usually include appreciably more elaborate and comfortable furnishings and chairs than telescoped seating. The cost of wagon systems varies considerably, but the total cost, including storage space expenditure, would be approximately US$1,500 (£900, €1,280) per seat (not including the chair).

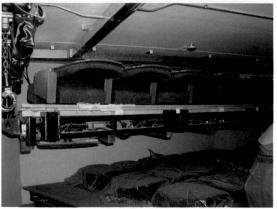

Top: Seating wagon using high pressure air castors from Solving; below: more steeply raked units being moved into store under an auditorium on low pressure air bearings, and seating wagons with folding seats hung above others to minimise storage requirements.

Photos - top: Solving, lower two: Techplan

Two systems from Japan by Kayaba Rae Stage (KYB): top: their Upright Seating System and below their Alti Seating System.

Seats rise out of floor

Seats under flaps in floor

Photos: Kayaba Rae Stage

Automated seating systems

Automated seating systems with a truly flexible rake are difficult to find. In one available system, theatre-style chairs are raised out of floor traps in risers, which allows a variable rake. In another, theatre-style chairs are flipped up from under flaps in risers, also allowing a variable rake to be created. Groups of chairs can also be rotated 90°. Two systems from Japan (Kotobuki/ KYB) use theatre-type trap mechanisms with elaborate floor-opening and chair-raising drive systems, set in groups on mechanical risers. They are more expensive: costing installed US$4,000–5,000 (£2,440–3,000, €3,400–4,250) per seat (not including the actual chair).

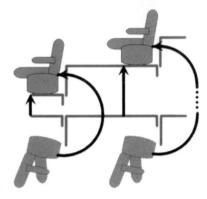

Theatre-style chairs are pivoted up from below the floor

Now a new, cleverly designed and straight-forward system made by the Gala Division of the PACO Corporation in Montreal, Canada achieves the same flexibility but is considerably less expensive (about US $2,500 (£1,500, €2,100) per seat).

In this, theatre-style chairs are pivoted up from below the floor of an integrated riser system, which allows a variable rake. The seats are stored on the underside of the mechanised risers and are pivoted up for use. The floor can be tiered up to 3.15 metres (10'-3") using the ingenious SPIRALIFT™ lifting mechanism which reduces the depth of the necessary pit below the floor to a minimum. Just about any chair on the market can be integrated into this system.

Seating risers by Gala Theatrical Equipment showing the individual riser sections and the pivoted seating which rotates into position when raised.

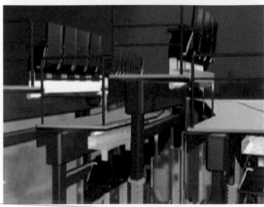

Photos: Gala Theatrical Equipment

Photo: Figueras

Tracked seating rows

Tracked seating rows

With the exception of the wagons, all other flexible systems will have some limitations with respect to the chairs that can be installed. In some cases the restricted storage space permits the use of only a narrow selection of chairs, often requiring special folding mechanisms that may reduce the seating stability and comfort.

Stacking chairs placed on tiered risers must be considered a bare bones solution for flexible seating with good sightlines. It should not be considered adequate for a quality venue and superior spectator well-being. A somewhat better solution can be achieved using special tracked seating rows from Spain (Figueras) that can be pushed onto the elevators manually and then tiered. Individual rows of chairs are guided on tracks manually between a storage area and the seating location. The cost, including the elevator system but without the chairs, would be about US$ 1,100 (£670, €935) per seat. Here again, storage space considerations can limit the design or selection of the chairs used.

Questions to be answered

Many questions, in addition to cost, sightlines, and changeover flexibility, will have to be answered. Does the system offer the architect or interior designer sufficient leeway in developing the seating configuration (row alignment and angling) and the hall ambience? Does the system offer a quality appearance? Does the system allow a variable hall capacity? Will the system conform to permissible building load requirements, and safety and escape route regulations? Are the system space requirements practicable? Is the system acoustically acceptable? Does the system possess sufficient structural stability and reliability? Will the floor maintain a good appearance without cracks, scuff marking, and wear when the chairs are not in use? Considering the costs involved, thorough study of these questions will be necessary.

Financial and other benefits

Almost all these systems reduce the conversion time and the corresponding labour costs considerably. Although labour costs depend on local conditions, a rough estimate of US$1.00 (£0.60, €0.85) per seat for a 'set-up/break-down' cycle shows that this is not the major factor for investment return. On the basis of two seating changeover cycles per week, between 5 and 30 years would be needed to return the investment through labour savings. On the other hand, if the conversion time can be reduced to less than 30 minutes, the frequency-of-use potential of a venue would probably be significantly increased.

Considering all time factors associated with successive uses of one multipurpose hall venue, it is generally possible to have only two different seating configurations on one day, or 14 per week at the most. The fully automated seating configuration changeover could increase this to three configurations per day, or a theoretical maximum of 21 different uses per week. Inasmuch as the tiered automated seating simultaneously offers new alternative use potentials, increased hall utilisation would be furthered.

A typical example would be a large hotel ballroom with a level floor. Using the classic ballroom or even stacking chairs, it would be difficult to run meetings later than the middle of the afternoon and arrange a banquet there the same evening. On the other hand, a meeting configuration will seldom be used in the evening. Usually this will mean that only two functions can take place during any one day. Using automated seating, the gap between meeting and banquet could be shorter while the quality of the meeting set-up would be significantly improved. The hall uses would be considerably enhanced in the evening if theatre-style seating were available, thus

Figueras Mutamut tracked seating row system.

Figueras International Seating
Head Offices
08186 Lliçà d'Amunt
Barcelona, Spain
Tel. +34-93 841 41 19
Or: +34-93 844 50 50
Fax. 34-93 844 50 61
Email:
headoffices@figueras.com
http://www.figueras.com

Gala Theatrical Equipment
Head Office
3185 First Street
St. Hubert, Quebec, Canada
J3Y 8Y6
Tel. +1 450 678 7226
Fax. +1 450 678 4060
Email: info@galainfo.com
http://www.galainfo.com

Kayaba
Head Office
Kayaba Rae Stage Co., Ltd
Fuji Bldg. 2-11-1
Shiba Daimon, Minato-ku
Tokyo 105-0012, Japan
Tel. +81-3-3578-1791
Fax. +81-3-3578-1789
http://www.kyb.co.jp

Kotobuki Corporation
Head Office
1-2-12, Yurakucho, Chiyoda-ku
Tokyo 100-0006, Japan
Tel. 03-5401-5090
Fax. 03-5401-5091
Email:
sales@kotobuki-seat.com
http://www.kotobuki-seat.com

also permitting cinema or theatre performances, a night club, or even exclusive sporting events. In particular, many of these activities would be possible on days with less demand, that would otherwise be harder to fill. Considering all these aspects, it seems reasonable to expect two to three potential additional uses per week.

Rental revenue

Increased rental revenue, even when combined with labour cost savings, is often only a small part of the total return on investment to be expected. Considering an assessment that, in year 2000, the average attendee of an event or performance generated a revenue of US$462 (£280, €390) direct spending, from Price Waterhouse Coopers Economic Impact Study Final Report for the World Council for Venue Management (WCVM) (information available on web-site http://www. venue. org/wcvm_eco.php), the likelihood of a short-term payback would be excellent.

In the long run, positive facility branding is probably even more significant than immediate revenue returns. Optimal seating configurations that ideally match event requirements and create interesting surroundings enhance the live experience. Confronted with a large selection of venues competing for guests, the well-configured hall becomes both the organisers' and spectators' preferred location.

The contact addresses and numbers for the main firms mentioned in this paper are given on the left. Ω

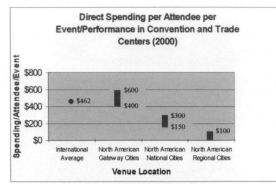

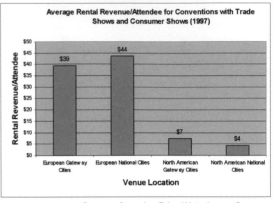

Source of graphs: Price Waterhouse Coopers

A major installation in a conference centre in which the seating is stored above the hinged ceiling.

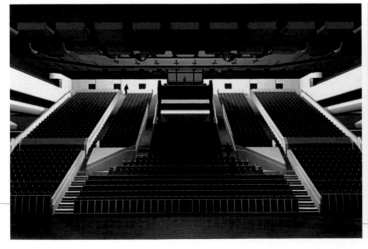

Chart provided by Professor Herrey which allows consideration of the many factors affecting seating type, choice and function.

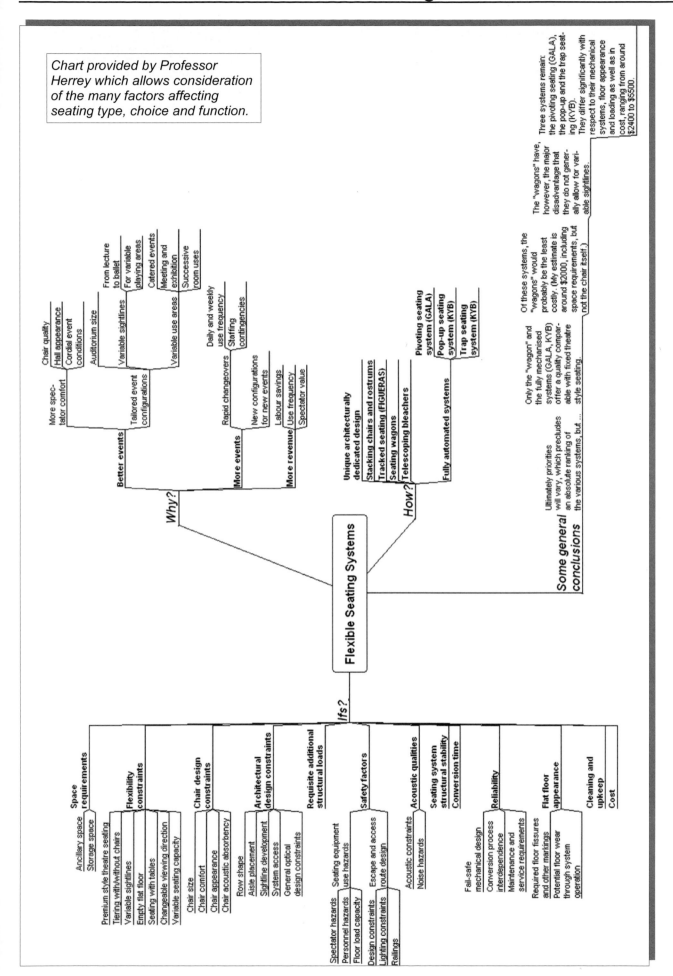

Low-pressure air bearings and blowers (orange) in seating wagons, and below: another type of low-pressure bearing moving over a step.

Stuart Wilson has a HNC in Mechanical Engineering and is a Grad IE (Aust). He has many years' experience of mechanical engineering for theatres. He re-joined Telestage Associates plc (now Waagner-Biro Stage Systems (UK)) in 1989 where he is Technical Manager, and is involved with the design of structures, hydraulics and transmission systems for projects worldwide.

Second speaker: Stuart Wilson

Air bearings, in the context of theatre wagons, provides a technique of moving loads supported on a thin film of air. Most people are familiar with the function of oil and grease as a bearing lubricant, where the lubricant separates the two moving parts and in which the coefficient of friction between the lubricant and the moving parts is minimal. In an air bearing the lubricant is air.

In a perfect air-bearing system, the coefficient of friction is significantly less than an oil or grease lubricated system, but in the application to theatre wagons the surface over which the wagon travels is much less than perfect, and much of this benefit is lost.

Compared with wheeled wagons with castors, wagons on air bearings can be larger, are more manoeuvrable, and require less effort to move. A tiered seating wagon some 8 x 4 metres (26'-3" x 13'-1") can easily be moved by two technicians in a well-engineered application. Larger wagons may need some form of motorised tug unit, particularly if the added loads are high, for example, when moving large scenery settings or acoustic towers. However, they are more expensive, and operational noise would generally exclude them from performance use.

The most common form of an air bearing is that of an annular ring, with air under pressure fed into the centre of the ring. The diagram below shows a vertical half section through a typical air bearing. The lifting capacity is a function of the air pressure and the area to which it is applied. Obviously, the higher the pressure within the bearing the greater the load that can be supported.

It is interesting to examine how these bearings work, as it indicates how important the selection of floor construction is to the performance of the bearing.

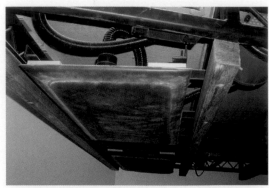

Photo: Techplan

Photo: Solving

The air bearings used mainly in the theatre operate at low pressure provided by small blowers. A perforated and flexible PVC or rubber membrane is formed over a backing board, forming an enclosed chamber between the board and the membrane. Air flow is introduced to the chamber through the board and this passes through the perforations. The membrane tends to form a circular seal with the floor around its perimeter, so that the net result is the formation of a pocket of air at pressure. It is this air at pressure which supports the load.

Another function of the flexible membrane is to accommodate differences in levels of the floor surface. Typically an air bearing will be able to operate over floors with height differences of up to 10 mm (0.4"). Obviously, a difference in floor levels of this magnitude will generate relatively large air-leakage paths and the system must therefore be sized accordingly.

To allow horizontal movement there must be air flow across the sealing zone, forming the lubrication layer. This is achieved by leakage from the air pocket, and is usually assisted by extending the perforations in the membrane into the sealing zone to ensure adequate air flow in this critical area.

Because of the way the bearings work, it is desirable that the working floor is smooth and consistent in texture. Also, rapid and large changes in height should be avoided by applying close tolerances to floor finishes and positional control of elevators.

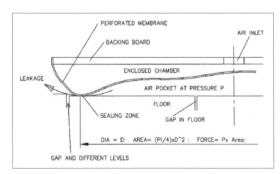

PERFORATED MEMBRANE
AIR INLET
BACKING BOARD
ENCLOSED CHAMBER
LEAKAGE
AIR POCKET AT PRESSURE P
FLOOR
SEALING ZONE
GAP IN FLOOR
$DIA = D$: $AREA = (Pi/4) \times D^2$: $FORCE = P \times Area$:
GAP AND DIFFERENT LEVELS

Section through a typical air bearing.

Photo: Waagner Biro Stage Systems

In practice, however, a stage floor might be boarded, with small gaps between individual boards, probably also with traps and covers, with gaps, to the fixed floor. Also, it is common that a wagon has to pass over the 10 mm (0.4") gap between adjacent elevators and fixed flooring, which may also have up to a 10 mm height difference. All of these conditions provide air-leakage paths, which vary throughout the travel of a wagon from one position to another.

To overcome these variations it is necessary to provide excess blower capacity. This ensures that there is always adequate air pressure to lift the load, and adequate flow to provide the lubrication layer. There is a relationship between air pressure and volume of air supplied from a blower. If flow volume is low, pressure is closer to maximum. If flow is high the pressure will be lower. Also, because of the shape of the performance curve, there is a point where a relatively small increase in flow rate, due to increased leakage, will produce a much more significant fall in pressure and load-bearing capacity.

Unfortunately, the provision of excess capacity can lead to another problem. If there is a wide range in the quality of the

Photo: Solving

floors over which a wagon is operated and the blowers are selected to work on the worst surface, vibration of the units can be caused when on the good surfaces. This is usually when stationary. It is caused by the membrane forming a much better seal with the floor, the pressure rising in the pocket and raising the wagon, then the seal breaking down so that the wagon falls. This is repeated at a frequency dependent upon the load, the blower capacity, and the floor surface.

This condition is most commonly met when a stage or auditorium floor is boarded with narrow, ill-fitting boards, and the storage area floor is power floated concrete, sealed and painted.

It would be possible to engineer some form of variable control for the blower, allowing the operator to modify performance to suit the floor surface, but this would be at extra cost and complexity. The practical and most cost-effective solution is to ensure that the stage or auditorium floor is well made and finished, with the numbers of traps and clearance gaps kept to a minimum. It should be noted that the satisfactory performance of an air-bearing system is dependent not only on the wagon design, but also on the floors over which it is to operate. A well-made and well-sealed floor has cost benefits for the client, as the number of air blowers required is minimised.

We are often asked if it is possible to use air bearings over carpets. Unfortunately this is not practical as the pressurised air can escape too easily. Technically it would be possible to design such a system, but the blower capacity would be so large as to make it uneconomical.

There are two forms of air bearing which are available commercially: low pressure and high pressure. The low-pressure system operates at pressures of between 1 and 2 psi (0.07–0.14 bar) and a typical unit would have a footprint of approximately 60 cms x 60 cms (2'-0" x 2'-0") and a lifting capacity of 300 kg (660 lbs). Low-pressure systems tend to have individual air blower units, or perhaps one blower feeding two bearings.

High-pressure systems operate at pressures of 10–15 psi (0.7–1 bar) or greater, and can therefore lift heavier loads. These systems usually have an external compressor or blower unit, with air being supplied to the wagon through a large diameter hose. Ω

Seating wagons on air bearings in store in the Waterfront Hall in Belfast.

High pressure air bearing as manufactured by Ab Solving Oy, Finland and used in major industrial installations.

Third speaker: Robert Heimbach

Robert Heimbach is President of Gala Theatrical Equipment, which is now known as Gala Systems. He began his career as designer of commercial passenger and freight elevator systems for a Canadian company, APV Inc. He joined Gala in 1992 and was part of the Research and Development team, developing electro-mechanical transformation systems for theatres and multi-use venues. He became Director of Engineering of this specialist company in 1997.

I want to explain the Jonquière Project which Gala undertook in Canada. This was to be a multi-purpose venue for the local community and was to be able to have the following functions:-

- Theatrical events.
    Local company and visiting companies
- Local University
    Art and Techniques of Media Class
- Community Groups
- Corporate uses
    (such as by Alcan Aluminum)
- Small Quebec Trade Shows
- Cultural Expositions
- Municipal Government Meetings
- Chamber Music
- Local School or Family-oriented Shows
- Others that are not yet known.

The building was to have 4 initial configurations:-

Large Theatre, 396 seats, diagram **A**

Small Theatre, 261 seats, diagram **B**

Cabaret, 267 seats, diagram **C**

Banquet, 301 seats, diagram **D**

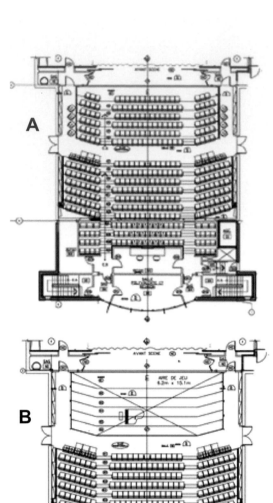

A

B

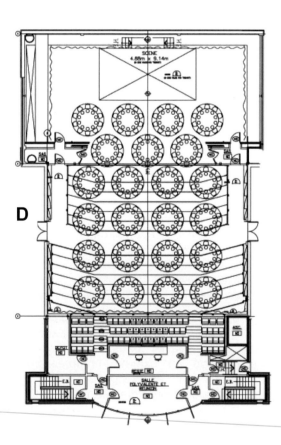

D

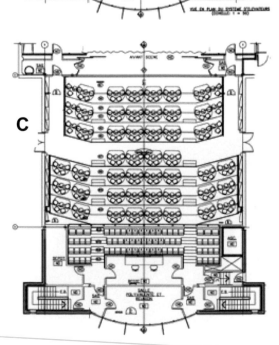

C

*Diagrams of the four initial configurations of the Jonquière Project. The stage area is shown only on **D**, the Banquet layout.*

The parameters that we had to comply with were:

- High quality transformable venue including 4 configurations and displaying the look of permanent installations.
- Transformation time lower than 10 minutes with no manual assistance.
- Highly comfortable seats with permanent look.
- Flooring sections without perforations of traps, etc.
- Structural stability equal to permanent flooring structure.
- High reliability.

Some computer generated models of the first solution for the Jonquière auditorium.

First solution

The first solution we explored was to rotate the seating blocks and this is illustrated on the right.

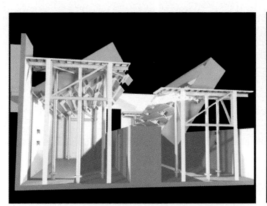
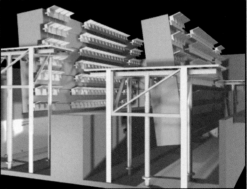

The second solution

But our new proposal, shown below, which respected the original criteria and added additional features, included:

- Possibility of angled rows,
- No guides on building walls, therefore a completely self-guided system,
- Added flexibility of multiple configurations including:
  - Conference setting
  - Extended stage configurations,
  - Extra handicapped rows,
- Fully standardized concept.

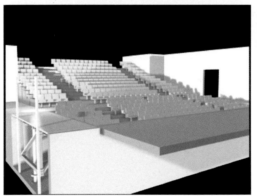
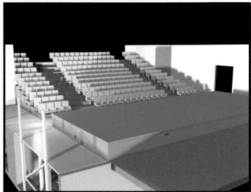

Images: Gala Theatrical Equipment

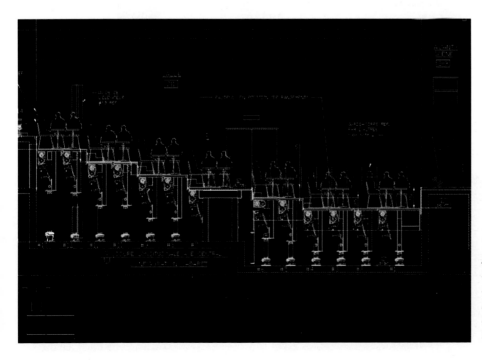

The second solution:
A section through the second solution showing the individual rows of seats in store and the cabaret tables set up.

The principle behind the changeable auditorium and the improved layout with angled seating rows.

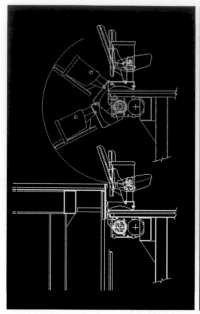

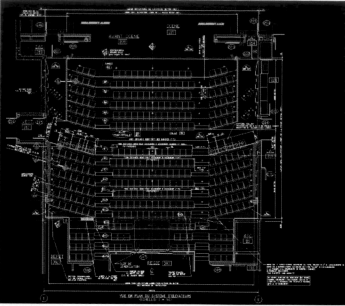

The new proposal was very beneficial in also complying with these parameters:-

- High quality
- Fast transformation time
- Comfortable seats
- No perforations
- Structural stability
- Reliability (a 6" Spiralift operates for a nominal 600,000 cycles)

The final data of the theatre is:

Number of platforms..................................... **12**
Total area of platforms...........................**194 m²**
Travel...**1.8 m to 3.7 m**
Change over time
  between configurations............................ **9 min.**
Lift speed... **0.03 m/s**
Number of reconfigurable seats..................... ...**320**
Total number of Spiralifts®............................. **60**
And the platforms are self guided.

The work on site showing the platforms being floored, the seat rotation mechanism and a factory load test on a Spiralift scissor lift.

Above: an exposed view of the riser lifts and seat rotating mechanisms.

Photos: Gala Theatrical Equipment

Fourth speaker: Jason Barnes

Although I am chairing this session, I have also been asked to speak. I want to contrast the technical descriptions we have heard by looking at detailed playmaking versus event management, that's the *frisson*, I think, of this session. I am the Production Manager of the Cottesloe Theatre of the National Theatre here in London. Lord Cottesloe was the Chairman of the South Bank Theatre Board that built the National Theatre, straight across Waterloo Bridge on the south side of the river. I've been with the company for 31 years, and the last 26 years I've devoted to working with the Cottesloe Theatre.

I think today I'm probably continuing to be what production managers are, and that is 'servers'. We serve by supporting the work. And in my case, I'm a playmaker, and I hopefully want to create an understanding about the difference between playmaking and the drama in all the other performing arts that we've been discussing at the Conference. And the work I've done is very, very specific to play-making.

The operation I work in is what's known as deficit funded; those of you who pay United Kingdom income tax pay 40% of my salary. And we manage to spend £13·5 (US$22.5, €19.2) million a year, but that's not uncommon because our art galleries and our museums tend to spend 100% of their turnover, so we're doing quite well.

I'm going to try and tell the story of the last 25 years of the Cottesloe theatre, covering something like 300 productions. I'm going to look at the principal interesting variants in terms of layout. One of the things that the Cottesloe can do is to make the different parts of the room available to actor, audience or technician, and to some extent we've done that over the years. I think the future for small dramatic work will be in what I call 'sheds'; a lorry outside with some platforms and handrails, scaffold spanner, and that's the lot.

Although he's not able to be here in person, I wanted to make sure that the person who conceived the Cottesloe, Iain Mackintosh, was here at least in spirit. This performance space was created in 1973 as a result of Peter Hall, the then Director of the National Theatre, saying that he would not move to the new building on the South Bank without a third auditorium. He said he would use this space as the kitchens of the National in order to create banquets to serve up on the

The Cottesloe at the National

Photo: Michael Mayhew

tables of the world. Indeed, if you look at the book that you can get from the National Theatre, called *Infinite Riches in a Little Room,* there is a table at the back that indicates the movement of work from the Cottesloe to the other auditoriums within the building, transfers to the West End, tours abroad and so on. But there have also been significant numbers of productions of authors' work in other theatres worldwide as a result of premier new writing.

At that time, Iain said that he saw the Cottesloe as an utterly simple space in which a performance could be given with the minimum of technical preparation. A flexible space in which far reaching experiments, possibly about the very nature of theatre, and certainly about actor/audience relationships, could be made.

"The central issue," he concluded, "is probably the opposing demand for simplicity on the one hand, and total flexibility on the other. The Cottesloe design proposals," he said, "are aimed at giving people enough, but no more than is necessary to experiment. Only by leaving a lot to the user can the designer of brand new theatres encourage the improvisation and vital response to the problems of theatrical relationship more often associated with converted premises, found spaces, and site-specific theatres."

Iain pointed out that a simple philosophy, a simple space in which a performance could be given with a minimum of technical preparation, is what he was trying to conceive. And the 1973 sketches, in a little pack that I inherited when I took over at the opening of the building, laid out what Iain imagined could be some of the uses of the space. These diagrams are on the next page. Top left is a short traverse. End stage, which represents something like

"The Mysteries" 1977 from the cover of the book "Infinite Riches in a Little Room", edited by Ronnie Mulryne and Margaret Shewring and first published in 1999. Jason Barnes was the Technical Editor.

Jason Barnes is the son of a painter and a poet/playwright. Following his West End debut as an actor he became a stage manager and lighting designer and later joined the National Theatre. Following the move to the South Bank, Jason was appointed Production Manager of the National Theatre's courtyard, the Cottesloe, where he has staged over 200 plays. He maintains many overseas links and has a particular interest in found spaces to many of which he has taken international tours from the National Theatre.

"Only by leaving a lot to the user can the designer encourage improvisation"

Iain Mackintosh on the design of the Cottesloe.

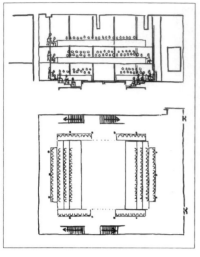

Short Traverse

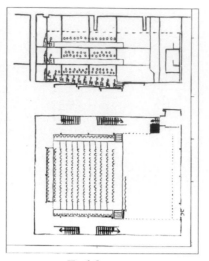

End Stage

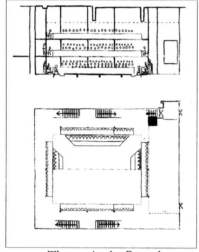

Theatre in the Round

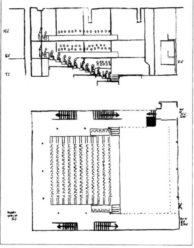

Cockpit

The concept design drawings of the Cottesloe Theatre: Iain Mackintosh 1973.

The empty Cottesloe – the last drawing made by Richard Leacroft before he died, which was presented to Jason Barnes.

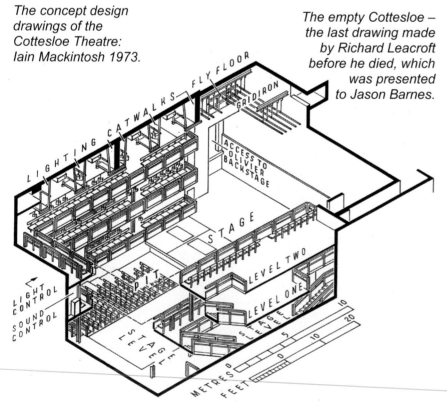

52% of our work over the last 25 years, making the point that only just less than half has been in the end stage format. Both theatre in the round, of which there is an example towards the end, and cockpit form are configurations that come into the history of the building. Total simplicity on one hand, and total flexibility on the other – what a tall order! So let's see how we've done.

The theatre had two fixed elements: the end stage performance area, which we've only used half the time, and the three encircling galleries, on the three sides. The end stage area is 9.9 x 9.1 metres (32'-6" x 30'-0"). I have to keep reminding my bosses that the stage of the Cottesloe has one of the biggest stages in London. They seem to think I can operate on budgets suited to The Pit, our sister theatre for the Royal Shakespeare Company at the Barbican, but The Pit's stage is often only a third of the stage area that we use. And whereas I often have an acting area bigger than the Lyttelton Theatre, I get something like 20% of their budget with which to mount plays. We also take less at the door at the Cottesloe, with a maximum of 400 seats compared with 900.

Bill Dudley, the scene designer, has been closely associated with work at the Cottesloe over the years, and he has been a guiding light to me. And it's been an enormous pleasure that I've done many productions with him. He countered the worry that the small space that Peter Hall demanded wouldn't keep up the quality of the complex: "There had been some active opposition to the opening of the third auditorium, as it was felt this space could not hope to sustain the high standards of the other two auditoria. In the event, the simplicity of the Cottesloe's courtyard-style environment, painted in black, proved its greatest asset."

What he's saying is that the simplicity has actually been its greatest asset. His reference to black is, of course, a disagreement with what I said earlier in the Conference about colour, and Tim Foster's suggestion that the most flexible tool for an architect is colour.

Now we will look at a whole series of different layouts. The first, on the next page, is traditional: *Half Life* with Sir John Gielgud, transferred to the West End; we had to cut a metre out of the width of it in order to get into a not-small West End theatre, just to give an example of how big the stage is!

Changeable auditorium techniques

Photo: John Haynes

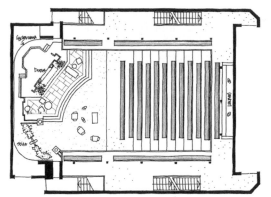

END STAGE
"Half Life" 1977
Designer: Jane Martin.
The pit tier, rising in
100 mm increments,
was formed in solid
plywood boxes, and
surrounded by a lower
pit level gallery.

The pictures below show the first of the promenade works; we did five major promenades over about 20 years, and this was the beginning of the *Mystery Plays* which lasted from 1977 until they were finally revived, after a 14-year gap, for the Millennium. And they have been played in all sorts of found spaces throughout Europe.

These use a flat-floored hall. So the boxes that were provided for the low risers that Iain originally conceived, with a ground-level gallery surrounding them, and therefore effectively creating a pit gallery, a first-level gallery and a second-level gallery, these wooden boxes, with screw-down chairs, were turned over into a lower pit, literally turned over, and fitted. That worked out, at no cost, and with no storage space needed initially.

The LINE DRAWINGS
reproduced throughout
this section are by
Tim Foster and later by
Miles King.

By the time we come to the addition of Part 2 of the Mysteries which was in fact the first part of the story of the Bible from the medieval mystery plays, we went to a full drop-in bar kit to fill in the lower pit, manufactured by Peter Kemp who for many years was a leading theatrical engineer in this country, now in retirement.

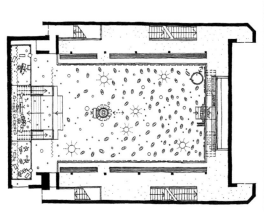

PROMENADE
"The Mysteries" 1977
Designer: Bill Dudley.
The pit boxes could be
turned over into the
lower pit to provide a
lower cockpit level,
surrounded by the pit
seating galleries with
their seats removed.

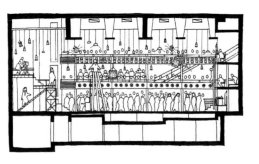

PROMENADE
"The Mysteries" 1980
Designer: Bill Dudley.
A pit infill kit allowed
250 members of the
audience to share the
pit level with the actors
and technicians within
the decorated room.

Photos: Michael Mayhew

The point about colour, I think, is that the Cottesloe is, literally, a room. We've all been talking about rooms as being the auditorium space, but the gallery surfaces in the Cottesloe are there to be changed, clipped onto, painted, unbolted. And here, the upper-level gallery has been celebrated with emblems of the working man – brewers' signs, dartboards and so on – and the lower level as a series of reproduction coal holes. For those of you from abroad, many of us who live in older Victorian houses have a round hole in our front path where the coalman pours the coal down into a coal cellar, and these were reproduced in the setting. And the cross-section elevation, which can't be seen on that drawing, was covered with agricultural implements in a sort of old-fashioned museum display.

That format went on until 1985 when Peter Hall closed the Cottesloe for six months, and we literally marched across Waterloo Bridge to the old Lyceum Theatre. This had been a dance hall since the second world war, and we closed it prior to its redevelopment. This was a very interesting example of a found space, like that used by Peter Brook and Jean-Guy Lecat, a theatre to be used in a different way. It was already in use as a dance hall, with what the Spanish call a *lisabetta*, a platform right out

into the auditorium. And, as Richard Pilbrow has pointed out earlier, up to about 1880 most classic Italian style playhouses had a stage absolutely level with the rear stalls or, in the case of a courtyard theatre, level to the rear, and therefore they were able to be boarded over in order to allow promenade performances. We've seen other recent examples of these during the course of the Conference.

We get into a little more scenery here; another promenade performance, *Lark Rise to Candleford*, was the Flora Thompson trilogy which we presented as two separate evenings developed about a year apart, and here we have horizontal scenery. We've talked about orchestra shells, but fortunately we don't have to provide music regularly in the Cottesloe and we don't have an orchestra shell to get in the way, but for this production we provided a sky cloth.

The Cottesloe is used here as a flat-floored rectilinear courtyard space. There are a number of examples of round-ended

PROMENADE "Lark Rise to Candleford" 1978 Designer: Bill Dudley. Work on these early productions discovered the strength of the space down its length; this led to 'set' pieces at each end of the promenade. At this time, however, there is not yet any requirement for trap access through the floor.

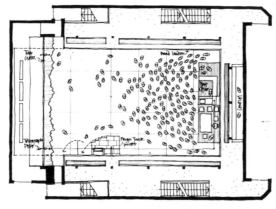

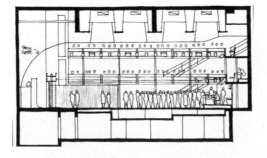

Photos: Michael Mayhew

Changeable auditorium techniques

galleried spaces; the Wilde Theatre at Bracknell is one, the Swan in Stratford upon Avon is another. But in my view, for really changeable courtyard galleried spaces run by a play-producing company such as the National Theatre, a rectilinear space is better because it gives you the opportunity of scenic treatment at what we still, even if we're in promenade configuration, call the downstage end.

There's been a lot of talk about how you create moments, and how you support the work, the moment of the play, providing you're not suffocating or uncomfortable on your chair, or you haven't tripped over a nosing, or you haven't been disturbed by a rubber seal on a door, all the things that we've been hearing about during the course of the Conference. If we get all those things right, then our job is to actually support the writing at any moment. And there are a lot of tools in our toolkit. One of them is sound, and in the case of the opening of these plays, the soundtrack of larks. We also used lighting on the bottom of the horizontal cyclorama to create a dawn effect, using skypans that we borrowed from Pinewood Studios – they're probably from about the 1930s, the beginning of filming there. These produced a completely soft light by virtue of passing through the diffusion of fabric which was a woven cloth, a sort of broadloom material that we used for cycloramas. The parallel is what you experience if you go into an art gallery and there's a piece of fabric stretched over the ceiling, and above that is a skylight with full daylight. And you could have sworn you were stood outside in a field in Oxfordshire at dawn; a real kind of environmental stimulus.

And so to theatre in the round and the floor of the performance space. We've just looked at various systems for poking chairs up in one place, and we've looked at those wonderful Spiralifts and other lifting systems on a number of occasions. But any examination of the matrix of the Cottesloe floor will not allow mechanisation. I have been working with Iain Mackintosh and George Ellerington of Theatre Projects on trying to discover any common rectangles for the various principal layouts required of the floor. If you draw a lot of lines in one direction and a lot in the other, you land up with 68 little squares of different shapes and sizes. If you popped a Spiralift or similar under each of them, how would you maintain enough space to get an actor to any of the trap apertures to make an entrance up a staircase? How would you

access it to put a loudspeaker underneath, to put a spotlight there, to withdraw a prop, or to put a costume down? All things that we have to do when we're playmaking in different parts of the theatre. Space under the floor is very important.

I usually say to consultants or to architects when they come to see me, "When you say to yourself you won't need audio tie lines in the foyer, put them in. If you can't put them in, leave a hole in the wall and stuff it up with proprietary fire-resistant material. If you don't think you need CCTV in the foyer, leave a hole so we can run the wire later, because the first cue on the first production will be a band playing in the foyer which will follow the audience in and they will need CCTV to see what's going on in the auditorium before they get in there."

Another thing: don't weld. For example, all the gallery fronts are bolted on and able to be removed. If you have a look at where we've punched through the floor, all the floor members were 18 mm (¾") ply, bolted down using self-tapping screws to steels which could also be unbolted and removed. We just went down with a spanner and took them out, removed the plywood and produced some vomitories for use in the action beneath the rented-seating tiers. And, during the course of this production of *Dispatches* a helicopter actually landed in the middle of the auditorium; again engineered by Peter Kemp.

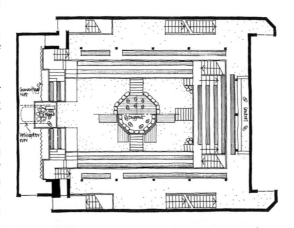

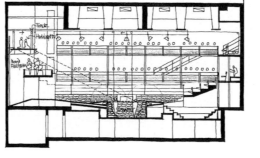

THEATRE IN THE ROUND "Dispatches" 1979 Designer: Bill Dudley Several experiments were made with raised seating – often rented and using sports seating units with a scaffold undercarriage. These, however, took several days to install and prevented repertoire performances of other productions. For the first time, we punched through the auditorium floor. Fortunately the structure is largely bolted together, which lends itself to flexibility. The moral of this is – don't weld!

*END STAGE —
RAISED PIT TIER
"Early Days" 1980
Designer:
Jocelyn Herbert.
Jocelyn Herbert was the
first to raise the pit
seating to meet the first
level gallery for this
production with
Ralph Richardson.
The tiers were built of
timber 'gate rostra' still
beloved of some opera
houses, but noisy,
dangerous and with
a will of their
own in storage!*

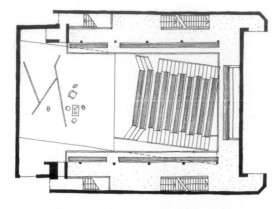

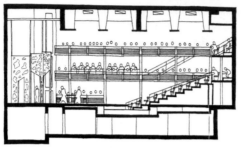

We had lusted after reaching the first-level gallery with the seating tier from the pit, from the datum stage level. And Jocelyn Herbert was the first person to actually make this connection – which Iain Mackintosh had anticipated in 1973. However, for this difficult, worrying play, she had turned the seats through 10½°.

This angle became known as 'Lindsay's Angle' after Lindsay Anderson, the Director. On being questioned about the angle he retorted, "It challenges the rectilinear nature of the space." The play was largely about disturbance of the mind, and this was the first production to purposely *fight* the room, and set a tension running.

One or two people have talked a little bit about discomfort in auditoria being used to suit the production. We're about to do a play about child molestation and murder, and the nature of the setting will be very simple but very severe. Tuning the

auditorium not only for acoustics but also for light, colour, material texture and quality and comfort or discomfort is something that's very useful for playmakers.

The next production is the only example of where Iain Mackintosh and I diverge. He always points out, I think quite interestingly, that certainly for comedy the centre of gravity of the audience must be beneath the actors' horizontal eye line. And actually as a performer in productions of English music hall in North America I know this; you play to the front row. If this relationship isn't right, the proxy relationship through the house won't work. And of course it doesn't work in this Conference room, as we know!

We are all dying to have any future Conference in a playhouse, because this will be set out where people can be heard, be lit and be seen, the front-row relationship will be correct and so on. And there are clear reasons why we moved to this steep-raked auditorium system, because half of it could be moved around at datum, as you'll see shortly, and the other half could be dealt with by moving them onto an elevator below datum which, indeed, Iain had again anticipated in his drawings.

We got a gift from the Greater London Council, when it was disbanded by Margaret Thatcher, of something like £100,000 (US $164,000, €140,000) and we were able to afford to buy a retractable seating bleacher system in two parts. This allowed us to move the steep terrace in about 35–40 minutes

*END STAGE – NEW
RAISED PIT TIER
"The Beggars' Opera"
Designer: John Gunter
1983
This production, by
Richard Eyre, made
use of a bridge linking
the ends of the 1st level
gallery, and the setting
grew out of the
theatre's architecture.
Gas lamps within the
auditorium created
the effect of a
Victorian workhouse.*

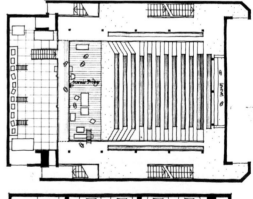

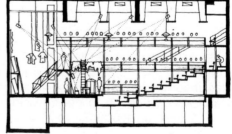

Photo: Jason Barnes

Changeable auditorium techniques

instead of taking seven or eight hours to dismantle folding-gate rostra. The bleacher seating, by Audience Systems, and the elevator, by Peter Kemp, are shown in this long section. The elevator is in fact an elevator and a half, anticipating the three-elevator system that Iain Mackintosh had suggested. This equipment had to be retro-fitted into the space and there are some problems with it, in that we cannot hide the whole of the upper seven-row bleacher beneath the floor on the elevator. This is because, being a retro-fitted unit, it won't pass behind the columns at the rear of the auditorium. But we manage. From time to time we've taken out the lower four-row bleacher because that's possible, but the big one is too heavy and too tall to actually manage to remove it out of the space.

Aha! Be still, my heart! The introduction of Steeldeck rostra. You're sitting on them at the back, but you probably don't know it. I've talked about sheds and a lorry outside with a lot of tube and some platforms, and that's the story from here on in. The point about a lot of seating systems – certainly retractable seating systems, and rostrum systems – is that they usually offer a series of heights but not anything you actually want. I'm a playmaker; I need to work with designers who, if they're good – and most of them are *very* good – design what they need for the production. And when they want a level, they want it the height they want it, not the height the manufacturer chose. This means we may want it exactly 372 mm or 492 mm because we're doing something else on top; setting out within those spaces is very important.

By 1988, Philip Parsons had introduced Steeldeck rostra, used for the first time in Peter Hall's production of the promenade play *Entertaining Strangers.* This offered decks based on a two-foot module in plan starting at just 178 mm (7") high, and by using standard inexpensive scaffold tube (48 mm diameter, or 1-29/32") allows an absolute choice of platform height – something rarely available in other proprietary deck or seating systems.

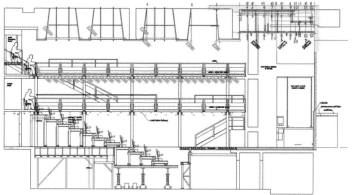

Long section through the Cottesloe Theatre showing the retractable bleacher seating system and the elevator under the front seating units.

This next arrangement shown, for the production *Shakespeare Late Plays,* follows, in a way, the sort of interior theatres of the late 17th century, in that we've got seats on the side galleries sold right the way up to the end stage and seats round the raked stage platform, which is also constructed using Steeldeck. We could now get rid of our steep-raked bleachers towards the rear of the auditorium – the upper bleacher is stored behind the curtain shown in the section and the lower bleacher used to go under the auditorium staircases at the rear of the auditorium. I said when we first got those seats that we spent £120,000 (US $200,000, €170,000) on not being able to not-have seats very quickly. Think of it that way!

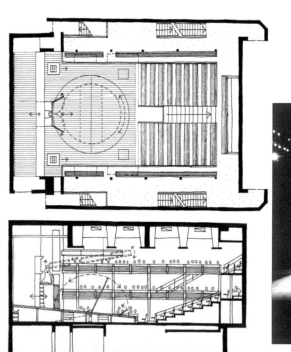

THEATRE ON 3 SIDES "Shakespeare Late Plays" 1988 Designer: Alison Chitty Director: Peter Hall

Photo: John Haynes

The section of the basic Steeldeck rostrum.

LONG TRAVERSE
"Fuente Ovejuna" 1989
Designer: Nick Omerod

Photo: Jason Barnes

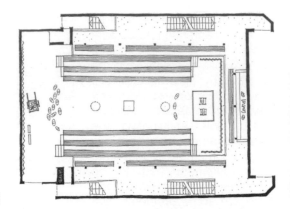

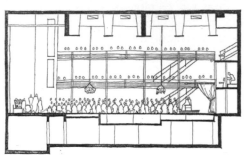

So we're into using boxes (rostra) and chairs. If we look now at the long traverse configuration, the Cottesloe is extremely strong down its long centre line, and it suits a lot of confrontation drama where there are basically two groups of protagonists. This particular play is the oldest play in the Spanish repertoire, and the most famous. It's their *Hamlet, "Fuente Ovejuna"* by Lope de Vega, and indeed we took this production on tour to the Lope de Vega Theatre in Seville where we played on their *lisabetta*, the platform out in the auditorium. They said that they use this form all the time which was very exciting. In this format the box seats in a traditional Italian theatre could actually see something of the action.

In the Cottesloe, the retractable bleacher seats were packed away under the rear gallery and beneath the audience staircases on each side. The elevator (not shown) was raised, and Steeldeck tiers ranged down the length of the room, which was set out as an upper throne room where the play is given. Simple linked stacking chairs were used for the first time. This marked the beginning of really flexible repertoire staging.

It's possible that the production that's standing on the Cottesloe stage now, may go to the Stadsschouwburg in Amsterdam, where I'm proposing for the first time in living memory that they do exactly the same. They told me when I went for the reconnoitre that they were going to reupholster the audience seating and were

thinking of making all the chairs removable. I asked why and when they said, "We don't really know." I said, 'I'll show you,' and I got the drawings out and plonked my theatre in the round setting in the middle of the auditorium. "Ooh, that's interesting," they said. "Now we know why we thought we'd make the chairs removable. Terrific!"

The set for *Ma Rainey's Black Bottom*, the August Wilson play, is an example of where the space becomes a room in which we all are actors, technicians, audience; the whole theatre was turned into a Chicago loft.

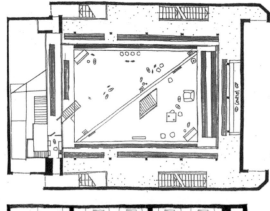

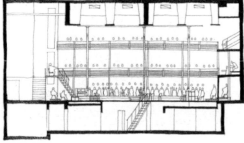

THEATRE IN THE ROUND
"Ma Rainey's Black Bottom" 1989
Designer: Bob Crowley

Photo: Jason Barnes

Changeable auditorium techniques

The play takes place in this building, and the loft building has been, in the play, converted into an early recording studio for the black jazz singer. For this production the bridge that was shown in *The Beggars' Opera,* is again in use, linking the end of the first-level galleries half-way up the end stage. And it has audience members seated on it for the first time.

Dermot Hayes created an interesting set for *The Shape of the Table.* I don't have any drawings of it, unfortunately, but it's in the round, with the audience placed in groups in the four corners of the arrangement, with a scenic unit representing a derelict Eastern European ballroom in the centre of each of the four sides. For the first time, handrails half way down the first level gallery were removed to allow for these apparently full height scenic pieces.

So in this case we were <u>outside</u> the room <u>looking in</u>, and it was extremely powerful. The set was actually built by Phil Parsons, the manufacturer of Steeldeck, and it included steel decks behind the upstage scenic panel. That is where we put the seven-row bleacher and we hid it with scenery.

THEATRE IN THE ROUND
"The Shape of the Table"
1990
Designer: Dermot Hayes

Photo: Nobby Clark

The first of the David Hare trilogy, *Racing Demon,* that was done in 1990 used a cruciform stage, and this play joined the other two in the Olivier Theatre; we did just the first one in the Cottesloe. This is the only time we've ever been able to re-use the Audience System's seven-row bleacher in any other position than normal steep-tiered end stage. That is how inflexible lumps of seats can be in a courtyard playhouse. We tried and they just don't fit, the sizes are wrong, the goings are wrong, and the acting area requirement fights with the plan area of those seats.

In *Richard II* by William Shakespeare there is a kind of jousting scene set in a piste. That gave rise to the whole layout of the otherwise long traverse arrangement that was used. The pitch of the side seats was increased to the legal maximum to give increased energy. One of the very dangerous things to do is to put people behind a handrail at the front of a terrace, like at a racing track or stadium. It's extremely dangerous. However, the present setup in the Cottesloe, which we'll look at right at the end of this presentation, shows the whole room with a rail round it, and that's something we did to try and overcome that danger. And it's absolutely to do with the relationship of the head and the eyes of the front row and the front of the playing space, to the millimetre. And if you get it right it'll work, and if you don't the play won't work.

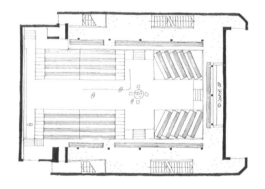

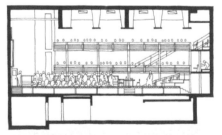

Photo: Jason Barnes

Richard II represents one of many productions where the lower four rows of the retractable tiers of seating needed to be removed from the floor of the theatre. It is

CRUCIFORM
(Mannequin Parade)
"Racing Demon" 1990
Designer: Bob Crowley

LIST or JOUSTING PISTE "Richard II" 1995 Designer: Hildegarde Bechtler.

Photo: Philip Carter

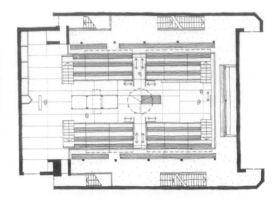

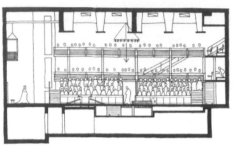

stored on the main elevator, with the void levelled off with more Steeldeck units. The empty space to one side was used for access to a trap in the floor representing the prison.

A lot of the floor in this set was brass sheet, which shone, and looked like molten gold; it was absolutely extraordinary. There was also a simple chandelier shown on the section drawing that flew in, was lit with real candles, and flew out again. We're not talking about the technical side of the Cottesloe, but flying in there is very rudimentary, although you can actually put a pulley anywhere and tie the line off on a cleat on the auditorium wall lining up on the second gallery, accessible to technician or audience or a cast member.

Tim Hatley set the Pam Gems play about the life of the British painter, Stanley Spencer, in a church – Spencer's life was totally wrapped up in his own approach to Christianity and his lifelong aspiration to work on church design schemes. Seats flanking the sides of the acting area were real church pews and stock decks, while the third side used the Audience System bleacher seating.

This was one of the most interesting productions I've ever worked on. Anthony Sher who played Spencer, and looked uncannily like him with a wig and spectacles and so on, is a painter. He did paint and continued an unfinished piece of work, that we reproduced bigger on a backcloth on the back wall, using a scaffolding, right through

the production. We had a trick panel because, towards the end of the run, he'd got too far to the end and we had to start him back again where he'd been, otherwise there would have been nothing left for him to paint!

Richard Eyre's production of *King Lear* uses three rows a side down the length of the theatre. The rear row in each case shares a floor level with row 2 as the head room below the balcony is tight. I talked a little about this production of *King Lear* in the Found Space session. The difficulty of headroom when needing steep sightlines is overcome in a way that many people have used: in the Royal Exchange upper levels,

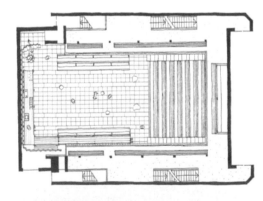

CHURCH "Stanley" 1996 Designer: Tim Hatley

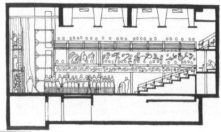

Photo: Philip Carter

Changeable auditorium techniques

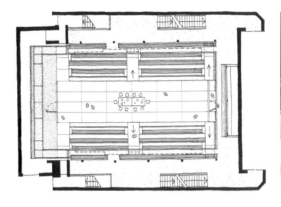

"King Lear"
Ian Holm takes the curtain call on the long transverse setting.

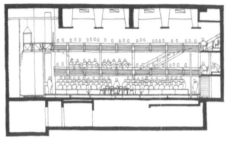

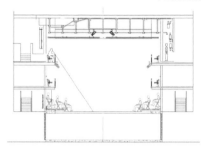

Photo: Jason Barnes

in those in the Swan at Stratford, and even those varying-height chairs that are used in a studio theatre in RADA. In the rear of three rows on the ground floor pit level, the chair is on a box and you clamber up onto it and you have a leaning rail and a foot rail. Indeed, there have been rear perch seats at the first level for the last three or four years in the Cottesloe, which are both inexpensive and offer quite a good view.

In the play *Blue Orange,* which is about two psychiatrists and one patient, we achieved almost our biggest ever capacity, with the smallest acting area, only 4·5 × 4·5 metres (14'-9" × 14'-9"). This was inspired by 19th-century medical lecture theatres, of which there is one at Guy's hospital. This is the first time that we started experimenting with setting Steeldeck in seating tiers. The seating is as precipitous as British law permits; 510 mm (1'-8") rise with a going of 915 mm (3'-0"). This production marked the introduction of a user-made seating tier system, using stock components from the Steeldeck range, together with trapezoidal and triangular special decks.

I have to remind everybody that we are a repertoire company and, although we are not doing many changeovers at the moment, because we're short of money, we normally do two or three repertoire changeovers each week in all three playhouses. If we're not careful this leads to traffic jams in the scenery corridor between the theatres on the ground floor. But this show was in repertoire with another complete arrangement, and generally we restrict ourselves to two layouts in any period, so if we lose one layout we can offer a third for an upcoming production. In this way we don't shoot ourselves in the foot in

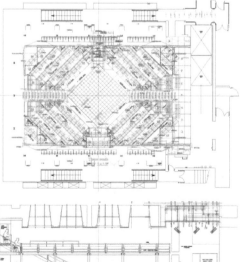

Photo: Philip Carter

THEATRE IN THE ROUND
"Blue Orange" 2000
Designer: Bill Dudley

terms of changeovers. Our changeovers are achieved usually by a large number of technicians working for a comparatively short amount of time, because we have them available. They probably work from 9 am until 3 pm, and then we drop down to about four technicians to finish off and run the performance at night. And the extra technicians go back to their own theatre where they haven't had a changeover on that day; that's how the Cottesloe generally operates.

Nicholas Wright's semi-biographical play *Vincent in Brixton* about Dutch painter van Gogh is set in a naturalistic kitchen in South London in 1873. Sunday lunch is prepared throughout Act One on a working Victorian cooking range. The acting area is realistically small, leaving space for the Cottesloe's largest capacity to date – 404 seats and 24 standing. The left-hand side is the Audience Systems upper seven-row seating block, set down to datum in plan, and the right-hand side is a Steeldeck terrace, as illustrated. This is in repertoire with end-stage work and we were pleased when the first changeover in the rep, which we'd never done before, was completed almost within four hours.

Some technical information about how we've done it is shown in the section. All the legs are terminated in ball castors on a spigot that passes up into the tube. They're held in with a bit of gaffer tape. We don't weld them because the ball-races and

Photo: Jason Barnes

castors do go wrong – my technicians tried welding at one time and we wasted a great deal of money.

The detail of the front leg of the second row, which would normally pass right down to the floor (as they do in the tier at the back of this room), are truncated at the level of the tier in front, terminated with a ball castor, and captured by a little bracket that bears down on the truss. Handrails are clipped on; there are again examples of those at the back of this room. Minimum amount of bracing is required to satisfy regulations; almost always an independent engineer will come and sign off the installation. I'm not a scaffolder, I don't have any qualifications, but you only need a very minimal amount of tube to satisfy live-load calculations.

These items are easy and flexible to store. One tier passes under the other by virtue of the ball races. Sandler chairs, made in America, but also available in this country, can be folded, stacked onto trolleys and wheeled away. Handrails, half-treads and chairs all need to be taken off before the tiers are closed up and moved to store. Very flexible and simple technology! Thank you. Ω

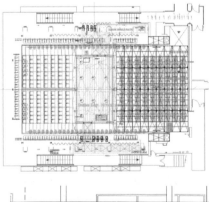

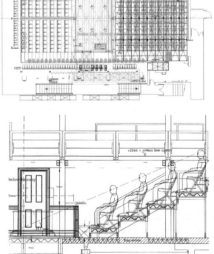

THEATRE IN THE ROUND
"Vincent in Brixton"
2002
Designer: Tim Hatley

Photo: Jason Barnes

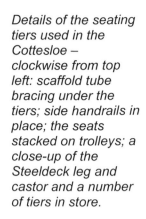

Details of the seating tiers used in the Cottesloe – clockwise from top left: scaffold tube bracing under the tiers; side handrails in place; the seats stacked on trolleys; a close-up of the Steeldeck leg and castor and a number of tiers in store.

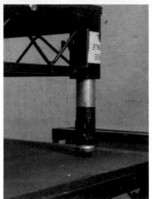

Photos: Jason Barnes

Questions and discussion

Jason Barnes, Chairman

The President of Steeldeck, Phil Parsons, is here with us today. He only has that title because there's now a factory in Los Angeles and a rental unit in New York. So for those of you in America, if you want Steeldeck, you can get it!

Question from the floor

One of the problems that we find is getting the warmed air into an auditorium. Getting it out is no problem – you take it up at the top – but getting it in at the bottom when you've got a lot of flexible seating and staging systems can be quite tricky.

Stuart Wilson, Speaker

We've certainly approached that problem; with seating wagons we have air fed into the seating units and out through the chairs in a fairly conventional way. It does add further openings in the floor which is a problem for air-bearing systems, but we've done at least two systems that way which are working quite satisfactorily, so it is possible.

Jason Barnes, Speaker

My experience of this is that we used to have a 24 sq ft (2.4 m^2) extract duct under the front of the end stage extension. And the minute you board in the floor at the datum level you obviously seal that off, so we then opened an aperture at the rear of the pit underneath the first-level gallery. This has hinged flaps which were designed to open with a steep terrace set out; it has a mesh grille to stop people and litter falling into it. I don't think we've opened these in the last 10 years, but we still manage, just about, because there are other extracts to balance our air flow. But the business of ventilation is an issue. We do have big problems with cold air descending from the input cowls, of which there are three or four in the overhead bays over the whole room, because when people are located up near the front of the galleries, they are in an air flow that nobody previously thought you would position a human being in! But this makes my point about flexibility – plan to allow human beings to be anywhere in the volume, make sure they can be there, because we'll get round to it, even if it takes us 25 years! Ω

*FURTHER IMAGES OF
CHANGEABLE AUDITORIA*

*Derngate, Northampton:
Part of the stage and
auditorium showing the
first tower removed into
the scene dock from the
concert platform format.
More information
about the changeover
operations is given by
the General Manager,
Roger Hopwood, in
Architecture and
Planning, section AP7.*

Photo: Techplan   Photo: Martin Charles

*The Vanbrugh Theatre
at RADA: a lecture is
given using the stepped
stalls seating; to the
right this is shown
levelled ready for the
seats to be removed.
The resulting flat floor
can be raised to
rear stalls /stage level.
Underneath: the screw-
jack and lever arm
mechanisms which
achieve this change.
A user's opinion on
RADA and the views of
the architect, Bryan
Avery, and others are
given in the
Architecture and
Planning Book.*

Photos: Techplan

*The main hall of the
Shizouka Convention
and Arts Centre in
Japan: here the seating
wagons are moved on
air bearings into the
shelves of an elevator.
The floor is marble and
the elevator is raised on
48 x 18" Spiralifts. The
raised elevator can form
a stage. The 58 metre
(190 ft) high room is
styled on a European
cathedral and is used for
all types of concerts and
community activities.*

Photos: Techplan and courtesy Shizouka Prefecture

Power and Harmonics

Chairman: Mark White, UK Sales Director, ETC Europe Ltd
Speakers: Adam Bennette, Technical Director, ETC Europe Ltd
Steve Barker, UK Business Manager, Siemens Variable Speed Drives
Dave Chapman, Copper Development Association

Mark White: Chairman

Welcome to this session on Power and Harmonics. The format of this session is that I'm going to give a very brief introduction about what electrical mains supplies are supposed to look like. I will be followed by Adam Bennette, who will describe what happens to mains supplies when single-phase devices are connected to them. Steve Barker will then talk about what happens when three-phase devices are connected, and we then have Dave Chapman of the Copper Development Association who will describe earthing, and provide information about functional and protective devices. This is in no way meant to be a heavy electrical-engineering session, but I can see quite a few electrical engineers amongst us anyway. These are the devices and effects which each of the three speakers will expand upon, and each of these devices does end up 'creating pollution', for want of a better expression, in some way.

We'll start with *power factor*. Power factor is one of the forgotten parts of electrical engineering now; we have this new thing to do with harmonics and power quality. Power factor is something which I guess tends to be ignored and we're about to rectify that a little.

In order to explain power factor, I also need to explain a little bit about electricity mains in general. I will just explain a few principles. The ideal mains supply is sinusoidal in shape. About the only time the mains appears like this is when it

comes out of the generator at the power station. We know it, in this country, as nominally 230V mains. It used to be 240V, but we're now at 230V due to European harmonisation. Being sinusoidal in shape, the 230V part of it is the root mean square (RMS), or the average value, of the waveform. So what we see is the sinusoidal shape, and indicated on the diagram are degrees at the bottom. If you imagine the area underneath this curve measured and the area converted to a rectangle of the same base, we end up what we call the RMS value.

We all tend to forget that there are peaks on either side of our AC mains; it goes 325V in one direction, 325V in the other, therefore we have a 650V swing. This is the reason for having mains cabling with a 660V insulation rating, so that when people doing electrical inspections come along, they need to make sure that the cabling within an enclosure is at least 660V rated.

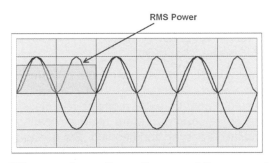

RMS Power

When we have the voltage and the current in synchronism, they're working together, if you like. The yellow part indicates the power that's being developed, or power being taken from the mains in one cycle. Again it's an RMS figure and it also swings negative.

Very few devices actually do take current from the mains in absolute synchrony. This is a bit like getting up in the morning, in that most electrical devices which we use have some sort of magnetic quality to them. In the case of, say, a motor, there's a certain

Mark White has been a chief electrician, a technical manager for a group of London West End theatres, and both a Theatre Consultant and a Project Manager for the development project at the Royal Opera House. As part of the latter project, he planned the stage lighting and technical power requirements and dealt with issues arising from mains-borne 'interference'. His interest in power quality stems from his earlier theatre experiences when attempting to discover why certain items of electrical equipment sometimes mysteriously refused to function.

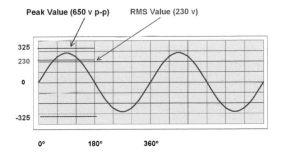

Peak Value (650 v p-p)   RMS Value (230 v)

Left: an ideal mains waveform as generated and, above, the RMS power taken from the mains when voltage and current are in synchrony, ie: 0° phase difference.

reluctance to actually get going, just like it is for us getting up in the morning! In the diagram below, the time you should get up is the black line and when you actually get up is the purple line. This is an uncorrected motor and, as we know that power is a product of voltage and current, we suddenly see that considerably more power is now taken out of the mains.

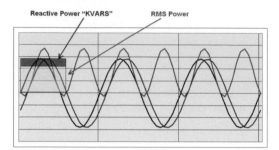

Actual power drawn when the current is lagging voltage by 30° includes the reactive power "KVARS".

We can see how the area has increased and should also notice that across the central section we're actually starting to see the power going backwards, if you like. This doesn't happen in reality; it only happens on this graph. What's happened, though, is that this extra power is called *reactive power* and this is the power that the electricity supply company has to supply without payment. It's actually true power, but the normal, age-old way of metering power meant that this power wasn't recorded. This is actually costing the electricity supply company money, so they do get quite excited about it. Now that there are improved metering facilities available, we are starting to have to pay for it. When the voltage and the current are all together in synchrony, this is what we describe as a power factor of 1, which is what we try to achieve.

What sort of devices do we have in theatres with a power factor of less than 1 and which therefore cost us extra money? The classic one is, of course, motors used in heating, ventilation and air conditioning. We're about to learn about the situation with stage machinery, in particular, when using inverters and other such things. These also start to affect the power factor. And simple things around the front of house, like the refrigerators used for the bars, the big cool stores that are in places like the Royal Opera House and others, where they have a lot of rotating machinery, actually start to cost you more money. We talked in an earlier session today about lighting and Part L of the Building Regulations which came into effect on April 1st of this year,

and how we all signed up to the Kyoto Agreement – or at least the Europeans did – in 1997. This means that in order to save power we'll end up having to use a lot more discharge lighting than we did before.

There's a lovely misconception within the theatrical industry. This is that because dimmers control incandescent sources, dimmers will therefore have a power factor of 1. As we are about to discover, they don't, if only for the simple fact that in the current range of dimmers there is inductance in the form of a choke, so that alone starts to knock back the power – but observe what Adam talks about in a minute. In other words, almost everything has a power factor of less than 1 in the theatre.

So how do we correct power factor? First of all we make a good choice of equipment so that we end up with fitted power-factor devices, power-factor correction already built into lighting ballasts, into motors and the like, and we look for a power factor of greater than 0·92 in practice. And when all that fails, we put capacitor banks in the electrical intake room to correct the overall power factor of all the installations in the building.

Now is this very effective? Well, up until a short time ago, it didn't really matter because the cost of power-factor correction equipment, particularly here in the UK, was fairly prohibitive. It tended not to be done in theatres. But recently we monitored the power-factor in a theatre not far from here which had a long-running musical in it, and it came out to be around 0·84, which meant that the client was paying each year just under £12,000 ($20,000, €17,000) for the 'real' electricity, for want of a better expression, plus another £2,500 ($4,000, €3,000) for the reactive power. The cost of installing the capacitor equipment to improve this was £3,500 ($5,740, €4,900) which gave a payback period of about 17 months. This becomes important to a theatre owner who is trying to hire out his theatre, as he can suddenly end up with a theatre which is slightly cheaper to run than his competitors' and therefore is more attractive to producers.

The power factor is nominally regarded as the cosine of the phase angle. Or is it? That's true if we have a pure sine wave. As we move away from a power factor of 1, the situation is worsened if harmonics are present, and Adam will now explain to us how that happens. Ω

Second speaker: Adam Bennette

Hello! I've given this paper a bit of an odd title 'Greeks, Guitars, Pretzels and a Frenchman', but there's method in my madness! The sub-title is "Everything you never wanted to know about dimmer power harmonics and some other stuff you never wanted to know either!"

Right, so this is going to be about harmonics; obviously we'll be talking about electrical harmonics, but I'm going to start somewhere else, because the story of harmonics actually goes back to no other person than Pythagoras. Pythagoras discovered a theory, and in fact invented the theory of music from this, which is still in use today, about ratios. He took a string with weights on it and plucked it and it vibrated with a certain tone, and he discovered that if he divided this in half the tone sounded pleasant with the original one, because it was exactly double the frequency; if he divided it into a third it still sounded pleasant, into a quarter it sounded pleasant, but if he divided it into other ratios or at some random point, the note produced didn't work well; it didn't sound good with the other notes.

The earliest mathematicians were interested in number theory; Pythagoras, Euclid and their followers discovered many interesting numeric properties, such as π (pi), the 3-4-5 triangle and the concept of ratios.

And this wasn't just about music; he and his fellow Greeks developed theories of the universe around these sort of concepts. They thought the universe consisted of concentric spheres and that the sizes of these spheres were in the ratio of the harmonics; one, then a half, then a third, then a quarter, then a fifth and so on. Their buildings were built on harmonic principles, so the heights of the openings were three or five times the width, in exact proportion. Pythagoras discovered this basic physical principle of ratios, and this turns up in a lot of different areas. We're going to be talking about dimmer harmonics, but these same principles can be use to explain why traffic bunches when it goes through tunnels, why raindrops coalesce in a certain pattern, and how to measure the breaking strain of 100 logs without breaking all of them, so it's a really fundamental basic physical phenomenon.

These special numbers appear again and again in the real world; there are many real-world phenomena based on 'magic' ratios – and harmonics is one of them.

Pythagoras discovered that if notes are related to each other by a simple ratio, like they're double, or three or four or five times, and you play them together, it sounds good; it's music. If they're not related by those ratios, they sound bad and the reason is that they don't work with each other, they don't resonate with each other. They never line up; the different notes never line up. We don't build musical instruments because we want to make them sound nice; we made musical instruments in the first instance out of what we could find, like a tube or a stretched string, and those natural things have the harmonic series built into them as a physical underlying principle.

So if you take the military bugle for instance – it's an instrument which is just a tube wrapped up on itself, with no valves or anything to alter the note – the only notes you can get out of it are the *harmonic series*, multiples of the wave corresponding to the full length of the tube. And if you blow harder you get the wave corresponding to half the length, and a third, then a quarter, then a fifth, and so on. That's why military bugle music all sounds a bit the same. All of the music is produced from the natural harmonic series and the relationship in music is this: the fundamental, the double, which is in other words halving the length of the string or the tube; three times, a third, which produces an interval of a fifth, and these are all musical intervals until you get up to quite high harmonics and then they don't kind of sound right any more.

I can demonstrate this. Pythagoras got a string – this is the length of the string, the part that can vibrate – and he hung it over two pivots with weights on the ends. If I vibrate it and place my finger halfway along the open string but without pressing hard, just to stop that initial wave, you get the next harmonic, that's the second harmonic, so that's a half the length; a third of the length, a quarter, a fifth, a sixth, a seventh and so on. It's the same as the bugle notes but coming off a string.

Basically harmonics are complete waves that fit into a given length and, in the case of musical instruments, a string or a tube. But you could also think of it as fitting into a given amount of time as well as, for example if you're drawing a waveform as occurring through time. The basic wave is known as the fundamental, one cycle of the

Adam Bennette
Adam is currently the Technical Director of ETC Europe Ltd. Prior to this, he was the Product Manager at ARRI GB. Adam started in the industry in 1975 building dimmers and lighting rock bands, moved on to work with several production companies and was involved in the early development of DMX512. He is the author of the DMX Recommended Practice Booklet. His interest in power harmonics spans many years and for several of them he was the PLASA representative on the BSI EMC committee.

sine wave, the second harmonic which is double the frequency, the third is three times, the fourth is four times, and so on. And it's the mixture of harmonics in a musical note that gives an instrument its quality, whether it sounds like a flute or a clarinet or an electric guitar. It's the proportions of those higher harmonics that give an instrument its sound quality.

Sine waves have 3 basic characteristics: the frequency, the amplitude and phase. And the phase is very important when you're studying harmonics in an electrical context. All of the harmonics are sine waves, at higher frequencies than the basic wave.

Frequency – How fast it repeats.
Amplitude – How big or loud is it.
Phase – When it starts at zero compared to other waves.

We've done the Greeks and the guitar, so now the Frenchman. This is Fourier, who was a mathematician who discovered a way of describing any wave, no matter how complex it is. Providing it repeats exactly, periodically, you can take one section of this repeating wave and decompose it into a series of sine waves. You start with the wave that exactly fits the period of time which is the fundamental, and then the next one up which is double, three times, four times and so on. He worked out the maths of how to reverse-calculate that for a random wave, which I'm not going to even attempt to explain. But actually, it's sort of obvious that in a given period of time, if a wave is repeating exactly, then the only things that can fit in between those two times must fit exactly, because they then have to repeat again. So an apparently jagged waveform like that of the word "Hello!" must consist of elements that fit exactly into that time.

What Fourier worked out was how to figure out which sine waves are present and what

their values are. If you have that information you can actually reconstruct the original waveform by literally adding together sine waves. That's what I've done on this next example. I recorded my voice for only half a second because it's very, very computer-intensive, and also very low quality because I had to keep the number of samples down so the computer could manage it. That was then put through Fourier's maths to produce a list of all of the waves present. There isn't really any such a thing as the zero harmonic – it's there for completeness – but it's actually equivalent to DC in electrical terms. The fundamental wave fits the entire length of the recording; and then there are the first, second, third harmonics and so on. I did this with 1,000 harmonics. Then taking information about those 1,000 sine waves, I reconstructed them all, added them all together, and produced a fairly accurate replica of the original sound, which is totally synthetic; it's made by a computer adding up numbers.

Now we move on to dimmers. Dimmers are just switches; they switch the power on and off once in each half-cycle, and the proportion of time-on to time-off determines the dimmer level. This happens very fast, so the light looks like it's set to a faded level. The mains power is a sine wave, so the output of the dimmer is the same sine wave as the mains power but with part of it chopped off. So Fourier's theorem means that you can decompose that waveform into a series of harmonics; and the illustrations on the right of the next page show what these look like.

The first and major amplitude signal is the 50 cycles (hertz); 50 cycles is the basic fundamental of the supply mains in Europe. Dimmers, for reasons I won't go into, produce only odd-numbered harmonics because of the switching edge. Then there's quite a lot of the 3rd harmonic, the 5th and 7th. A curious effect there; both 5th and 7th are exactly the same amplitude. Then 9, 11, 13, 15 and so on up the series of the odd-numbered harmonics, more or less infinitely. But they become a bit irrelevant much after this; there's not much power in those above the 15th harmonic.

If we look at the phases, notice that the phase of the fundamental waveform has been shifted, as Mark pointed out, so when you've got a dimmer set to a level other than full even the fundamental gets phase-shifted, apart from all the other harmonics.

A small part of the Fourier transform of the waveform of the spoken word "Hello!"

h#	data	dc adj	fft	real	phase	corr ph.
0	350	328.3936	0	0	0	0
1	-757	-778.606	-43673.9079271154-12459.7947419478i	22.17602	-164.077	-74.077
2	482	460.3936	-99435.7857255847-8438.14323816956i	48.72714	-175.149	-85.1495
3	504	482.3936	-8427.42615442381+148430.93558201i	72.59277	93.24958	183.2496
4	26	4.393555	96589.4271958697-75740.9016614874i	59.93382	-38.1019	51.89812
5	-726	-747.606	58302.4839238027+5725.49751309779i	28.60495	5.608652	95.60865
6	-512	-533.606	22534.2658126392-12538.5683420947i	12.59168	-29.0925	60.90746
7	1108	1086.394	-3405.83814483798-22967.8647648283i	11.33741	-98.4348	-8.43476
8	1442	1420.394	18432.0914790951+2760.68864300082i	9.100433	8.518225	98.51822
9	-56	-77.6064	-7029.36591808023-15324.9871666573i	8.232532	-114.64	-24.6403
10	-1070	-1091.61	15317.5730572437-6687.79411822591i	8.161087	-23.5865	66.41347
11	-657	-678.606	-18602.8871859928+9471.366172811141i	10.19297	153.0178	243.0178
12	445	423.3936	18160.3637664766-4075.28137245725i	9.087893	-12.6479	77.35205
13	1331	1309.394	17901.5872691977+3166.46374611738i	8.876697	10.03082	100.0308
14	-926	-947.606	9509.6157769841-5966.08448390297i	5.48153	-32.1031	57.89691
15	-4367	-4388.61	-160.925353873552-658.232141353666i	0.330868	-103.738	-13.7383

You've also got the 3rd harmonic at about 90° out of phase; 5th harmonic is at −90° out of phase, and so on.

We can add these harmonics together as I did with the audio recording of my voice. With just the 1st and the 3rd, it doesn't really look much like a dimmer set to half. But you add more of them and it starts to look like the real thing. With 127 harmonics, it starts to look pretty much like the output of a dimmer. And this is just done by adding sine waves together.

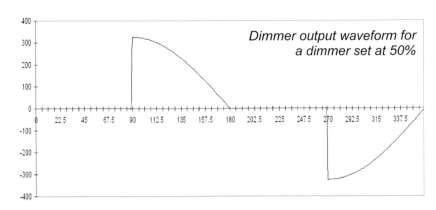

Dimmer output waveform for a dimmer set at 50%

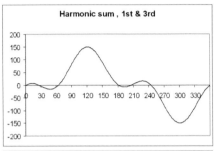

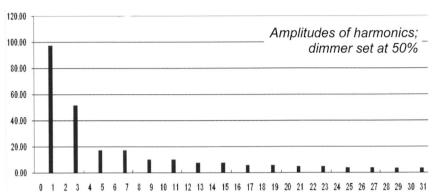

Amplitudes of harmonics; dimmer set at 50%

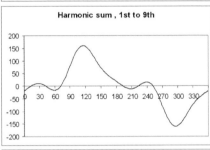

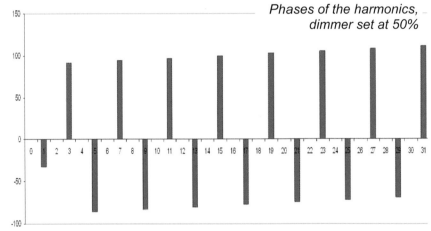

Phases of the harmonics, dimmer set at 50%

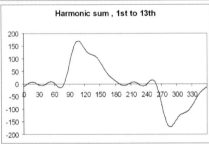

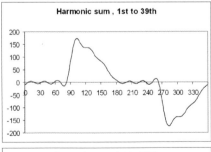

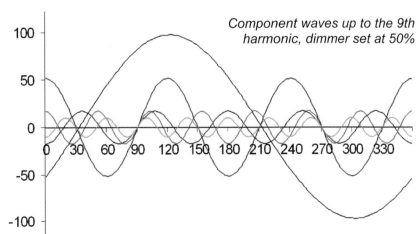

Component waves up to the 9th harmonic, dimmer set at 50%

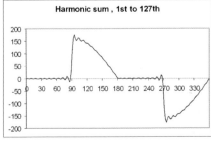

The construction of the dimmer output waveform from the harmonics.

A dimmer is only a single-phase device but large dimmer racks spread the load across the three phases. With various dimmer settings the current in the neutral can exceed the line current.

The supply voltage coming from the power company is pretty much a sine wave. But the current consumed by the dimmer is not. The current is being switched on and off, and it contains all of those harmonics we just defined. Because there are resistances between the point of supply and the equipment, those currents will produce harmonic voltages; they will produce voltages basically of these waveforms in various parts of the wiring and in transformers and in anything that has a resistance between the generator in the power station and the load equipment. These currents are really a problem for the power-generating people, essentially because they have to deliver heavy currents into their wiring systems. For the companies to try and compensate for them uses up money and power and so on. These harmonic voltages are problematic for a range of equipment connected to the power supply as it can misbehave if distortion is present. Dimmers don't like to have distortion around the zero-crossing point because they can't synchronise properly and they flicker.

The supply voltage is a sine wave, but the current consumed by the dimmer is not! To summarise:

- when you pass a current through a resistance you get a voltage.

- All power wiring has resistance, right back to the generator in the power station

- So drawing a harmonic current produces harmonic voltages in the supply system

Harmonic *currents* are problematic for the supply industry.

Harmonic *voltages* are problematic for equipment (especially dimmers as they rely on zero-cross synchronisation).

Why is the neutral getting hot?

Now a point slightly out of sequence, actually, but this is an effect that you may have heard about, which is a bit odd and important. In a normal power system you can expect that the currents on the different phases will cancel or partly cancel in the neutral, and the neutral will either have no current in it at all (if there's perfect cancellation), or some current up to the worst case when there is no cancellation. This is because you're drawing everything on one phase and so the neutral current is the same as the line current. If you have a number of dimmers on each phase which

chop up the waveform and they are set to different levels, the neutral current can actually go <u>higher</u> than any of the phase currents. The diagram above represents the neutral current with one dimmer set to full on one phase, one dimmer on another set to half, and the other phase is not used. The neutral current, if you only have the one dimmer at full, would be just the same as the phase current. But because you're turning on another dimmer at half, it's adding to the neutral, not cancelling out, and the end result is that the neutral, in this case, is about 25% higher than the phase. So if you've got, say, a 3 × 100A service in the theatre, and you set your dimmers like this – everything on Phase 1 at full, everything on Phase 2 at 90° and nothing on Phase 3 – you will have 125A in the neutral, and the circuit breaker might open or even the wiring might fail.

Harmonics are bad because they cause losses and the currents cause heating in the supply system. The supply grid, intercity wiring and so on, have got a tendency to resonate at the 5th harmonic. The electricity supply people don't like the 5th harmonic; that's the one that causes them the most problems. They install great banks of capacitors in various locations to try and deal with this. And in one case, several years ago, one of those banks of capacitors blew up, because of excessive 5th harmonics.

There are also problems in transformer equipment; some of the harmonics get absorbed in the substation transformer, basically the ones that are called the *triplins*, which are 3, 9, 15, 21 and so on. Some of these get absorbed in the transformer, some of them get back into the national grid, some get back into the generating systems, and they all cause problems. They also cause problems within a theatre facility because, as I said, a 4-pole breaker rated 100A feeding a dimming system may actually be required to deliver 125A on the neutral. To put it another way, you can actually get out of that supply through the breaker only 80% of what you thought you could. And the neutral wiring can get hot. It's all to do with harmonic currents.

Harmonic voltages can cause problems in user equipment. AC motors, for instance, can overheat as they have a tendency to absorb harmonics. That's actually quite a positive thing about AC motors, providing they can tolerate the absorption, they have the effect of cleaning the system. But that's only if your using completely conventional magnetic AC motors. Then you've got power-factor circuits that can go wrong, as they don't like harmonics.

The position in law is that harmonics are tolerated from phase-angle dimmers because it is the prevailing technology and if they had been forbidden there wouldn't be any dimming, for the most part. So while it is permitted to connect this harmonic polluting equipment, you have to have both a concession from the electricity authority, and a low enough impedance power supply to minimise the harmonic voltage.

You can measure harmonics; it is possible to purchase a meter with probes that you just put on your facility and it will give you readings directly of how many percent of which given harmonic you've got.

Total harmonic distortion (THD) is a term that you might come across. And unlike normal ranges of distortion, in this case it can go above 100%. It's the proportion of harmonics relative to the fundamental. If you don't have much fundamental, the THD can be very high. If you've got *no* fundamental, the THD can be infinite.

You can't eliminate harmonic current coming out of a phase-angle dimmer. There is nothing that can be done about it. You can't filter it; there's nothing you can do. What you can do is you can minimise the effect that it has on the system in producing harmonic voltages that can interfere with equipment, and essentially you do that by getting the impedance of the power supply as low as possible. Filtering doesn't work, because the harmonics vary according to the settings of the dimmers. If you designed a filter that was tuned for, say, the 3rd harmonic, to reject it at one level, you could set all your dimmers at another level and the harmonics would all be completely out of phase, and that filter could, in fact, make the situation worse. It could even resonate and actually produce more pollution. And in any case, it would be absurdly big – by which I don't mean the size of a dimmer rack, I mean the size of the whole dimmer room – to filter the sort of currents that are often in use in theatres.

Large installations must obtain consent from the electricity supplier:

- The supplier has the right to refuse connection of a large dimmer system to an unsuitable supply.

- The criteria measured is the 'RSCE' or the ratio of short-circuit current to service current. High short-circuit current indicates a low supply impedance.

A low-impedance supply is the most important aspect in a new theatre building or in a new installation of dimming equipment. You need to have a very direct route with heavy wiring to the substation transformer. There are other systems available. The Royal Opera House, for instance, has a very large power supply system which is feeding IT equipment and machinery and so on. It has harmonic cancelling amplifiers installed. These are devices that sense what is being put onto the mains as a harmonic current and literally inject the reverse phase current of that particular harmonic to cancel it out. They're quite expensive, they're quite difficult to set up and they're not really necessary if you've got a good low-impedance supply.

You may come across harmonic cancelling transformers, but in fact they don't work with dimmers; they're designed for fixed loads, and like filtering they can make things worse on dimmers because they won't be tuned for every possible combination of harmonics and levels from the dimmer. Passive harmonic filters based on chokes and capacitors and line conditioners will also not work with the huge variation of harmonic phases and levels from dimmers.

Also, do ensure you oversize the neutral. There could be 25% more current on the neutral than you calculate for the phases. Specify over-sized neutrals; at least the next size up from the calculated correct size for the phases. Use 3-pole circuit breakers with hard neutrals or, if you're going to use a 4-pole circuit breaker expect it to have only about 80% of its rating. And run private wiring for dimming separated from other supplies to prevent pollution interference. Run separate feeds for the dimmers all the way from the 'point of common coupling'. And if you are providing new supply transformers, specify 'K' rated types with enhanced harmonic tolerance.

> The supplier has the right to refuse connection of a large dimmer system to an unsuitable supply.

Trailing-edge dimmers, which turn the current off, create an identical problem. It's absolutely the same situation, it's just the phases of the harmonics are opposite. So the phase is inverted; everything else is the same, the levels and relative proportions of them are all the same. Trailing-edge dimmers offer no improvement at all in low-frequency harmonic emissions. They may offer some reduction in higher-frequency harmonics, but at the expense of greater heat output.

So now to the last element of my title, the pretzel. If you plot a given harmonic from the dimmer you get a pretzel! The illustrations show the 5th, with its zero-zero point in the centre of the graph. As you increase the level, the distance from the centre represents the value, the magnitude of the harmonic, and the angle around it represents the phase. So as you increase the level of a dimmer, the diagrams show what happens to the harmonic.

The real big peak is when the dimmer is set to half, with quite a lot of 5th harmonic which keeps increasing in level until you get up to full. Then there are no harmonics; it's just on, like a switch. What this means is that if you had a dimmer set, for instance, to fire at 140°, which is quite dim, and another one set down at around 97½°, the 5th harmonic from those two dimmers would more or less cancel. Another pretzel shows the 7th harmonic, where the same sort of thing happens. As you increase the level, the magnitude of the harmonic changes and its phase rotates around this graph.

This means that you can get some cancellation. Bigger dimming systems are never going to produce as much harmonic pollution as a single dimmer, as shown in the example; one channel set to half, large amount of 5th harmonic, you add another

channel set to about three-quarters, assume four channels here, and another five there. Under these conditions, the 5th harmonic has almost gone.

Remember that the phase of the harmonics depends on the dimmer level:

- Harmonics of similar amplitude but opposite phase cancel each other.
- As more channels are added, each with different levels, some harmonic cancellation will occur.
- The worst case of all channels on at half is unlikely to happen often in a real lighting rig.
- It is more likely that *some* cancellation will occur.

What this means is that, in practice, you can't have the slightest idea of what the harmonics are going to be on a multi-channel dimming system. We're considering just two channels here and it's getting complicated; if you've got hundreds of channels there is no way of figuring it out. You're going to have completely random sets of harmonic pollution throughout the course of a play or a show.

A few words in closing about sine-wave dimmers. They don't produce any low-frequency harmonics at all, because they're effectively just varying the height of a sine wave. But they've got some problems. They're quite expensive; they're quite complicated; they produce harmonic output at very, very much higher frequencies up in the radio spectrum, which means they're very difficult to suppress and they have to be installed with great care. And if you take the other precautions of low-impedance power supply, sensible wiring practices, you don't really need them to deal with harmonic problems although they may have other benefits. Thank you. Ω

Multi-channel chaos (or "help yourself to a pretzel...")

Harmonic "pretzels" with cancelling imaginary components of current marked.

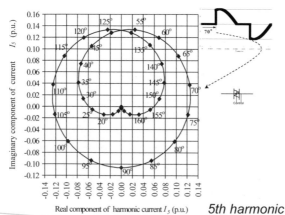

5th harmonic

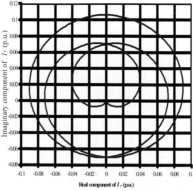

7th harmonic

Pretzels courtesy Ralf Gretsch

Second speaker: Steve Barker

I'd like to build on what Adam's told you about single-phase harmonics and then expand that a little bit to cover three-phase harmonics. And as a specific example, I'm going to talk about variable-speed drives, inverters, adjustable-speed drives, whatever you tend to call them. I'm the Business Manager of Siemens variable-speed drives in the UK, so you can see why this is such an important issue for me.

First, a very brief instruction to variable-speed drives. I'll also cover some of the practical and regulatory issues regarding harmonics, then review some of the harmonic elimination techniques that are available to us, and give you a quick comparison of some of these techniques.

But why do we use variable-speed drives? At the end of the day it's really all about improved motion control in some form or other. Very often, compared to other, older techniques, typically mechanical or hydraulic methods for example, electrical variable speed drives offer a reduced maintenance requirement, and quite often also give a longer system life. We tend to talk about totally integrated automation as well, because with these new electronic devices it's very easy to integrate them into your overall control scheme. Within the electronic variable speed drive you've also got comprehensive motor protection, so you don't need to introduce that in addition.

One of the biggest uses at the moment of variable speed drives is actually in energy-saving applications, predominantly with fans in ventilation systems, where we can often reduce the flow and save significant amounts of energy.

Typical sorts of applications are, therefore, ventilation control, air conditioning, pump control, refrigeration compressors, and similar. Some of the more esoteric applications include power flying hoist systems where you need a full range of variable speed. This is quite a difficult application – it's fairly dynamic, you've got to be able to hold the load, so you need electrical braking – but it's something that we can accommodate quite easily with modern equipment. Any kind of stage control system is moving more towards the variable-speed electronic drive control.

There are other topologies of variable-frequency drives but the diagram probably

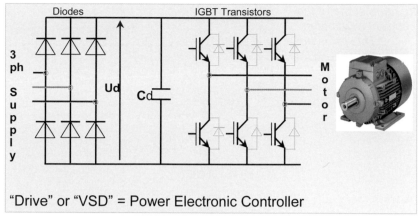

"Drive" or "VSD" = Power Electronic Controller

This can also be single phase for low power ratings!

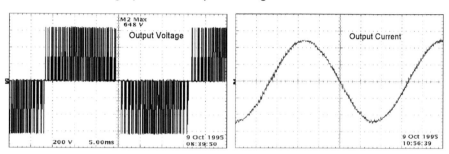

A basic variable-speed drive and the output voltage and current waveforms made up of many fully-controlled pulses.

covers 99% of those which are in use today. Just to give a very brief overview, what we do is we take the power supply, in this case three-phase although there are also single-phase units for lower-power applications. We simply rectify the AC into a fixed DC voltage, so in effect it's almost like a large battery. We then use the output transistors, IGBTs as we call them, to switch that fixed DC voltage in certain patterns and sequences onto the motor.

The output voltage of such a device is a whole series of individual output pulses. We have full control of all these output pulses, both in terms of the width of the pulse and also we can turn it into the negative direction, so you can see that we've actually synthesised a positive and negative half-cycle. This waveform is pretty much in block format at the moment, but when we actually connect it to the motor, because the motor consists of a lot of windings and therefore has a high inductance, by the time that the actual current flows it's fairly sinusoidal. At the end of the day what we're trying to achieve with variable-frequency control of a motor is to provide the motor with a variable-voltage, variable-frequency supply. And that's what this topology does.

Steve Barker is a Chartered Electrical Engineer who graduated in 1984 in Electrical and Electronic Engineering. He has been working in electrical drives and automation for some 18 years, the last 12 years of which he has been with Siemens. He has experience of the special needs of drives for theatres, has been Chairman of the Variable Speed Drives Group of GAMBICA and is a past leader of IEC WG26 on Inverter Driven Motors.

The practical effects of harmonics on the supply and, right, some of the current regulations. This list is not exhaustive!

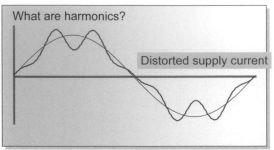

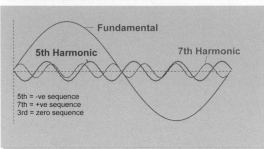

We've already seen the effects of harmonics, and the purple line on the waveform above shows the distorted input-current wave form, for example, to a drive. Adam also showed you the principle of superposition whereby we can separate out the individual harmonics and put them back together again. This example that I've shown here is based on a very simple example with only 5th and 7th harmonics. I'll show you later the typical sort of harmonics which you do get with a three-phase drive.

Why do we worry about these harmonics? Well, the actual harmonic voltages which can be present on your power supply can cause other equipment to malfunction, and there's no way of knowing exactly what's causing the problem or predicting what the problem will be. Power-factor correction capacitors, as Adam mentioned, can literally explode, which is quite dangerous. Energy meters can read incorrectly and, of course, you've probably guessed that they read in the wrong direction, so you pay more rather than less, unfortunately. If you have harmonics, then any transformers have to supply the additional harmonic currents as well as the sinusoidal current, therefore you have to effectively over-rate the transformers.

Additional harmonic currents will also create additional harmonic losses in your system, and will therefore reduce your overall system efficiency. We've heard about problems with excess neutral currents, and they have been a real problem where people have undersized their neutrals. There are problems with

lighting equipment, more particularly things like fluorescent lights, which can be quite susceptible.

The relevant authorities are quite worried about these losses from a power-system point of view, and there is a whole plethora of standards and regulations which try to regulate the amount of pollution, particularly that which users can actually transmit back into the mains power supply. Because the electricity providers have a duty to supply good quality power to the next consumer, they have to introduce requirements to control the harmonics which you generate back into the supply. And we can do that, actually, in three ways. First of all we can control harmonics at the product level, and there are certain product standards which limit harmonics. Last year, Regulation G5/4 was introduced, and then there is the utility level, EN 50160, which is concerned with the actual quality of the supply. There's a whole number of these, but there's nothing that actually specifies what the harmonic distortion should be inside your building. But you do need to worry about that because it can cause you problems like reducing the life of equipment and so on.

How do we cope with these problems? One solution which has been mentioned is to have a very strong power supply, and a strong power supply is characterised by

Harmonic Mitigation Techniques

➢ Very strong power supplies!
   (high fault levels)
➢ Parallel passive filtering
➢ Increase converter "pulse number"
➢ Clean Power Technology
➢ Active filtering
➢ Common DC bus solutions......

one that has a high fault level. It's not always too easy to actually modify what your supplier is giving you, unless you're prepared to pay a lot of money, but it's worth bearing in mind. Parallel passive filtering, increasing the converter-pulse number, active filtering, common DC bus solutions; I'll mention some of these in little bit more detail.

Parallel Tuned Filters

There are many designs, but typically these are based on circuits which effectively conduct the harmonic currents away from the mains supply. The problem with these is that they need a very careful design. It's very rare that you would have the correct system parameters, to the required accuracy, to enable a good filter design, so you have to incorporate a lot of compromises, otherwise you're likely to introduce resonance rather than get rid of it. Because they're essentially capacitive, you can introduce some capacitive-reactive power, which may be a good thing if your power supply is poor. Resonance can be a major problem. If you have many different filters all in the same installation, you can get a lot of problems with the filters interfering with each other and, of course, they are not cheap, either.

Twelve-pulse Drive Solution

As far as the drives and some of the power electronic equipment is concerned, we can increase the pulse numbers. If you contrast

this with the original diagram that I showed of the drive, we've now introduced a second rectifier section. What we do with the second rectifier section is to feed it, essentially, with a phase-shifted supply. And by feeding the two bridges from a supply which is phase-shifted by 30° from each other, we can demonstrate some cancellation of harmonics.

I'm showing here a typical induction motor, but it could as well be a servo motor by the way for motion-control type applications. This is a 12-pulse scenario, but sometimes, in special cases, we can extend that to 18- or even 24-pulse. These start to get a little bit elaborate and there are better solutions.

Graphs of the idealised harmonic current spectra are on the right. I say 'idealised' as these are based on theoretical calculations using Fourier analysis. For the 5th harmonic the theoretical value of at least 20% is basically the reciprocal of the number 1/5, so the 7th harmonic would be 14%, the 11th would be 9% and so forth. That's the theoretical evaluation for a six-pulse drive. On a 12-pulse unit, we get some cancellation, so, theoretically, the 5th and the 7th would cancel. The 17th and the 19th would also in theory cancel. The 11th and the 13th would remain, but they were smaller than the 5th and the 7th in the first place. This is a widely used technique overall for higher-power variable-speed drives.

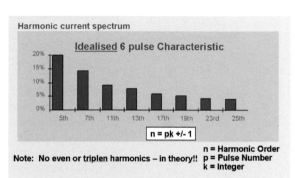

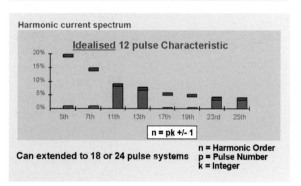

Left: parallel tuned filter circuit and right: a twelve-pulse drive.

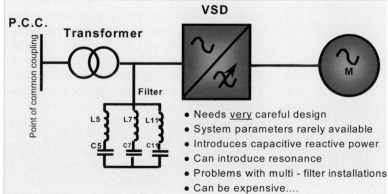

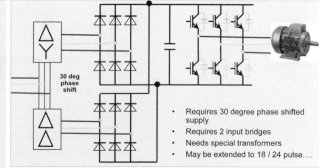

Fast internal switching together with a special filter ensures a near perfect sinusoidal current waveform is drawn from the supply...

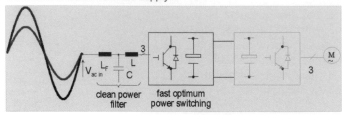

clean power filter

fast optimum power switching

- Harmonic distortion is negligible under all conditions
- No complex harmonic filters or 12/24 pulse solutions......

Harmonic Current Distortion - Example

Harmonic Number (Hz) on 50 Hz supply	6 pulse	6 Pulse with reactor	12 Pulse	CPT
5th (250Hz)	50%	28%	2.5%	0.98%
7th (350Hz)	29%	11%	1.2%	0.87%
11th (550Hz)	9.0%	9.5%	9.0%	0.26%
13th (650Hz)	6.2%	3.9%	7.1%	0.05%
17th (850Hz)	3.4%	5.5%	0.3%	0.40%
19th (950Hz)	1.9%	3.5%	0.3%	0.05%
23rd (1150Hz)	2.1%	3.9%	3.3%	0.07%
25th (1250Hz)	1.5%	1.8%	2.9%	0.02%

Examples only - actual values depend on product design and system characteristics

A Clean Power Technology Drive (CPT) and a comparison of harmonic current distortion for different drives.

Clean Power Technology

In terms of newer technology, we have a design called Clean Power Technology. Rather than mitigating the effect of the harmonics once we've created them, with this type of design we don't actually create the harmonics in the first place. Compared with the original drive diagram, we've replaced the rectifier section, which was constructed with typical diode rectifiers, with high-speed transistor rectifiers. The design of that and the associated software is quite complicated, but the effect is that we actually draw a sinusoidal current from the supply.

There are other added benefits of this technology: it's very tolerant of power-supply disturbances. It can easily ride through power dips and so forth. It's inherently regenerative, so for braking applications like hoists it's absolutely ideal. Normally we set it to take a unity power factor, but we can actually control the power factor to be basically whatever you like. One possibility would therefore be to oversize the drive, and use part of the rating of the drive as power-factor correction which will work independently of the actual drive operation.

With this type of product the harmonic distortion is negligible under all conditions. And there is no need any of the complex arrangements with 12- or 24-pulse systems or any of the additional parallel filters. So this is probably the solution of the future, certainly in higher power ratings.

The table above summarises harmonic current distortion. A three-phase drive without a line reactor on the input side creates, typically, a 5th harmonic current of 50%, a 7th of 29% and so on. If we add a line reactor, which is always a good thing to do, you can see that there's quite a significant reduction in the harmonic currents which are generated.

When we move to a 12-pulse design, nothing is actually 100% perfect, so you do get what we call a 'spill' of harmonics left, for example, on the 5th and the 7th. Typically you get approximately 10% of the 6-pulse value, so this gives 2.5%, and 1.2%, but still quite a dramatic reduction. With the clean power technology it's hardly worth measuring.

To show you how that relates to actual voltage distortion – which is what will actually cause practical problems in your building – the graph on the next page is an example with a 132 kW inverter. The blue shows the 6-pulse harmonic voltages, the green shows the 12-pulse. The tiny red blip at the bottom is the harmonic voltage distortion using clean power technology. That is the dramatic kind of difference that you get using the clean power techniques.

I've already mentioned what we describe as active filtering, which is possibly a good solution in some cases for three-phrase applications. On the opposite page is an example with a number of harmonic generating devices like variable-speed drives, with a representation of what the input current might look like. What we can do is introduce the so-called *active filter* solution. What the active filter does is to monitor what is happening on the network, and then feed back impulses of voltage to basically counteract the unwanted distortion that is being produced. The original load current is shown on the graph which also shows the spikes on that waveform. The active filter is measuring this and is injecting current in anti-phase. When these are added up on the actual network current, it cancels out. The good thing about active filtering is that the equipment is very easy to retro-fit after an initial installation and, once you've got the equipment on site, the compensation is very programmable, variable and flexible.

To give you a feeling as to what your overall strategy should be, we suggest that you should identify and characterise the possible harmonic sources. Remember there are differences between three-phase and single-phase devices, and take account of whatever you have. And remember that just about anything you've got in your installations, anything electronic, is going to generate harmonics of some description.

Calculate the distortion levels in the system; there are software tools available to do that. Are you likely to have any harmonic problems? If you are, then look at the possible methods of controlling those harmonics, whether it be clean power units, 12-pulse devices, additional filters, or whatever. And once you've installed the equipment, it's always wise to go back and do some measurements and confirm that you have actually achieved the harmonic reduction you expected.

Where can you get further information? 'Gambica' is the trade association for industrial control and automation. Through them we produced a guide to managing harmonics. It's specifically a reference to the UK regulations G5/4, but you will find a lot of other useful information in there. You can actually download it as a PDF file from their website: www.gambica.org.uk.

In conclusion, variable-speed drives can offer significant application benefits, including energy savings particularly for fan

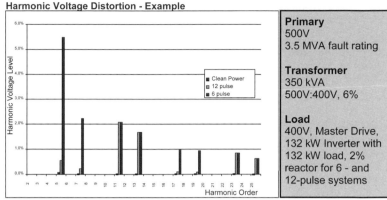

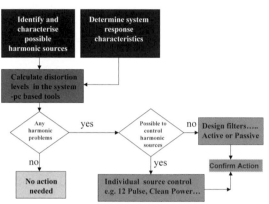

Comparisons of Harmonic Voltage Distortion showing the benefits of Clean Power Technology and the logic of a design process to reduce the effects of harmonics.

and certain pump-type applications. But do remember that all non-linear loads produce harmonics in the supply that you need to take into consideration. And those harmonic disturbances can cause problems. You need to think of harmonics as the low-frequency equivalent of EMC. They're just two elements of the same phenomenon.

Observe the regulatory requirements such as G5/4 here in the UK, IEEE 519 that they have in the States and whatever applies in your country. I've mentioned the traditional solutions such as 12-pulse drives and passive filters, but do consider some of the newer techniques like the clean power drives and active filters. A knowledge of these new techniques can actually save you a lot of money, a lot of trouble and lot of time in the long run.

My final point would be just to say that harmonics are a potential problem. They're just one of a number of design considerations that, as design engineers, we need to take into account when we're designing our systems. Thank you very much. Ω

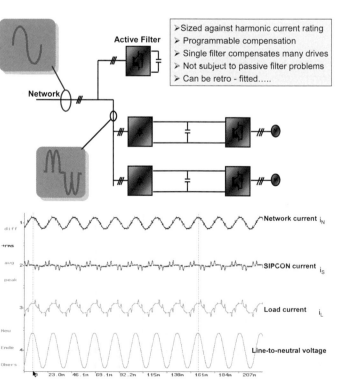

The circuit of a typical Active Filter with the resultant current and voltage waveforms.

David Chapman
trained as an electrical engineer and spent several years in research into dielectrics for power capacitors and cables. His career experience includes early work on optical fibre communication systems, electronic hardware and software design, and project and general management. Five years ago he returned to the power engineering field with a particular interest in power quality issues. He is the co-author of several of the Copper Development Association publications, including *Electrical Design – A Good Practice Guide* and presents the CDA's *Harmonics in Power Installations* seminars.

Third speaker: Dave Chapman

The Copper Development Association promotes the use of copper. So I'm very pleased to hear about all these low-impedance supplies that we need to install in order to get rid of the harmonics – very pleased indeed!

I'm going to talk about earthing, which of course is another subject we're interested in, although doing this in 20 minutes is perhaps something of a challenge; 20 hours might be more appropriate; we'd probably need 40 speakers to do it justice. All I can hope to give you is an overview of some of the problems that you might face, and perhaps give you an idea of an approach that you can use when thinking about earthing.

The first priority for earthing is *safety*. This is pretty well understood – basically people know what they're doing these days. The second consideration is *protection*, that's protection against overcurrent and, of course, fault currents and protection against lightning and transients. In the UK, lightning protection is not a really big issue, but it is serious in many parts of the world, so it is important nevertheless. And the third thing is *functionality*, of course. Earthing is important to ensure electromagnetic compatibility; it's essential that we maintain an equipotential plane – I'll talk about that later – for signal interfaces. And we have to take into account the wide frequency range of signals which are now flowing around our earthing systems, many of them pretty uncontrolled.

There's an alternative way to summarise this basically: No 1 is *safety* (don't kill anybody), No 2 is *protection* (don't burn the theatre down) and the third one is *functionality* (don't stop the show). And they come roughly in that order.

Safety

From the point of view of safety, which is basically shock protection, the important things to consider are proper bonding and proper shielding of live parts. That's understood. But there's another issue, which is becoming more and more important these days, and that's the issue of earth leakage currents. When Adam and Steve were talking about harmonics, just about everything that produces harmonics uses some sort of switch during the cycle. And these items therefore produce fast-rising edges and radio frequency

interference. It's necessary to filter these out, so just about everything that we've been talking about has a filter on the front of it. These are filters which take the high frequencies down to the protective earth line. Because the filter is a capacitor, there's also a small fundamental current flowing in it, about a milliamp, maybe. Its limited by regulations to something quite small, but there will be a few milliamps of fundamental current flowing to ground. For three-phase devices, that's not too important because it's balanced and the current is cancelled out. With single-phase systems, it doesn't cancel out, and these currents add, so that you can get quite significant amounts of earth-leakage current flowing in the neutral lines.

Shock hazards

The problem, of course, is that the earth connection is usually a single wire and often quite an ignored single wire. So, if you do have a problem with your earth lead, then you have a potential electrocution situation where the exposed parts will rise to half the supply voltage because of the nature of the filter capacitors. It's a particular problem in installations such as the one we have in this Conference venue where we have a number of multi-way blocks, and I'd take a bet that they're actually connected in series, so that one feeds another, which feeds yet another. So we could quite easily have, perhaps, 10 or 15 milliamps of mains current flowing down the earth. Now if we do get a fault on that earth cable, the earth points of all this equipment will rise to 120V and that's potentially lethal. It's something which is often overlooked; it's covered in the Regulations, and it's something that really needs to be looked at quite carefully. The relevant section of the Wiring Regulations in the UK is 607; the European regulations are not yet so strong, but the next edition will be, so it becomes a world standard issue ultimately. So it's worth thinking about earth leakage when you are installing equipment such as this.

Fault currents

That deals with the shock hazard. As far as overcurrent is concerned, the important thing is that the fault current can flow. It's the fault current flowing which causes overload on the current-overload device – the circuit-breaker or the fuse – and removes the voltage and therefore the source of danger. So the important things are that we have low impedance to ground, a low loop impedance around the system, and that the current overload devices have been chosen with proper discrimination in mind, so that when you have a fault on a sub-circuit you take out only the sub-circuit, not the whole theatre.

Systems of earthing

I want to have a quick look at the systems of earthing that are in normal use. These are the systems that are defined by standards, and they're also the ones in common use. Just quick word about the nomenclature: the T here is from the French for earth, *terre*, so if we just replace the T by 'earth' it's easy to translate what they mean.

In the first case (1), TN-S, it means that the neutral conductor is earthed and it is are brought into the installation separately. So we have here a five-wire system; we have red, yellow and blue phases, a neutral and a green earth, all brought in separately. Neutral and earth are connected at the source of supply and not anywhere else. The 'equipment' is meant to represent the whole of the installation. There is a point of common coupling at which the supplier's responsibility ends and the installation's responsibility begins. The advantage of the TN-S system is, of course, that you have a nice metallic conductor right back to the source of energy which has been provided by the supplier at the same time as the electricity supply and therefore is properly rated to give you a low loop impedance. So it's a robust system. But of course it's more expensive because it's five-wire not four-wire, and you can have quite a long earth path, which can have integrity issues. You can also have EMC issues because you've got a long single wire which has inductance.

The next system (2), TN-C, is the earthed neutral with combined wire, so we have a four-wire system, the neutral being earthed back at the supply and at many points along its path; but there is no separate earth connection. This is not used in the UK, but is used in many parts of Europe. It's lower-cost; it has the advantage of having many points of connection to earth, so it offers a quite low earth impedance. But there are EMC issues with it, because the installation also has a common neutral and ground and therefore you have neutral currents flowing in the earth wiring, which is never good news. And also you have

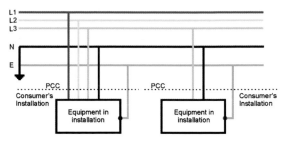

Earthing System 1
TN-S
+ *Dedicated metallic earth return*
− *More expensive for Supplier*
− *Long earth path, low integrity*

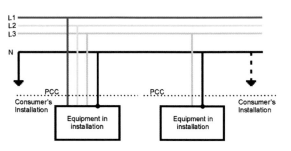

Earthing System 2
TN-C
+ *Lower cost*
+ *Multiple earth connections*
− *EMC issues*
− *Rogue currents in metalwork*

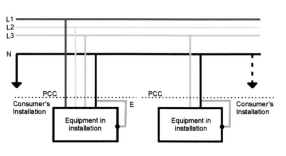

Earthing System 3
TN-C-S
+ *Lower cost*
+ *Multiple earth connections*
+ *Better EMC*
+ *Multiple earth connections*

rogue currents in the metalwork, because most of the metalwork in the building will be grounded somehow, either accidentally or by design, and that means that you can import earth currents from elsewhere, which can flow through the building. That's a bit of an issue with the TN-C systems.

The derivation of this is the TN-C-S system (3). This is a sort of half-way house which has many advantages and is the system used generally in the UK. The neutral is earthed; it's common as far as the supplier is concerned but once it comes into the installation it is separated and remains separated throughout the installation. This is more or less the approach now promoted by international standards, and most other standards will be moving this way in the next few years. It's been the situation in the UK for the best part of 50 years, so we have a lot of experience of using it. In this country it's relatively well implemented, in that the earth and neutral are kept separate once they're inside the installation. In many countries who have a long history of TN-C, installers trying to use TN-C-S are finding it very difficult to ensure that they do keep the earth and neutral separate because they've been so used to considering them as just one wire.

Earthing System 4
TT
+ No rogue currents
– No metallic return
– Good ground
electrode required

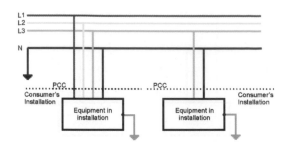

With this system we have the benefit of the lower cost, because it's four-wire, not five-wire. We still have multiple earth connections; we have slightly better EMC conditions, because inside the building we can keep the earth and the neutral separate, we don't get them mixed up. But we still have rogue currents flowing because the metalwork in the building, which is bonded to earth, is sitting in the ground and can pick up other earth currents. This is, however, the system that most of us have to live with.

I'll quickly explain system (4), TT; it's popular still in some countries. In this case, both the supply and the installation have an earth, but they're not the same earth. They're independent. The neutral, which comes into the installation, is earthed by the supplier, but it is not regarded as earth; the earth is provided separately. In this situation, of course, there aren't any rogue currents because you have your own earth. As you can keep this quite clean, it's actually not a bad idea. There is no metallic return and therefore there's no low loop impedance, so you can't rely on over-current protection devices to operate; you have to work on residual current breakers. And if you're actually going to make success of this system, you need a very good ground electrode to keep the impedance down, because it is entirely your responsibility to make sure that you are grounded. You have no other connection to earth, no fall-back.

There is another system, IT, but we won't look at that because it's not very often used.

Functionality

Obviously compliance with Section 607 of the Wiring Regulations here in the UK is also a functional aspect because the leakage current needs to flow from the filter, so that's a bit functional. You need to be careful to make sure that you bond all the metalwork as far as possible directly to the main earth terminal. If you've got a steel structure and it's sitting in the ground,

then you will get currents flowing up the steel structure and back down again because it's an easier path than flowing across all that soil. Beware; if you bond the metalwork randomly, then you'll have currents flowing randomly around it. If you bond it all as it comes out of the ground, straight back to the main earth terminal, then you effectively sweep those currents into the earth terminal and stop them distributing throughout the building.

Obviously it is important to keep the protective earth and the neutral separate – don't go back to TN-C because it's a really bad idea – and keep the earth impedance low. Earth impedance needs to be low over a very wide frequency. What we're really talking about is establishing an *equipotential* plane; it doesn't really matter so much what the equipotential is with regard to true earth – if there's any such thing as true earth – but it does matter that it's the same everywhere at all frequencies, because it's carrying high-frequency noise currents, leakage currents, and the results of filtered transients, and all those have to be conducted away.

Signal transmission

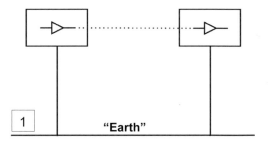

If we look at a simple signal transmission system (1), we have a couple of devices that have to communicate. And we have an ideal equipotential plane. These things are working and therefore we're getting noise currents, we're getting leakage currents, we're getting transients, running down these earth lines to this idealised equipotential earth plane. What's actually happening is that the noise current is flowing through an impedance, partly inductive, partly resistive – and don't forget we're talking about a complete installation here, so this could be a long tree of earth cabling.

So what happens is that we get a noise voltage that appears in the earth side of the device, (2) and (3). When you stick some signals on, it's pretty clear that out of this side of the device you're going to get a signal which is composed not only of the

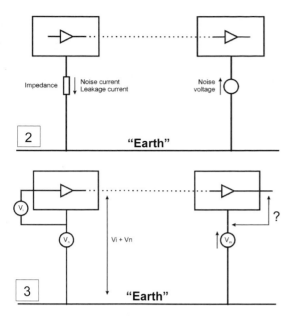

The simple solution is, of course, to use differential signalling as shown above (4). Here we have a differential amplifier, and positive and negative signals that are translated back to a single one on the output. This gives us a degree of improvement, but it's not perfect because this amplifier responds not only to the difference but also to the absolute voltage to ground. So it also sees some of this noise voltage. And it can't be relied on to have a perfect 'common mode rejection ratio', that is rejection of the common mode noise.

But this helps. The fact is that most communication systems work. The reason why they work is because we have designed error-protection coding, which detects errors and corrects them, we've designed software that takes that into account and does retransmission and that

required inputs but also of noise. And by the time you get over to the receiver, well, who knows what you've got? Whether this matters depends on how big this noise voltage is and whether this is an analogue or digital system. It also depends on how much radiated noise you're picking up on the interconnection cables.

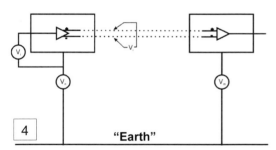

sort of thing, and basically we have covered the issue in other ways. But of course none of this is perfect. Every time you do a retransmission, you're reducing throughput; if it's an analogue signal you're retransmitting the noise that you're getting straight away, so you can cover this to a certain extent. But sometimes, under some circumstances and with some equipment, you just cross the boundary, and a differential amplifier no longer discriminates or the error-correction software no longer copes, and the retransmission rate becomes too high, and everything falls in a heap. And often it's difficult to identify exactly what the last straw was.

You have to look at the earth as a complex impedance carrying a set of complex signals – I couldn't resist 'Ground Rules' for the summary of this! And you have to think very carefully about where your signals are travelling and how they're travelling. It's not enough just to connect to the green wire, basically. You have got to use grids in intensive situations where you really need to keep the EMC under control. Obviously, keep neutral and protective earth separate, keep the ground as clean as you can, and use high-resilience protective conductors. I hope that it's clear that there really is just one ground; there's no such thing as power ground, clean earth, telecoms earth, computer earth. They're all the same thing, because they all go to the same place, and what we have at the end of it all is just a very complex impedance carrying a lot of complex currents and generating a lot of complex voltages! And you have to be very careful how you make your connections to complex system in order to make sure that you don't have problems. Ω

"GROUND" RULES

Low impedance, wide frequency
➢ use grids where required

Keep neutral and PE separate
➢ keep signal grounds clean

Use high resilience PE connections
➢ bond all conduits, trays and ladders
  - but don't rely on them as PE conductors.

Questions and discussion

Don MacLean, Cirque du Soleil

In the discussion about single-phase harmonics and harmonic control, there was one item that we skipped over, which was the K-rated transformer. Could you talk a little bit about the applicability of K-rated transformers to audio mix systems, and the difference between the K13 and K20 and which you feel is more applicable.

Adam Bennette, Speaker

The first thing I'd say is that the K-rated transformer really is an American product, and I'm not aware of them being used here to any significant degree. I looked into this when I was preparing my presentation, and all of the K-rated transformer manufacturers are based in the United States. It seems that the tradition here is to use a normal transformer of a larger size, and a K-rated transformer isn't quite that. It's designed in a different type of construction. It's got a different amount of iron in it, of a different grade, the windings are wound with gaps and it's got a different cooling arrangement, so it can tolerate the kind of heating you get from harmonic currents and still be basically smaller and, I guess, more cost-effective than an oversized conventional transformer.

There are four or five K-ratings that go up to, I think, K20 which is for installations like medical facilities with requirements for exceptionally low harmonic pollution and the ability to absorb quite large harmonic currents from, I guess, X-ray equipment, electron microscopes and other strange equipment. Then there's a one called a K13 transformer, which is rated for slightly less onerous situations. And then as I recall, there's a K5, which is the next one down, and typically, it seems in America, the K5 is being specified, and sometimes the K13, for lighting power supplies. These transformers are basically designed to tolerate the heat and circulating currents due to harmonics and to be effective in size and cost. But they're not in use in Europe as far as I know.

Dave Chapman, Speaker

Can I just add something on that? There is an article on K-rated transformers on our website, www.cda.org.uk. This indicates how to work out what K rating you need, and how to do the calculations.

William Conner, Schuler & Shook

I was curious about the effect of the so-called low-harmonics dimmers where you combine reverse-phase and forward-phase dimmers in the same system. Could you tell us if you looked at that at all, and what its total effect, or its proportional effect is, on harmonics from dimming systems?

Adam Bennette, Speaker

The idea here is that alternate channels are either trailing or leading edge. And so if two channels were set, for instance, to half, one would take the first half of the half-cycle, the other would take the second half of the half-cycle, and the net result would be that between the two of them they would consume exactly a half-cycle's worth of sine-wave current, and in that scenario you'd have no pollution at all. So in principle they offer the possibility of a great deal of cancellation of harmonics. I haven't done an analysis of this, but as you saw from those pretzel diagrams the phase of a given harmonic depends critically on the firing angle, so you will rarely get a situation where the alternative of trailing and leading edge offers proper cancellation. I would argue that it may be just as likely that you would get cancellation on either a fully leading- or a fully trailing-edge design on the basis of different firing angles being set on different channels.

Although in principle, conceptually, it's possible that you could get complete elimination on a trailing/leading-edge mix, that would only be the case if all of the channels on the trailing edge were set to exactly the mirror-image levels of all the channels on the leading edge, which will never happen in a proper show-lighting situation. In a fixed-lighting situation, like an architectural lighting situation where you know in advance what channels are loaded with what, and the kind of levels they may be set to then, maybe, you could design your system in such a way that you get a very high degree of cancellation. But for a dramatic or musical presentation type environment, you can't; there are too many variables to calculate whether you get cancellation or addition. When you go beyond a couple of channels it's just an astronomical amount of computation to work it out, so you're left with basically a statistical probability of cancellation.

Dave Ludlam, Barbican Centre

A question for Steve Barker: referring to the Clean Power Technology Drives, are they still only in the 100 kW range of sizes or are they actually in the sort of drive sizes we use for hoists in the theatre, the 11–18 kW sort of range?

Steve Barker, Speaker

We bring them down to about 2.2 kW in principle. In terms of economics and the applications generally, it's tens of kW and upwards where the majority of the use is.

Dave Ludlam, Barbican Centre

So the other question has to be how much more expensive are they? Are we talking twice the price?

Steve Barker, Speaker

It's a difficult question to answer. I'm not wriggling out of it, but you have to look at the whole system cost with Clean Power drives. Because you're not generating the harmonic currents maybe your supply transformers can be smaller, they can be standard transformers rather than converter-rated transformers, or K-rated transformers, and your cabling may be smaller because your currents are lower, and so forth. So you have to take the whole package into consideration.

Mark White, Chairman

Well wriggled out! Ladies and gentlemen, thank you all very much. My thanks also go to our three speakers. Ω

Siemens MC+ Master Drives, installed in Göteborgs Stadsteater as part of a 66-axis power-flying system supplied totally by Stage Technologies (ST). The installation uses Maxis ID technology, a joint development by ST and Siemens which incorporates the motion control component of the system within the drive. ST purchased the 400,000th Master Drive from Siemens in 2003.

Photos: Techplan

Power and Harmonics

Left: power transformers in Göteborgs Operans in Sweden and right: transformers during installation in the Opera Project in Copenhagen in Denmark.

Right: transformers and grounding connections in the Royal Opera House in London, England.

Left and above: Harmonic filters in the Royal Opera House and, right and below: the power factor correction equipment.

Photos: Techplan and Mark White

Working at heights

Chairman: Jeff Phillips, Project Manager and Consultant, Royal Opera House
Speakers: Paul Edwards, UK Safety Network Ltd
Chris Blakeley, Technical Consultant and Trainer, Lyon Equipment
Chris Higgs, Rigging and Access Trainer, Total Fabrications

Introduction: Jeff Phillips

The crews at theatre and performance venues have always had to work at height in one way or another, at all sorts of levels above the stage, be it focusing lights, rigging or just doing up that last pin-hinge that somebody forgot on the very top of the flat at the back. We've always taken all sorts of risks and chances, and thought nothing of it. I've seen somebody shin up the back of a French flat quite happily, and stand on the rail, which is only probably held together with a couple of those wiggly hammer-in nails, and fortunately he didn't come to any harm; but one day somebody will.

Not many technicians, are aware, either, that there's really a maximum height of 2 metres (6'-6") at which you may work without being guarded or strapped on, or enclosed by handrails. But these guys are going to tell you a lot more about that as we go along. There's a sub-committee now of the HSE; they're currently drafting a new working-at-height regulation. I've had a sneak preview of the direction in which they're going and although it's in very early stages yet it looks generally to be fairly sensible. However, it is going to become law and we are going to be forced to do certain things properly. Anyway, with no more ado, I'm going to ask Paul Edwards to take us through the first stage.

First Speaker: Paul Edwards

Some of you have met me before, so some of what I say you will have heard before, but I'm going to expand on it. I notice that many of you are from outside the UK. Forgive me, but I will be focusing on UK law. This is, thankfully, based on European law, so it's going to be very relevant to those of you working in Europe as well.

Aside from talking about regulations, what I shall develop is an approach based on good, practical common sense. A common sense approach to how we control safety. These safety management principles are fine for anywhere in the world; it's just that when I talk about specific regulations these might not be of direct relevance to everybody.

Let's look at some of the issues that are at stake here – we're interested in *work at height*. When we look at the UK definition of *work at height*, we start looking at working at anything over 2 metres (6'-6"), or anywhere where somebody could suffer injury if they were to fall, so standing on these rostra here at this Conference could be deemed to be working at height. If it's possible that I could fall into something that could injure me, or the nature of my fall could be such that I could be injured, that would be considered working at height. And it's well worth bearing in mind that the 2-metre reference is just a guideline, and to work at anything over that height we *must* consider the management controls that we might use.

Let's be sure we're all using the same terminology. We want to know about *hazards* and *risk* and *risk management*. A hazard is something with the potential to do harm. That's a good generic statement. When we start looking at *risk*, we are looking at the likelihood of things going wrong and how bad it could be if it did go wrong. Risk assessment and risk evaluation are areas where people frequently get things wrong. But the idea of risk can be understood if we explain that to go from *hazard* to *risk* we must have people exposed to a *hazard*. So when we ask people to go and work at height, of course they're exposed to a hazard. This hazard is a big drop with a sudden stop likely to cause injury at the bottom. Or the risk that while working at height they might drop something on somebody else.

Paul Edwards. After working on Harrier jets with the Royal Air Force, training as a teacher and rising to become a senior lecturer, Paul became a freelance training and safety consultant and is currently an advisor to the electrical and construction industries on safety, installation design, inspection and testing. He has amateur experience of theatre, both on- and back-stage and delivers training to theatres and arts organisations. He also publishes training materials for health and safety, electrical and electro-mechanical engineering.

RISK ASSESSMENT

Step 1 – Identify the hazards;

Step 2 – Eliminate hazards, where possible;

Step 3 – Implement risk control measures to eliminate or minimise risks;

Step 4 – Monitor the operation of risk control measures to ensure their effectiveness;

Step 5 – Check that compliance with statutory requirements is achieved.

A key element in dealing with these problems, the ultimate solution, is to eliminate the hazard – eliminate that need to go and work at height. While that might put at lot of riggers out of a job, it is clearly the ultimate solution. It is strange that we never seem to look seriously at the idea of eliminating the hazards from the workplace; we always look for ways in which we might control the hazards. I wish that during the design of theatres Health and Safety was given more thought. We do need to design out some of the problems that we're actually still designing in on some schemes. I had to bite my tongue in one of the presentations earlier, because some access solutions that were developed some 30 years ago and seen then as very practicable, are still being built into modern theatres. We've moved on since then. These solutions no longer comply with current regulations.

No theatre is in the business of running a safety company, but they do have to see that they run a safe company. Theatres cannot be driven primarily by the idea that they are trying to create a totally risk-free workplace; in fact, if they were to try and aim for that, they'd stop theatre production straightaway.

So what are we aiming to do? We're aiming increasingly to move towards a safer working environment. We're trying to reduce the risk to what would be seen as a *reasonable level* of risk. I doubt if any of you believe that you are paid enough money to risk life and limb every day at work. What should we aim for? No more risk than crossing the road with a bit of care. No more risk than carrying the shopping home with a bit of care. That's the sort of level of risk we should be facing. We're not employed to take risks. But the theatre company can't afford to make the whole workplace safe now; they've got shows to produce and run. What we need to do is to look for ways in which we can argue for tackling risks that are manageable now, and delay in tackling other areas until later. We need to start asking, "Well, how much risk are we facing?"

Many organisations use a risk-factor rating so they can say, "The things with a high risk level we'll deal with now, and things with a low risk level we'll tackle later." This is fine; we need to assess the *likelihood* of any harm being realised, of the activity going wrong, and then the *severity*, how bad it would be if it did go wrong. This is where risk assessment often fails because frequently people will look at the idea of the *likelihood* – but they'll be considering what could go wrong and what the worst-case scenario might be? And they conclude that it's possible that somebody could die. As an example, when they're trying to work out the *likelihood* of someone tripping, instead of working out the *likelihood* of that happening, they start trying to evaluate the *likelihood* of somebody tripping to their death. That's a different thing altogether. What's the *likelihood* of tripping? It's the *likelihood* we should be assessing first – and then the likely *severity* of that trip afterwards. That's quite important and I will develop further this example of tripping.

We must carry out an evaluation to try to make things as safe as is *reasonably practicable*. Sometimes we're not allowed to do that, by the way. Let's consider a hazard or a risk at work, doesn't matter what it is. What should I do in Step 1, when I'm trying to identify how that hazard or risk might be controlled? Suppose it's climbing on a vertical ladder to get to a lighting truss, so the risk is that I might fall from it and be injured as a result. Step 1 in my risk assessment process must be to get details about the hazard itself, the nature of the hazard, the nature of the activities occurring. Step 2 requires me to try and eliminate the activity. Do I have to try? Yes. Almost any set of regulations says '*If you can, you must eliminate the hazard*'. If we can't eliminate it, we move to Step 3, to control the risk. How do I decide what standard to use to control it? This is the gap in most people's risk assessment. Step 3 should be: What does the law say I've got to do? And I must do that to start with.

There are many sets of regulations where we are not given this luxury of deciding what is reasonably practicable. There are many sets of regulations that say '*If you have this, you must do that*'. I won't say that the theatre is one of the worst industries for ignoring this, but it is quite common. Everyone wants to look for solutions they think are reasonably practicable. If a regulation says '*the employer shall*' or '*the employer must*' that defines it. No ifs or buts; '*the employer shall*' or '*the employer must*'. Only where it goes on to say '*so far as is practicable*' can you start looking at what is possible in terms of technology, so far as is reasonably practicable, getting it down to as low level of risk as possible for a reasonable level of cost.

When we start looking at the level of risk against the cost, the cost item is evaluated not just in terms of the financial implications, but also in terms of technical difficulty, in terms of time, resources and so on. Generally we have to look at trying to reduce risk so far as is reasonably practicable, and that's fine. Working at height can be an example of this. We have a set of regulations and an approved code of practice for working at height. In the UK that approved code of practice has a semi-legal status – that's to say that it can be used as evidence in a court of law. That means it could be used to define the standard that should be met. If you have not met that standard – you've used some other kind of judgement, come up with another means of controlling things – you may have to defend that in a court of law. You may have to demonstrate how your system is as equally effective as the system specified in the code of practice. It might therefore be much easier just to implement what the code says, but it is possible to do a cost–benefit analysis.

The regulations tell us we should eliminate the need to work at height, we should fence or guard any area where someone could fall more than 2 metres or fall so that they might hurt themselves, and *only if we can't do that* do we start moving on to other things like using things like a catch-net or a safety harness and so on.

For carrying out the risk-rating, one of the things that we often do is to give a point system to things like the *likelihood* – if it's a remote possibility give it a point score of 1, if it's unlikely a point score of 2. *Remote* means you can't discount it entirely but you can imagine it could happen. *Unlikely* is a little bit more likely than not so you can't discount it entirely. *Possible* indicates that you can see it happening sooner or later. When we get into *likely*, this is sooner rather than later, and then *probable*, which means that you can't believe it hasn't already happened. That gives you a gut feel for what kind of a point score to give each term. And remember, no matter how wide this numerical range is, you'll always have somebody who says, "Yeah, I want to give it 4½."! Perhaps some people shouldn't be doing risk assessments!

Likelihood	Risk Rating
Remote	1
Unlikely	2
Possible	3
Likely	4
Probable	5

Severity	Risk Rating
Minor Injury	1
Acute Illness	2
Chronic Injury (RIDDOR)	3
Major Injury/ Disease (RIDDOR)	4
Death	5

	Minor Injury 1	Acute Illness 2	Chronic injury 3	Major injury 4	Fatality 5
Probable 5	5	10	15	20	25
Likely 4	4	8	12	16	24
Possible 3	3	6	9	12	15
Unlikely 2	2	4	6	8	10
Remote 1	1	2	3	4	5
Calculation of Risk	Minor Injury 1	Acute Illness 2	Chronic injury 3	Major injury 4	Fatality 5

Examples of Risk Evaluation tables.

Some organisations, by the way, spread the table out even further than that; I've seen a 10 × 10 point system. But when we look at severity: *minor injury*, possibly no injury at all, give it a point score of 1; *acute injury*, something that will be fixed in the short term, point score of 2; *chronic injury*, takes a bit longer and could put you out of work for some time, 3; *major injury*, implies permanent disability, 4; and then *fatality*, 5. Some people also go further and include multiple fatalities on their assessments.

What do we do with the points once we've evaluated the *likelihood* and the *severity*? We just multiply one by the other; simple. The colour matrix just makes it easier to understand. Where we have 1 × 1, that's going to be a very low risk. If we're into the 2–5 band (grey) then we've got low risk. It increases through medium-risk band (gold), to the high-risk band (amber), and to the very high-risk band (red). This is done so that we can start to look at the idea of offsetting when we're going to tackle hazards. We can perhaps decide that if a particular area has come out as high risk or very high risk, we can justify a more costly solution than if it's much lower risk. And we need to take action more urgently.

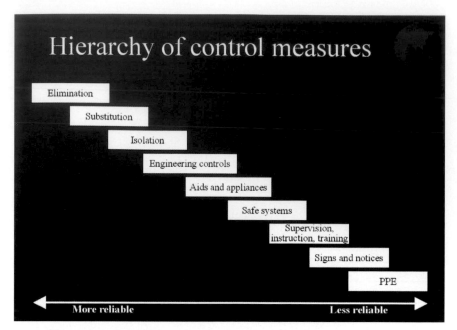

Hierarchy of control measures

Elimination
Substitution
Isolation
Engineering controls
Aids and appliances
Safe systems
Supervision, instruction, training
Signs and notices
PPE

← More reliable   Less reliable →

Hierarchy of control measures: start from top left. (PPE refers to Personal Protective Equipment).

This is a well recognised hierarchy of control measures; in other words showing what's very effective set against what's less effective, in terms of risk management. Those risks at the top of the block, in the red zone, have to be *eliminated*. There is no question, they have to be removed to achieve a complete end of the problem. *Substitution*; a safer form of the same thing, but difficult to apply to working at height. *Isolation*; keeping people and the hazard as far apart as possible. Here we could use fencing and guarding, so people can't accidentally fall or others get beneath the working area. This is applied in theatres by preventing unauthorised people from gaining access to the fly gallery or to the grid. That is a way in which we can isolate people from the hazards quite effectively.

By the way, if you do employ that system, using some kind of a pass door, you do want it to be a *lockable* door and you must insist that the operators *keep it locked*. How many times have you seen pass doors and similar, including fire doors, in all sorts of buildings, including theatres, wedged open? And often a fire extinguisher, otherwise known as a 'British Standard doorstop', is used for the purpose!

Engineering controls can be employed. This would be implemented by using systems or equipment that will reduce the risk. As an example, we might use winches to lower equipment down to a lower level to work on it. That might be considered to be an engineering control for working at height

purposes. *Aids and appliances*; how about using a long stick for adjusting the barn doors instead of having to climb up there? They are used in television studios. *Safe systems of work* refers to a technique for doing the work; that is one that is relied on a lot for working at height. *Supervision, instruction, training*; if you are going to introduce any safe system, you have got to make sure that people are competent to operate the system safely.

We'll talk about competence in a moment. But now, how effective are *signs and notices*? Let me remind you of a classic one which we all know is pretty ineffective: FIRE DOOR: MUST BE KEPT SHUT. What more do I need to say? Signs and notices can seldom be relied on.

And then *personal protective equipment (PPE)* which we rely on a lot for working at height. I am aware of a company (I cannot disclose who or where) who are taking very great risks. Their means of protecting an operator who has to climb onto an overhead lighting truss twice every show is minimal. This person clips himself on to the lighting truss – there is no other provision, he just clips on to the lighting truss. The company have been advised by the truss suppliers that the anchor points of the lighting truss will not absorb the energy of a person falling. So we have to ask what they are relying on for his and their safety. They are taking a huge risk.

When I see things like this, I worry about risk 'appetite', which is defined as somebody's judgement in terms of what is acceptable or unacceptable in terms of a level of risk. My risk appetite may be very different from that of someone else. Riggers and technicians and similar people become accustomed to working at height and are quite happy with it. Believe it or not, I was a high springboard diver in my youth, so standing on the edge of a considerable fall doesn't worry me. Having a slightly higher risk appetite than is good for a person, and for the company employing him or her, can greatly affect whether a safe system of work is truly safe. It certainly affects whether people bother to operate a safe system of work. But if the safe system goes wrong on this lighting truss I described and, even if they're wearing their full body harnesses clipped on properly, even with dual clipping as well, they've got little to save them if the anchor points cannot take the loads.

They're relying on their competence. What is *competence*? Adequate skills, knowledge and experience. Only when we've got this overlap of adequate *skills*, *knowledge* and *experience* have we truly achieved competence.

I have a little demonstration for you about competence which I will perform with a volunteer from the audience. This man, despite outward appearances of being such a healthy young man, has got a brain tumour. But don't worry – you're in safe hands – I'm a doctor. You know I'm a doctor because on my business card it's got lot of letters after my name – so you can trust it, can't you? And I wear a white coat, and I work in a hospital. So that must make you happy. How did I become a doctor? Study didn't make me a doctor. How did I become a doctor? I bought the white coat? I passed the exams; so here we are – I've written papers and passed exams of all sorts on the theory of brain surgery. Happy? I've got a book on it here, look, there's the HSE guide on brain surgery – are you happy now?

Clearly, if I was going to do brain surgery on you, you'd want a bit more than proof that I knew not only the theory of brain surgery but had had practical training. You would want some kind of practical test. I could claim that I've done lots of these operations, and that not many people had died!

I tell you that my competence was assessed not just by exams but that I've got an National Vocational Qualification (NVQ) in brain surgery! Now you can be really happy, can't you? An NVQ does more than just test knowledge; it tests skills as well. Therefore we've got this blend of skills, knowledge and experience and to pass an NVQ, you are tested on not just your knowledge by exams and questions, but also your skills, your ability to do the job.

There is a slight problem in how we prove that people are competent. We've got this idea that even if they've got the skills, knowledge and experience they need to be assessed. Note here that I do not mention the word *qualification*. It's not that I don't value qualifications, but I don't see that they're proof of *competence*. They may be an indication of knowledge, they may be an indication of a combination of knowledge and skills. The question is how do you know who is *competent* within your organisation? Operating the equipment that

is specified and installed relies on the *competence* of the operator. If you're responsible for operators, you're relying on the *competence* of those operators. How do you prove that they are competent? From a CV or from their qualifications? One has to discover whether it was a theory-based examination or a test like an NVQ, which would have included skills. NVQs are relatively useful, but references seldom tell you anything objectively – just that the applicant didn't mess up the previous job! A direct practical assessment might get nearer, but that relies on the quality of the assessment and therefore on the quality of the assessor. This is a problem, and what we need to determine true competence is, of course, a blend of all these things.

I'm going to finish with some practical advice. There is on the Health and Safety Executive website (www.hse.gov.uk) a bit of guidance on working at height in the entertainment and broadcasting industry. There is also an approved Code of Practice for workplace health and safety welfare which includes working at height. You should look at that and apply it. There is also a code of practice from the ABTT, which is being updated as we speak. One last thing; the UK government is considering authorising the Health and Safety Executive to be able to snooping on us and to look at our emails and so on. That means consultants like me daren't put in an email any more, *God, that's lethal – what you are asking those guys to do?* What are they going to do next? Thank you! Keep doing your risk assessments! Ω

A more formal set of notes on Risk Assessment, as prepared by Paul Edwards, appears on page ET10-24 at the end of this section.

The overlap of skills, knowledge and experience that leads to competence.

Second speaker: Chris Blakeley

Photos: Lyon Equipment

Chris Blakeley works as a technical consultant and trainer. His background was in industrial rope access; he is a member of Industrial Rope Access Trade Association (IRATA) which is a quasi-governing body throughout the UK and Europe, and he is qualified at level 3T. He has a background of being in suspension all the time, not necessarily in theatres, but in more wide-ranging environments including on- and off-shore. He has developed more recently an involvement in testing, evaluation and development of items used as personal protective equipment. He works for Lyon Equipment who are equipment suppliers and training providers to the entertainment and other industries.

Following on from what Paul has said about risk assessments, let's consider the access to overstage lighting. This is something which is a common 'work at height' task that technicians all need to do – just the simple focusing of lights.

We're already looking at personal protective equipment (PPE) in action here, something which might not yet be in common use at your place of work. The technician here is looking quite comfortable. For simplicity I'll refer to our technician throughout as male, while acknowledging the number of female technicians in the industry. He's able to reach and do his task quite efficiently, he's using both hands; he's completely supported by his PPE. We'll look at the limitations as well as the possibilities of the PPE.

The company I work for, Lyon Equipment, started by just supplying equipment, but we have developed into technical rescue and access specialists. We carry out annual research programmes and are also members of the British Standards Institute. This enables us to contribute to, and hopefully assist with, the development of realistic standards. We specify systems which are not termed as *safe systems of work* – we do try to avoid the word 'safe' because, as already mentioned, it's a very tenuous area.

Let's now consider modern techniques for working at height in the entertainment industry. The full hierarchy of risks, which Paul mentioned, is developed in the Entertainment Sheet, No. 6 in the series by the Health & Safety Executive. This talks specifically about working at height in the entertainment industry, and gives a four-step hierarchy for the prevention of risks or reducing the hazards associated with working at height.

The main hazard, of course, is taking a fall. There are four steps to reducing the risk of a fall: first, provision of a safe working platform that includes handrails, mesh guards and toe boards to stop us kicking objects off the side. Such platforms would be great if they were practicable for all our work. The use of scissor lifts or mobile working platforms is often the best option, but unfortunately this is impractical in many theatre and entertainment situations.

When a safety system is not reasonably practicable by whatever method we try to do it, we move a step down in the hierarchy of risk, which in this case is to the application of a safety harness. To use these we then need training and appropriate supervision, and maybe qualifications or a level of competence. We'll implement this step to protect our technician, to reduce the risk or apparent hazard.

We'll consider three very simple items of equipment. The first thing is a helmet, which should be worn whenever you're working at height or exposed to a risk associated with others working at height. If I'm on stage and someone is working at height above me, then I'm exposed to risks from people working at height, so I should wear a safety helmet all the time.

Secondly, our technician is wearing a full body harness, consisting of a lower part and an upper-chest attachment point. We tend to see a lot of climbing-based sit-harnesses creeping into the entertainment industry. These are not an appropriate measure – it is important to use a full body harness.

Thirdly, he's wearing a pair of lanyards as well. 'Twin lanyarding', that is having two

Hierarchy of risk:
- Safe systems
- Supervision, Instruction, Training
- Signs and Notices
- Personal Protective Equipment

Suitable Personal Protective Equipment for working at height.

Photos: Lyon Equipment

lanyards, ensures that he can *always* be attached to whatever structure he is on, even when transferring from one point to another. These lanyards do a very important job. If we do take a fall, then that lanyard is the item that's going to stop us hitting the ground. But the important thing about lanyards is that they should reduce the energy that's created by the fall to, hopefully, an acceptable level. This is a level which will not cause damage to the attachment point, or injury to the falling person. A lot of systems don't achieve this, so we have to be very aware that the right equipment has been specified and that we are using this in the correct way.

Our technician in his or her full body harness is able to move around on a steel structure, one which is suitable for climbing on. The sketch illustrates how the use of two lanyards protects during movement. Even if climbing above the anchor point, it's possible only to climb to the limit of the length of the lanyard, and from there on to clip with the next one, always keeping the anchors as high as possible.

The thing to remember about these lanyards with which we're protecting ourselves is that that is all they are for. Their sole purpose is to protect us from a fall, or the effects of the fall. They're not for getting us into a position where we can work with both of our hands free. We do that with another system; a lanyard which is adjustable in length – and this is where we really start to see the benefits of PPE. It can not only give us protection against a fall, but can actually give us the facility to work more efficiently. There are real

difficulties involved in hanging onto a truss or a piece of structure with one hand, leaning out, trying to do up a nut and bolt, getting things out of your pocket, using your Leatherman, just getting it out of the pouch while under a bit of stress, all of which might cause you to drop something on your mate. As soon as you can hang, be suspended, get somewhere comfortable, we're already beginning to reduce those risks and hazards. The stress levels also decrease, as we can work in a more relaxed way; it might even be quicker and more efficient.

Quite often one can work in a state of semi-suspension with your feet taking most of your weight and the system taking a little as well. Your lanyards must be attached in case any of the remainder of the system that you are relying upon should fail. Always have two points of attachment.

One can use exactly the same equipment to gain access below an item. The picture below right shows two of us both suspended from a lighting truss, completely in suspension in the full body harness – but we've still got our back-up lanyards in place. These are the lanyards which are the ones which will hold us if we were to fall; they're designed to do that job.

We should consider using a very similar setup, two separate systems, to climb a wire-sided, or a flexible-sided, ladder to gain access to a work position that's above us, whether it's a truss, a flown bridge or lighting bars. We've got the ladder itself, again another full body harness, and this time we're using another protection system, so we've always got two in place.

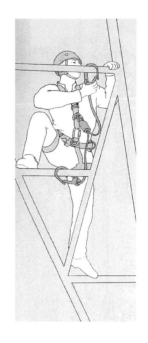

*From left:
a technician being trained in the use of his Personal Protection Equipment; being shown how to take up a work position; and suspended safely to work below a truss or other equipment.*

Photos: Lyon Equipment

Climbing a flexible ladder and right: a technician who has fallen and been restrained by his lanyard.

One of them is the technician's hands and feet, or perhaps the ladder. If any of those should fail, we need that second protection system, and this time it takes the form of a flexible line, or flexible anchorage, with a device which moves up and down with the technician. The flexible line can be very simply placed; it can be made off on a suitably rated truss; maybe, if it's scenery we're talking about (climbing up and down timber frames was mentioned earlier),

Photos: Lyon Equipment

we would take the anchor point of the flexible line right up to the structure in the building, maybe to the grid. We can move it around as we need to in order to accommodate the work on stage. It might also be that it's permanently attached to the structure which you're going to climb.

So that is the correct approach and all the advantages of using the correct equipment. But what actually happens if it does go pear-shaped? The guy looks away for a minute, his pal also looks away and knocks him on one side, or he just takes a little bit of a tumble, and takes that fall.

When our technician has taken a fall, his lanyards have deployed and have reduced

the energy of the fall, but he's now in suspension and he's unable to help himself. This the main problem that we have with working at height. If everybody just fell straight to the ground, it would make everybody's lives a lot easier – or at least everybody else's lives a lot easier! The picture doesn't truly replicate exactly how you hang in a full body harness, because the technician is not unconscious. It's very, very difficult to replicate unconsciousness, or the full effects of hanging in a harness, because even in rescue practice when the 'victim' is conscious and uninjured they will suffer bad physical effects from hanging limply in a harness. Consequently, there's a little bit

of a shortage of research in this area. The technician is sitting a bit more upright here than he might be if he were unconscious. But you can see the advantage of a full body harness. If he was in a climber's-type harness with a low attachment point, his spine would be more extended, and he would be in a much more awkward position.

But there remain a few concerns. We need to think about how we're going to rescue him. There are a number of factors which will guide us here. How severe was the fall? If it was a massive fall, then he's definitely going to need some kind of a rescue, and that will point us to a few things that we must consider. If it was only a minor fall, perhaps another technician could go over and assist him; that might be all he needs. But has he damaged the structure? If he is attached to an aluminium truss which is loaded up with public address loudspeakers, lights and cables, then perhaps the very nature of his fall has damaged the truss structure to a point that it is not safe for another person to go and get him. What method can we use? Are we going to drive a working platform onto the stage or an area beneath him and go up and get him, or am I going to climb out and expose myself to some more, and possibly greater, risks as well? Who's going to do this rescue? How many of the technicians in your theatre who are trained to use personal protective equipment for working at height are also trained to be rescuers? Do you train just one? It's more expensive to train a person for rescue, so it is quite likely that we'll have only one technician

trained for rescue. Who are you going to ask to do the more complex technical job? Probably the guy who's trained for rescue, because he'll be more experienced or better qualified. Perhaps it's him that's taken the fall – so now what do we do? Should we train everybody to be able to rescue?

There is another very important point that we must consider: a risk assessment. Have we done a risk assessment and a method statement for a rescue of this nature? If we look at a lot of current legislation, one of the most important things it will say is that before you undertake any work at height make sure you've got adequate provision for rescue from the outset, before you even get off stage level.

So how long is this rescue going to take? This technician fell off the truss a quarter of an hour ago. Have any of you heard of suspension trauma? I've come across this phenomenon and it is something which has recently come to the attention of the HSE. It's a problem associated with being in one position for a period of time. Again we've got a number of variables which will affect suspension trauma, and we'll just have a quick look at them.

1   The severity of the fall.

2   The attitude of suspension – that's what I was describing before, the difference in the harnesses that we wear. Ensuring we're hanging in a comfortable position might give us a little bit more time.

The procedure for rescuing someone who has fallen from a truss or similar construction.

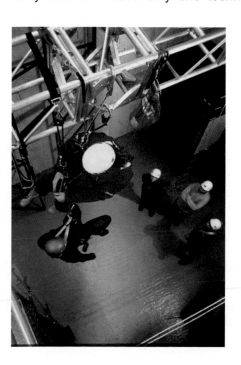  

Photos: Lyon Equipment

3   The nature of his injuries – does he have a massive head injury, is that a matter of concern?

4   The location of the attachment point on the harness – many scaffolders' or riggers' harnesses have rear attachment points; this is very, very different to the modern harnesses for fall-arrest or for work positioning with high attachment points at the front.

5   How long has the casualty actually been there? Did you see him fall, or have you just seen him hanging there, unconscious? In the case of an *unconscious* casualty, the rescue has *got to be performed* within 6–8 minutes to reduce the risk of heart failure and death. If we don't do that, if we know we can't get there for 20 minutes, then really you might as well just take your time because it will be too late.

> "In the case of an unconscious casualty, rescue must be performed within 6–8 minutes to reduce the risk of heart failure and death"

It's very real, is this – it's a massively real risk. I can't emphasise it enough. Let's consider what happens when you're in suspension. The harness is constricting various areas on your body. It doesn't matter what kind of harness you have, whether it's an all-singing, all-dancing one, or whether it's a budget one; it's doing the same sort of things with its attachment points. It will still be, no matter what type it is, constricting various areas on your body.

As the casualty hangs there unconscious, his muscles are still working and still producing waste products which are building up. He will have an attachment point, leg loops probably, and straps around his chest, under his arms, round his waist. Waste products build up in those areas, and can't be pumped round the body. That's not really a problem while he is suspended; he can cope with that because his heart and brain are not constricted and they're dealing with things okay. After about 6–8 minutes, though, he has got enough of this build-up to cause him a problem later on, although I'm still quite happy as things are. However, when the casualty is rescued and lowered to the ground, all his mates rush round him, they lie him flat and maybe cut his harness off or take otherwise ease the pressures on him. Now all the constrictions have gone, the waste products which have built up inside him rush into the rest of his body, the liver, the kidneys, the heart – the right ventricle of the heart in particular. These organs can't cope with that sort of deluge and he passes away on the floor in front of them all. Remember, only 6–8 minutes!

With that lesson learned, we've got our systems in place and we know what's required. We've got a rescue kit which is on site all the time there's any work at height being done. Everyone knows where it is. We've got enough people trained. The unconscious technician is hanging beneath the truss. The second technician has made his way to him and he's deployed a rescue kit. In this case, the truss has been established to be strong enough, but maybe we go for an anchor point above or some strong-point which is completely separate from the truss.

We then deploy the rescue kit, and the guy in the red overalls in the pictures is in the process of attaching the rescue kit to the casualty. The problem is that the casualty's suspension point, his lanyards, are tight. They've deployed as well and maybe they're so long that we cannot reach him. And we definitely can't pick him up. Don't, for one minute, think you can pick a guy up and just unclip his lanyards – it just cannot be done. You need some sort of mechanical advantage to do this.

So we get the rescue kit attached; this is a little rope-based hauling system, just enough to lift the casualty and take the weight from the lanyards. The casualty's lanyards are now slack; the guy in red is removing those lanyards – it might be a case of cutting them with a knife to save a bit of time, but nine times out of ten you reach out with your knife and you will drop it or cut the wrong thing. Knives are not always a good idea. A Leatherman is good for one thing, but make sure you keep those blades folded. It is horribly easy for a bit of tape or webbing to get cut accidentally with a sharp knife. No knives are required.

A little lift, his lanyards are taken off, and then we're free to get him down to the ground. We've got the lowering system fixed and we've got plenty rope to lower him to the floor – if that's the best place and that's what you're going to do. Maybe you'd want to lift him up somewhere, but that must be determined before you start. So the little rope-hauling system lowers him to the ground.

On the ground you would normally have arranged a reception crew so that you don't have to deal with everything yourself. In the event of any rescue, you're bound to be a bit excited; a lot of people are likely to have heard about it and they will all be rushing round to give you a hand. This is an added risk that needs to be controlled. Whether we are training or carrying out a rescue for real, we need to keep people out of the way. A crowd of people underneath would be just as dangerous in training as it is in real life.

If we refer back to the image that we had at the very beginning, it seemed quite simple. Our technician had lowered himself over the side of a lighting bridge or similar – but this is over an auditorium. Another risk associated with a fall can be that there's no clear space to land a person in an emergency.

Having considered all those possibilities of personal protective gear, and the limitations as well, we can see that there's more involved in this working-at-height business than just chucking PPE at the crew and saying, "This'll be fine; I'll get you on a training course, you know how to use a harness and a pair of twin lanyards, you can go and rig anywhere." It's important to have a little bit more than just focusing lights on your mind.

I'll leave you to think about all that, and pass you on to Chris Higgs. Ω

Third speaker: Chris Higgs

I work for a company called Total Fabrications in Birmingham, here in England. Total Fabrications are best known for aluminium outdoor stages and similar structures but we do a lot of other things as well; the Rugby World Cup rig in South Africa, for example, and we've recently started doing a lot more stage sets. In fact, we have just finished doing Kylie Minogue's world tour set and lighting equipment.

I was employed by Total Fabrications four years ago, after I had a bit of a heart attack and some heart surgery. Having spent 25 years hanging equipment up for people, I started to try and put a little bit back into the industry. I felt this was very important, because when I first started there were a lot of people doing the work, but there wasn't that much overhead rigging equipment. Now you can get the equipment pretty much anywhere; if you've got the money to rent it, you can use it. And because the equipment is readily available, it means that people are starting to use it and they are therefore going to start working at height.

I'd like to concentrate on just two things. One is a safety solution that uses existing Personal Protective Equipment, which Chris has already mentioned, and the other is a new product which has been out for a couple of years now, but I think you'll see its relevance, having listened to both Paul and Chris. I think that there were in the construction industry, back in 2000, some 73 fatalities caused by falls from a height – this was 25% of all fatalities, which is too many. We've also had a few in the entertainment industry and these must be eliminated as far as possible.

Chris Higgs is a keen climber to whom work above stage became a particular interest while working in subsidised rep., touring theatre and dance and music venues. Chris founded a rigging service company and later began to provide training for riggers. He contributed to the writing of BTEC and NVQ rigging standards and has been involved in a number of recent training initiatives. Since he joined Total Fabrications in 1998 over 600 people from UK and overseas have attended his training classes.

Structures created by Total Fabrications: Rugby World Cup in South Africa and the setting for Engineering Impact.

Photos: Total Fabrications

Top: a crew working on a stage in a workshop – in present-day terms this is not a safe place of work, and below: the ceiling-refurbishment access platform in the Royal Albert Hall.

Photos: Total Fabrications

Eighteen percent of all fatalities were caused by falling objects, so there's a lot to think about there, and it's a major part of a revitalised health and safety campaign by the HSE at the moment.

I am sure that you have also heard about the limitation on working at a height of more than 2 metres (6'-6"). A crew were actually building the Commonwealth Games opening ceremony stage in our warehouse the other day, and I had to point out to them that the guy standing on the platform was 'working at height'. He was within 2 metres of an unprotected edge, and the staging was actually just over 2 metres high. This is a very easy mistake to make. He could even have been working by the manhole; when that stage comes together, there will be a 2-metre drop through the hole that the other crewman is standing in. That is not classified as a safe place of work.

These are the three hazards which are identified in the broadsheet that both Paul and Chris referred to, the ETIS 6, which, I think, has been out since around 1989. We're only going to concentrate on falls, because we don't have time to talk about the rest of them, interesting as they can be!

Many situations give rise to unexpected risks. I know that the increment at the bottom of the upright truss in the picture below is half a metre (18"), so if you count them up, this guy is standing just a bit over 2 metres. But he's only going to be there for a second. "Oh, I'll just nip up there and do that." That's the kind of thing we're faced with, day in, day out, isn't it? "By the time I've got all that protective gear on, I'd have done the job." It's a real risk.

> "There are three main hazards in working at height:
> - Falls
> - Falling objects
> - Falls from collapsing structures"
>
> Source: HSE ETIS 6

The ceiling-refurbishment access platform in the Royal Albert Hall is a structure which we built. It was designed originally to do the access job, but there are now going to be people up there for a long period of time. As Chris mentioned, the crew are not necessarily thinking about dropping things, and people do get a bit complacent about tying things down or restraining them. Also, when you're busy doing a job, you just, *just* have to go and fetch something: "I was only just going over there," and that's when the fall occurs. Risk increases considerably when there's a long period of duration or exposure.

Ladders

Everyone should be aware of the Temporary Working at Height directive that's soon to be with us. In the UK, the HSE have identified that outside the construction industry there are over half a million users of ladders who require training because that is one recommendation of the directive! In contrast, interestingly enough, most people who've had some training on scaffolding will actually comply with the regulations already. These regulations are not out until 2003 or the year after. The good old Zargees (aluminium step-ladders), which we've all used, are not actually

Illustrations of the risk of working on trusses and ladders.

classified as being a place of work and haven't been for some time. Ladders are to provide a means of access, unless you can justify the use of a ladder to do a particular type of work. We should not forget the importance of that; in all industries the majority of the falls are from ladders.

We're not talking about balancing about at heights, the activity that I used to do and which Chris still does. The risks arise when equipment is not used properly: standing on orange boxes rather than getting access equipment, getting on the fly rail, standing on the rails of a Tallescope. These parts of equipment like this are not designed for standing on. It's that kind of misuse that's going to cause the injuries. It's the actions of people and the interaction between people and equipment that can create the risk. Being aware of this kind of thing is very important.

Access Equipment

The good old access platform, the Tallescope, has been much maligned, largely because they are often not used correctly. This new Directive will require that if you use a Tallescope, you're going to have to receive some training on how to use it. And proper training is available; there are at least two companies, to my certain knowledge, that provide training on the correct use of Tallescopes. This is not difficult and not rocket science, but it is nevertheless very important.

The argument that theatre people often use about needing to move mobile access equipment while people are up in the basket is really not as strong as it used to be. You can now get little machines which you can drive around from the top; they pass through an opening not much bigger than a standard door, and they don't weigh as much as they used. I've had a lot of health and safety people telling me over the years, "You don't want to be doing that, you should be using a cherry-picker." Well, even if you could get that very large thing up the ramp, through the get-in doors, it would probably break the stage when you drove it around,

Photo: Techplan

A Tallescope and a wheeled lighting boom with step-ladder access at the side of the Royal Opera House stage.

or, as happened on one famous occasion, when someone got one wheel over the edge of the stage into the orchestra pit!

So these powered access units are available – they can be used for focusing plants, for example. As long as they don't use them for watering the lamps!

Mention was made of the risk-reduction principle, which is very important. We shouldn't have to work where we're exposed to risk. Now a fly tower grid would be a good demonstration of that, and again this new Directive will require, wherever possible, that you justify the reason for doing work in the way that you're doing it. What it doesn't mention, at the moment anyway, is this risk-reduction principle. It assumes that you've already taken that step and decided that your ladder, tower, orange-box or whatever you are using is the way to do the work. While working on a grid, you are exposing other people to more risk than yourself, although as I've seen someone go through an old timber grid up to his shoulders maybe that isn't always the case!

A modern theatre grid, whether steel channels or grille, still has to be fitted with edge protection. The safety of those below must also be considered in terms of loose items on any grid. The sheet from the HSE that I referred to has edge protection as the first item. The second is using safety harnesses, which have to be fitted and used properly. A number of large exhibition centres, particularly in this country, insist

Left and centre photos: Techplan

Photo: Total Fabrications

Theatre grids – left: Steel channels in the Milton Keynes Theatre, centre: grille decking in Kwai Tsing Theatre in Hong Kong (note the hazard markings), and right: an unsatisfactory temporary protection barrier.

that their riggers do wear harnesses – but they do not enforce the use of the lanyards or that they be clipped to anything! They enforce just the *wearing* of harnesses. The third is maintaining a safe distance from edges. Safety nets are the last thing in the hierarchy, for reasons we'll look at later.

Control Measure Hierarchy - First level

The right-hand picture above shows some hi-tech edge protection – good old tape! You can see what that is indicating, but it's not actually very effective as protection. You could walk backwards into that quite easily, carrying the other end of the spreader beam that you were wandering around with, or maybe even forwards if somebody happened to turn the work lights off. This is an example of poor edge protection but, done properly, barriers represent the first level of the safety hierarchy, because you don't need to rely on equipment.

Control Measure Hierarchy - Second level

The second level can be illustrated by the crew at Glyndebourne using harnesses. The harnesses are necessary because rigging on the lighting bars can be a bit hazardous. If you kneel down – as I'm sure a lot of us have done – and you just want to reach back to that barn door when you've been told it isn't quite correct, and there is a fall hazard – you could slip through the gaps. It's not practicable to have mesh guards or kick edges or anything like that in such a situation.

The advent of tension-wire grids has changed this in some venues. However, these chaps, with their Petzl equipment (we're not the distributors!) are using their fall-arrest equipment in addition to walking on a very secure platform, because the risk of falling still exists. It's not difficult, these days, to rig the safety equipment; there are

suitable anchor points around. The lighting bridges are a big steel construction with an ample safe working load; its something like 6 tonnes on the structure, and they have with good access. So this is an example of belt and braces, I suppose, to use an old analogy.

Something which is not particularly new, but its application in the theatre and entertainment business dawned on me a few years ago, is the Vertical Rope Fall Arrest System. By installing one of these you can use your harness and your hooks but you also have a separate and secure fall arrest system. I've seen people clip onto the back of the 1" (25 mm) bits of steel framing on scenery flats that haven't any chance of stopping you from falling; all they're going to do is pull the scenery apart and you'll still

Photo: Total Fabrications

Technicians using safety harnesses on the lighting bridges at Glyndebourne Opera House in Sussex.

end up in a heap on the floor. It occurred to me the best anchor is exactly what we're anchoring everything else overhead to – the grid, or the structure above the grid, or to a combination of the two. It's also a system that we're used to dealing with in theatres – pulling up spot-lines, whether it's a mirror board or the top of a lighting boom. So it's an easy process to deal with.

You need an *adequate* – I was actually going to say a *reasonable* – anchor point, as we use an energy-absorber at the top which limits the force on the anchor point, and on you, to less than about 6 kN (1,350 lbf). Typically it's a little bit less than that, but that's what the Standards require; a force of less than 6 kN. The system gives about a 30° operating envelope; you could probably make it a little more extreme than that, but there doesn't seem to be any point in tempting fate. Obviously you can rig this to almost any height you like, within reason – but I've yet to see a theatre which would be too high in which to use one of those systems.

What this system means is that the person is protected from the second they leave the ground. The shock absorber is at the top – it's part of the system, rather than something that the technician's got to remember to hook up to; it's already installed. The safety line is very flexible, so you can move it around. In fact there's a number of jobs that we've done where we've actually installed a whole number of these, and crew were able to move between them safely with considerable ease. They could connect to an adjacent line before releasing themselves from the first, so they didn't have to come back to the ground all the time.

Vertical Rope Fall Arrest systems are not commonplace yet, but a word of caution; don't use them on Tallescopes and Zargee ladders and similar things, for the reasons that Chris set out. If you are up in the Tallescope basket with your harness attached to a fall-arrest system, or to an inertia reel anchored to a strong place, which may seem to be the obvious thing to do, this may encourage you to take a few

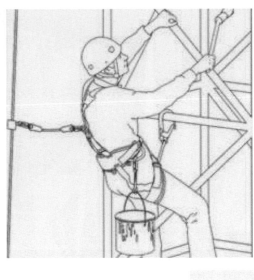

more risks – your risk appetite has gone up a little because you're clipped on to something, and it's secure, and it's got EN numbers, and you've been trained in its use. Then the Tallescope falls down a hole, the Zargee keels over, or whatever occurs, and you're left suspended up there. You were probably up there on the only piece of equipment that could get you that high in the building, and now you've just fallen off it and are left suspended. How are the rest of the crew going to get you down? So the minute you put on a harness, and this is said by Total Fabrications, Lyon Equipment and others in the industry, think about the rescue kit and the rescue procedures. Do the risk assessment!

Rescue from a Vertical Rope Fall Arrest installation must be organised in exactly the way that Chris was showing you. There are two ways of doing it. You can either hook the lifting device onto the top of the vertical rope where you can get to it in the grid, or you can actually reach just through the grid in the traditional manner and attach a rope-clamp upside down and lower the whole lifting unit down to the ground. In this way the ground crew can actually use the slack in the line to steer the victim through any scenery or equipment on stage down to the ground, where the ambulance should be waiting.

Application and details of a Vertical Rope Fall Arrest System.

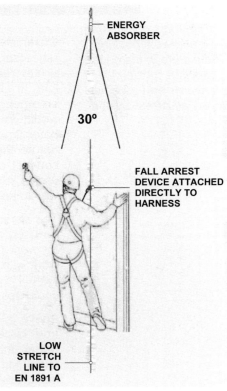

ENERGY ABSORBER

30°

FALL ARREST DEVICE ATTACHED DIRECTLY TO HARNESS

LOW STRETCH LINE TO EN 1891 A

Line drawings based on those by Safety Equipment Suppliers, Petzel.

Photos: Total Fabrications

Examples of both bad and good work positions. The picture in the centre shows a correct use of lanyards and a Vertical Rope Fall Arrest System.

Obviously this needs training, practice and rehearsal, so that when it does happen you're ready for it. The 6 minutes is not long at all. Many people believe that in an emergency on a front-of-house truss they would lower the whole truss down. We have timed this; it was about 27 minutes before they got the safety lines off! The concept of secondary suspension to back up the suspension hoists is fine but not the way to lower a casualty.

The Vertical Rope Fall Arrest system could be used as support for this operation and for work positioning as well. You shouldn't work with a shock absorber fitted, because there's a possibility it could deploy, but you could use a similar technique.

Above is an illustration of work positioning from Israel. This guy is working on a tower rather than a truss, but it's still on an aluminium structure. He's connected with his work-position lanyard which, in this case, just looks like an ordinary strap. He's also got a fall-arrest device. The big hook at about knee level is connected to a vertical tube, which is not necessarily a good thing to do with that hook. It's not going to load it very efficiently in the event of a fall. He also has a shock-absorber of a sort, not a proper industrial fitting, and there is doubt about its shock-absorbing qualities. The shock if he falls is probably going to be quite severe.

The danger is that he's not using a proper industrial piece of gear. His greatest period of risk is unclipping and moving back down or further up the tower. That's the time he's most likely to fall and he could fall quite a way. He is also wearing a sit-harness, so there's every chance he's going to break his back. Not a good system to be using, and the attachment certainly doesn't do the aluminium truss any good.

The centre illustration shows what we've been talking about. This guy has shot up one of these vertical wire-rope ladder systems and he was connected to this fall-arrest device from the second he left the floor. He's attached a fall-arrest lanyard, the blue and yellow one, to a strong-point which happens to be above the hoist. He's also got the other one clipped to something out of the picture, because like me he's a pessimist! He's arranging his work-positioning lanyard so he can do whatever it is he wants. That bit's easy – it always has been. Notice that the fall-arrest rope, by the ladder, is not attached to the truss, but attached to the roof, which is a lot stronger. It's also independent of the other systems, so there is some redundancy there.

The next point to consider is movement along the truss shown on the right. This can be done using twin lanyards. One is attached at the front, and he's just about to detach the one nearest him so that he can move forward. It's a bit of an art, although it's not as arduous as people think. And on structures that will actually tolerate the forces if the worst should happen, it's a very acceptable way of protecting yourself; maintaining constant attachment. The danger is that if you were to fall you could impose a 6 kN load (1,350 lbf), which is a bit more than half a tonne, on some point on the truss and we don't know where you're going to fall off. Is the truss

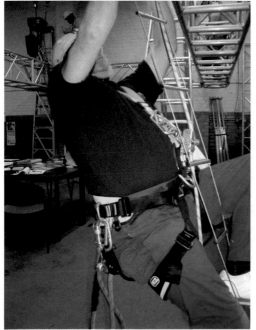

Photos: Total Fabrications

designed to do this job? The fact is, 90% of the trusses of which I am aware, are *not* designed for this shock load. If it was a heavily-loaded truss, or a particularly long truss, or on a cantilever or something like that, you would really be in trouble.

Control Measure Hierarchy - Third level

Maintaining a safe distance from an edge does not need describing in detail, but obviously one must assess just how far is, in fact, safe – and be able to justify it!

Control Measure Hierarchy - Fourth level

The last level in the HSE hierarchy is safety nets. You've got to be very careful with nets, because the standards require that certain fixings are capable of sustaining the same force as your fall-arrest lanyard (6 kN, 1,350 lbf). The next fixing would have to sustain 4 kN (900 lbf), not 6 kN, but the one after that would again be 6 kN. The specification for the distance between attachments which, I think, is 2.5 metres (8'-2"), means that the net is a lot weaker at the edge than it is at the centre. You usually fall into the middle of a net, unless you get caught up in it, and the loads have therefore to considered at 45° to the horizontal. The majority of lighting trusses are not designed to sustain these forces at 45° any more than they are to sustain the loading from a fall-arrest lanyard. So you have to be very careful where safety nets are attached.

With properly engineered net systems these loads are not so much of a problem, but they are something to be aware of. When a safety net does suffer a fall, you've got to replace it; a safety net is a one-time-use item. Nets can also easily get damaged and so while they do have their uses they're the last thing in the hierarchy.

Horizontal safety lines

The next thing, which brings me round to the product that I want to tell you about, is horizontal safety lines. These are an obvious approach and are something that the construction industry has used for some time. You can buy them as kits, they're highly portable, very flexible, you can coil them up and chuck them in your bag. However, you've got to be very careful about what you attach them to. It is important that they are attached to substantial anchorages, such as can be found in many grids, some front of house positions or on circle fronts, places like that.

Top: traversing a truss using two lanyards. Centre: a horizontal safety line in use on a construction site. Bottom: starting the climb up a wire-rope ladder while attached to a vertical fall arrest rope.

Below: local failure on a truss caused by excessive point loading.

Examination of the forces that could be created in horizontal safety lines and their anchorages when a fall is arrested.

Consider a bridle with a static load of 1 kN (0.112 ton-force). There will be a deflection of about 2.6 m (8'-6"). The force at each end will be 3 times the load applied.

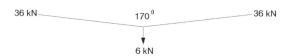

Now pull on the ends to make the bridle quite taut. The deflection will be reduced to about 0.8 m (2'-7"). The force at each end will now be 6 times the load applied.

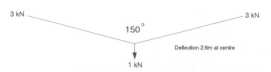

The loads at each end of the safety line in the event of someone falling with a plain webbing lanyard could be of the order of 36 kN (4 ton-force).

But never attach horizontal safety lines to an aluminium truss.

I'm not an engineer, I'm a rigger. So the basic physics is shown in the diagrams on the left. The result is that in the event of a fall the load on the horizontal safety line and its anchor points will be 6 times the load caused by your fall. And the casualty is hanging nearly a metre (3'-3") below the truss. How would you reach him or her? People say they would climb up their own lanyard; this is above your head – try it! Another theory is to grab hold of the lanyard and pull the person up. You can't do it. In order to reach the guy we've got to make that line tighter to reduce the deflection – but look at the loads that are already imposed on the line and the anchorage.

Because an amount of energy is absorbed in the line, whatever it is, there are a number of different systems, such as ropes, webbing, even devices that pay out a little bit of slack, that can reduce the total loading. But it is still likely to be over a tonne. The majority of trusses of a workable length, say 12 metres (40 ft), could be carrying up to tonne anyway, and they aren't designed for this type of additional loading. We need to be able to climb on trusses from time to time. A safe system of work is required, and that is where the Total Fabrications T2 trussing comes in.

The T2 truss

T2 is a short truss, an advanced truss. The idea is that it's a safe system that works. You can move permanently attached along the truss. The wire-rope ladder is attached by a device that actually loads the truss in the correct manner, but I stress again, accessing and climbing on a truss is the <u>last thing you should do</u>. If there's any alternative method – Tallescopes, Genie towers, etc, that are safe to use – then use these. *Climbing on the truss must be the last resort.* Not only because of the obvious risk of falling off, but because of the difficulty of rescue in the event of a fall.

Total Fabrications have produced T2 in both flown systems and ground-support equipment. The components use square tube, rather than round, and the diagonals aren't in the open sides of the truss, but actually through the centre, because if somebody was to fall off, the truss is obviously going to want to lurch to one side or the other. It also uses a ribbed extrusion,

T2 trussing in use as an advance lighting bar in the Sunderland Empire.

Photo: Total Fabrications

so it's easy to grip. This is also a very sneaky way of getting more aluminium into the cross-section, which makes it a lot stronger. It uses a genderless connection, so it doesn't matter which way round you put it, it can always be fitted together. It uses a Clevis pin joint which is extremely clever. And it's got a continuous T-slot which runs right the way through it, apart from one direction on a corner-block. Effectively you've got a slot, much like Unistrut, that runs right the length of the truss, in all the chords.

The T2 truss has been load tested with up to 2½ tonnes in the centre of an 18-metre (58'-6") span. The truss lifted all the test weight before it failed technically at that point, because some of the connections pulled out. The engineers stress that this was not an actual failure, the truss had not broken. It will still take your weight. I can't tell you the total load it will carry, as otherwise irresponsible people may try to load it excessively.

Training is part of the system; you can't buy the system without getting the training. And we try explain to people that they shouldn't feel imposed upon; to use the system properly you need a certain amount of information – that's all it is, really.

The PPE side of this equipment has been very carefully considered and we strive to incorporate the correct standards. It includes a twin lanyard with a mobile anchor-point and the vertical fall-arrest system. As one never knows where the fall is going to occur, T2 effectively takes a rated loading condition of a 1.5 tonnes (3,360 lbs) over 12 metres (40 ft), but it allows for that roving 6 kN (1,350 lbf) load as well. The user must allow for this extra 6 kN in each of the truss supports or suspensions.

For attaching lighting there is a part called a T-clamp which completely eliminates hook clamps and all the damage which is done by hook clamps to trussing. It's effectively a quarter-turn connector, much like a Unistrut fitting. The beauty about it, from a lighting designer's point of view if not from the technician's, is that it will fit into the continuous slots anywhere on a truss. You can fit it on a connection, you can attach it on the top, hang it on the bottom, put it anywhere you like. Each lighting attachment T-clamp is also rated at 100 kg (220 lbs).

Detail of the T2 truss showing the ribbed chords and connectors.

Photos: Total Fabrications

To conclude, it may be helpful to list the standards that apply to Personal Protective Equipment:

- Helmet to EN 12492 and EN 397
- Harness to EN 361
- Twin lanyard to EN 355
- Mobile anchor point to EN 795

Think T2. That's it. Thank you. Ω

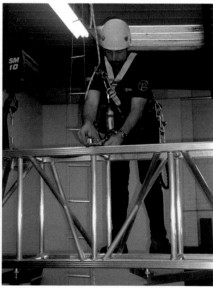

Top: Mobile Anchor Point for the T2 truss.
Left: The T-clamp for lighting suspension on the T2 truss.
Right: Personal Protection Equipment.

Photos: Total Fabrications

Questions and discussion

Bert Pronk, Het Muziektheater, Amsterdam

Why is Personal Protective Equipment rated lower in risk-reduction than safety signs? I didn't understand that.

Paul Edwards, Speaker

Arguably, safety signs don't belong as a risk-control measure at all, because in truth they prevent nothing. So you can argue that they don't belong there. But what they often do, if you have a safe system of work that you are requiring to be operated and you have trained people and so on, is to reinforce that, to remind people of the process that should be operated. So if it belongs anywhere, it's got to be much lower than these. We always say PPE is the last resort. So you could argue, take it out and throw it away, but if you're going to have it in, PPE is always the last resort.

Andy Hayles, Theatre Projects Consultants

I think the step-ladder thing is probably the thing that scares me most about all this, because I guess most of us come across working at height over 2 metres (6'-6") on step-ladders rather than on trusses. Something that we've had a problem with recently is HSE saying that they're not happy with people rigging from step-ladders, or indeed from Tallescopes. They don't like platforms being used to carry lanterns around, or these being rigged from these platforms. There will be a serious effect on the lower end of the market, like studio theatres that have a grid at, say, 5 metres (16'-3"). Perhaps the only way of rigging that grid would be off a step-ladder or from a mobile platform, but many small studios don't run to the kind of budget necessary to pay for that kind of kit. Are the panel aware of any clever systems or ways of getting around that, or any ways of assessing the risk and eliminating the risk in that process?

Comments from the panel

Eliminating the risk's easy ... Don't do it!

Chris Higgs, Speaker

Absolutely. And unfortunately I've had this argument recently with somebody, and you can't balance focusing a light compared with lying in hospital. What you've got to do is think, well, okay, we shouldn't be using step-ladders either because we've been told we shouldn't or because it clearly isn't a safe system of work. You've got to think of an alternative such as a mobile tower, maybe an alloy tower, which is possible unless you've got weird floor-level changes.

Paul Edwards, Speaker

But you mustn't use the tower as a method of hauling equipment up, like a loader, by attaching lifting equipment to it, or as a means of actually moving equipment at height to the place where you're going to use it. Don't hang the gear all over it; there I've got to agree with HSE.

Chris Blakeley, Speaker

It's the same, if you think about it, if you were using your personal protective equipment you'd never clip to a handrail of an alloy tower scaffold. It's a working platform, and what they're trying to get you to do – as they do throughout industry – is to work back up that hierarchy. You can climb up the inside of the tower and so on, but when you get into position on your mobile platform or alloy tower scaffold you must then haul your lights up attached to your lighting grid, the lighting bar or whatever. You could use a little pulley system, but not on the tower.

These mobile towers aren't as expensive as you think. There are fibre-glass ones which are really lightweight; you know, a little bit more electrical awareness as well, GRP towers, carbon towers ...

David Adams, Chairman, ABTT Safety Committee

I'm tasked by the HSE to write what we've agreed is the procedure for the use of Tallescopes. I think it's quite important to reinforce what the panel said, that you can't use Tallescopes for the purposes of hauling kit up and down; they're not intended for that. They are perfectly acceptable as a working platform, and indeed the HSE recognise that Tallescopes are essential for the focusing of lights in smaller theatres where lighting bridges are not possible. The argument, which is partially relevant to this meeting, is not actually about the use of Tallescopes for focusing lights, it's whether you can move people in the basket of a Tallescope. And I'm delighted to say that the HSE are perfectly happy with this if the Risk Assessment shows that the man's going up and down the ladder 50 times in order to focus the No. 1 lighting bar would expose him to a greater risk than if he had stayed at the top. If certain precautions are taken, the Tallescope may be moved. The precautions they agree on are that some form of fall-arrest system must be installed, or the Tallescope is used it as it was instructed, with the braces on, and the man comes down. What they won't accept is the possibility of two strong persons, even if they're as fit as the best here, being able to stop the tower turning over, because once you look at the mechanics of it, they can't.

Paul Edwards, Speaker

A small point to pick up on that. Whatever the HSE say, I have to point out that they don't decide what the law means. The courts decide what the law means. So if you do go down the route where you say, "We've decided by Risk Assessment process that it's safer for somebody to stay up there and we push them along, than it is for them to climb up and down," you've also got to justify that you could reduce how much they're going up and down in any one period, and change the people who are doing it so that they get a chance to recover, and so on. You've got a lot to justify before you can possibly say going up and down is not possible.

David Adams, Chairman, ABTT Safety Committee

The work for the HSE has actually been suspended whilst we finish quibbling over the wording of temporary or permanent Work at Height documents, in which the work's all going wrong for us. But in terms of Tallescopes they still feel that there is a very good case to justify moving a chap along a bar focusing lights. And they're not pressing very hard. I agree that if there was a coroner's inquest in a court, they could be overturned, but the courts have accepted that if you are following an HSE Guidance Note, and that is what I have been asked to draft, most courts will accept that as evidence that you have been sufficiently careful. This note will be in the series that you have been quoting from, Work at Heights No 6.

Paul Edwards, Speaker

I disagree with you there. If it's an approved code of practice they will; if it's guidance they won't.

David Adams, Chairman, ABTT Safety Committee

It's not an approved code of practice. It's the same thing as the document you were talking about earlier, which they say ... it is not a quasi-legal document which ...

Paul Edwards, Speaker

Because the courts decide what the statutory instrument was intended to mean ... I'm sorry, in fact they don't even do that. They decide what the actual words of the statutory instrument mean, and they don't care whether HSE's interpretation is different to anybody else's. They only decide on law. If the Regulations want changing, that can be influenced, but that's a different thing.

David Adams, Chairman, ABTT Safety Committee

I think you're absolutely technically correct, but if you are found guilty of an offence when you were working to the HSE's guideline ...

Paul Edwards, Speaker

It can be used in mitigation.....

David Adams, Chairman, ABTT Safety Committee

... and the fine is likely to be quite slight.

Paul Edwards, Speaker

Doesn't absolve you, though.

Charles Haines, Harkness Hall

Just a quick question, because I didn't hear any reference to this in the presentations. We've recently specified an inertia-reel safety-line system with an engineer's rescue handle on the side of it. I just wondered what your opinions are of this item of equipment.

Chris Higgs, Speaker

Their use on vertical fall-arrest blocks? The hardest thing about a vertical fall-arrest block is the fact that you need to inspect it every time you use it, like any item of PPE. It's a constant test, so you need to go right to the top of it and have a look before you attach to it. If you then need to recover someone from it who's hanging in mid-air, you need to get to the device to operate it. We've recently carried out training and supply of PPE equipment to a big organisation who previously had more than £60,000 ($36,000, €51,000) of vertical fall-arrest blocks installed and found that they were pointless, really. I'm not saying that applies in every situation, but you've also got to be really careful with them. Just bringing one down and then letting go of it – which everybody will do – causing it to wind up under its own inertia, will require a re-build and re-test of the unit. The angle of use you can get to with these items is also fairly limited.

> "... they're actually applying standards for the testing of passenger lifts to the tension-wire grid"

Louis Janssen, HWP Theateradvies bv, Amsterdam

Are there any regulations about the use of tensioned-wire grids?

Paul Edwards, Speaker

They come under work equipment regulations. So we've got to take account of the working at height regulations, but we've also got working equipment. They're in use as was discussed in the Conference session on RADA and the use of a tensioned-wire grid.

Andy Hayles, Theatre Projects Consultants

In Newham, in east London, they've decided that the tensioned-wire grid is a series of wires that suspend people. What else does that conform to? Er, passenger lifts. So they're actually applying standards for testing of passenger lifts to the tension-wire grid, which actually requires a manufacturer's inspection and certification twice a year!

Paul Edwards, Speaker

It's crazy isn't it? What is a tensioned-wire grid? It's part of the building structure. It's like walking on a floor, like anything else, isn't it?

Andy Hayles, Theatre Projects Consultants

And conversely, the grid in RADA, which is in Camden (another local authority in London), hasn't been tested since it was installed, and has no regime at all.

Paul Edwards, Speaker

Do they have the same requirement on the grid in a fly tower?

Jeff Phillips, Chairman

You only have to inspect it although everybody says 'test'. It's actually tested once, when it's first put in, and then you inspect it regularly.

David Adams, Chairman, ABTT Safety Committee

I think the use of the word 'test' should be banned. 'Load-test', yes.

Jeff Phillips, Chairman

Its clear we could go on for another hour with this discussion, but I'm afraid we have to stop ...

Paul Edwards

As we have to finish, can I give the parting shot? Let us remember that the majority of people are caused by accidents. Ω

The last thing you should consider is climbing on the truss. Use alternative means wherever possible.

RISK ASSESSMENT by Paul Edwards

1.0 Health and safety management

Risk assessment is a key element in managing safety in the workplace. There are several sets of regulations that specifically require that risk assessments are completed:

- Management of Health and Safety at Work Regulations;

- Manual Handling Operations Regulations;

- Personal Protective Equipment at Work Regulations;

- Health and Safety (Display Screen Equipment) Regulations;

- Noise at Work Regulations;

- Control of Substances Hazardous to Health Regulations;

- Control of Asbestos at Work Regulations;

- Control of Lead at Work Regulations.

To ensure that risk is satisfactorily managed it is necessary to:

- Identify the hazards;

- Eliminate hazards, where possible;

- Implement risk control measures to eliminate or minimise risks;

- Monitor the operation of risk control measures to ensure their effectiveness;

- Check that compliance with statutory requirements is achieved.

1.1 Risk assessment process

Risk assessment forms an integral part of business planning. Specific legislation is applicable: Regulation 3 of the Management of Health and Safety at Work Regulations 1992.

This Regulation stipulates that risk assessments must be carried out on all hazardous environments, dangerous plant and equipment and hazardous tasks and activities and the significant results must be recorded where there are five or more employees.

If tackled systematically, risk assessment need not be an arduous task and may lead to more effective and efficient working.

To complete a risk assessment:

1. Identify the environment/plant and equipment/task/activity to be assessed;

2. Identify specific and associated hazards;

3. Identify the at risk population;

4. Assess the likelihood of injury occurring;

5. Assess the probable severity of injury should it occur;

6. Evaluate the level risks posed by the hazards;

7. Identify means of eliminating the hazard, if possible;

8. If elimination is not possible, identify means of combating the risks at source;

9. If combating at source is not possible, identify control measures that minimise risks;

10. Communicate the results of the risk assessment to those affected.

1.2 Hazard Identification

A hazard is something that has the potential to cause harm. Hazards can include:

- Working at height;

- Equipment or structures collapsing or overturning;

- Moving vehicles;

- Electricity or an electrical discharge;

- Falling/flying objects during mechanised handling of materials;

- Moving machinery or material being machined;

- Hot or harmful substances.

There are other hazards that do not necessarily lead to fatalities but do cause injury, or can result in damage to property, or loss of time, with subsequent financial loss. These must also be considered.

1.3 Risk Evaluation

To simplify risk assessments, risks can be evaluated using a points scoring system:
Risk Factor = Likelihood x Severity

Or this may be expressed as **R = L x S** where **(L) Likelihood** is the likelihood that harm will be realised and **(S) Severity** is how bad the probable harm that would arise would be.

Likelihood	Risk Rating
Remote	1
Unlikely	2
Possible	3
Likely	4
Probable	5

Severity	Risk Rating
Minor Injury	1
Acute Illness	2
Reportable Injury (RIDDOR)	3
Major Injury/ Disease (RIDDOR)	4
Death	5

Likelihood/Severity Rating System:

The points attributed to the risk are then multiplied, as shown above, to arrive at a risk factor. For ease of calculation, a risk factor matrix, like that set out below, is sometimes used:

	Minor Injury 1	Acute Illness 2	Reportable Injury 3	Major injury 4	Fatality 5
Probable 5	5	10	15	20	25
Likely 4	4	8	12	16	24
Possible 3	3	6	9	12	15
Unlikely 2	2	4	6	8	10
Remote 1	1	2	3	4	5

1.4 Priority

Having identified the level of risk, the risks will need to be prioritised. What level of priority is allocated to different risk bands is entirely arbitrary, but the following is an example of priority ranges:

Range	Level of risk	Action Required
1	Negligible	At the first opportunity
2-5	Low risk	Within a month
6-12	Medium risk	Within a week
15-20	High risk	This day
20-25	Very high risk	Immediately

2.0 Primary control measures

Where levels of risk rated above negligible have been identified for hazards in the workplace, control measures must be implemented to manage those risks. The best measures are those that protect everyone in the workplace:

Avoid risk: Where possible, exposure to hazards is avoided by the use of alternatives such as equipment design improvements, change of process (this is usually the responsibility of the designer of the equipment, work area or activity), a different environment, etc.;

Combat risk at source: If it is not possible to avoid the risk, it should be combated at source by enclosure, removal (e.g. extract facility), substitution (e.g. replace a hazardous chemical with a less hazardous one), etc.

2.1 Minimising risk

Where hazards can not be eliminated from the workplace, or avoided or combated at source, other control measures will need to be considered. Priority must be given to control measures which would protect all people in a workplace rather than individual operatives who are directly involved with the hazard.

The control measures will be selected using a hierarchical system:

1. Elimination of the hazard from the workplace;

2. Substitution of the hazard for a safer alternative;

3. Isolation from the hazard;

4. Engineering control methods (e.g. extract fans, trip mechanisms, etc.);

5. Jigs, appliances and holders;

6. Safe systems of work;

7. Supervision, instruction and training;

8. Warnings, signs and notices;

9. Personal protective equipment (PPE).

2.2 Information

The results of the risk assessment must be communicated to those people who are affected by it. They must be informed of the hazard, its effects, the likelihood of harm and any control measures which have been determined as necessary. Additionally, they should be instructed on how the control measures work to protect them and they should be instructed how they need to work to ensure that control is maintained.

3.0 Competence

Before entrusting a task to an employee, under the Management of Health and Safety at Work Regulations, 1998, the employer is obliged to ensure that the employee is competent to carry out that task safely. If a safe system of work is to be relied upon, it will require operatives to be competent.

3.1 What is competence?

Competence is indicated by:

Only where there is an overlap between all three elements can competence be claimed.

3.1 Supervision, instruction, training

Where competence can not be assured, the employer must provide adequate information, instruction and/or training, as well as close supervision.

Whenever a new item of plant or equipment, or a new system of work (including safe systems of work), is introduced, close supervision will be needed until the employer can be sure that competence has been achieved.

Once the employer is certain that those for whom she/he has responsibility are competent, supervision can be reduced.

3.3 Supervision model

The level and type of supervision required relates to the level of skills available:

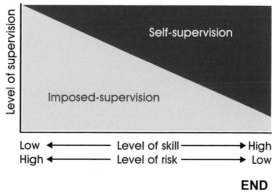

END

Reviews and Sponsors of the 2002 Conference, and plans for 2006

THEATRE ENGINEERING AND ARCHITECTURE 2002

It is my pleasure to congratulate you on organising such a marvellous event. The professionalism and competency of all the lecturers and the setup of the sessions was outstanding. I am also impressed with the overall event organisation and efficiency.

Maciej Wojciechowski
THEATRE TECHNOLOGIST
EMWU PROJEKT, WARSAW

We would like to congratulate you on the tremendous success of the *Theatre Engineering and Architecture 2002 Conference* last week. You managed an extraordinary achievement by arranging this event, the first in the UK, of what we hope will become a regular occurrence in the future.

Andy Whitworth and John Tune
STREETCRANE EXPRESS
MULTISTAGE INTERNATIONAL

In my opinion, this year's event was very successful, and I didn't meet anyone there who didn't think that the event should not be repeated. Once again, thank you very much for all of your tireless energy in putting this year's event together, and I look forward to hearing about the next.

Robert Shook
THEATER CONSULTANT
SCHULER SHOOK

PLATINUM SPONSOR

Waagner Biro Stage Systems.......................... www.waagner-biro.com

GOLD SPONSORS

Stage Technologies .... www.stagetech.com
Unusual Rigging .... www.unusual.co.uk

SILVER SPONSORS

Bytecraft Automation .... www.bytecraft.com.au
Delstar Engineering .... www.delstar.co.uk
Gala Theatrical Equipment .... www.galainfo.com
Gerriets.. www.gi-info.com
Mitsubishi Heavy Industries .... www.mhi.co.jp
Sansei Yusoki.. www.sanseiyusoki.com
SBS Bűhnentechnik... www.sbs-dresden.de
Serapid Rigid Chain Engineering.......................... www.serapid.com
Street CraneXpress .... www.scx.co.uk
Triple E www.3-eee.com

BRONZE SPONSORS

Arts Team.. www.artsteam.co.uk
AVW Controls.. www.avw.co.uk
Carr and Angier .... www.carrandangier.co.uk
Centre Stage Engineering .... www.centre-stage.co.uk
Gardiner & Theobald .... www.gardiner.com
Rexroth Bosch Group .... www.boschrexroth.com
Riskotec.. www.riskotec.fi
Techplan.. www.thestagehouse.com
Telmaco... www.telmaco.gr
Theatreplan .... www.theatreplan.net
Theatre Projects Consultants .... www.tpcworld.com
The Theatres Trust .... www.theatrestrust.org.uk

OTHER ASSISTANCE

Association of British Theatre Technicians .... www.abtt.org.uk
AT Sound Hire and Production .... www.atsound.co.uk
ETC Lighting... www.etcconnect.com
OISTAT .... www.oistat.org
Steeldeck.. www.steeldeck.co.uk
Trade Partners UK... www.tradepartners.gov.uk
White Light .... www.whitelightgroup.co.uk

THEATRE ENGINEERING AND ARCHITECTURE 2006

Four-year cycle agreed by many to be suitable for major conference on performing arts buildings

It is generally felt that significant changes in the technology and in the planning and construction of venues for the performing arts do not occur rapidly, and that a period of four years between gatherings of those involved in these activities gives time for important issues to be considered.

Many new buildings will have opened by 2006 and have had sufficient use to be suitable for assessment

Certainly, that is the plan for the 2006 Conference. A number of both small and large projects worldwide have opened since 2002, a selection of which need to be analysed. Work on these projects will have extended the experience of a great many people who need to explain their approach and identify the pitfalls they experienced in this very specialised business. Despite the wide range of topics covered previously, there are many others that are already being raised and the industry internationally will benefit from a further major Conference in 2006.

Location and venue for 2006 will need to take account of the considerable interest generated by previous event

International issues that have already been marked down for consideration include matters like the negative effects a poor client can have on his own project, the way in projects can be expedited or delayed by the way in which contracts are let, the new technology in recent theatres of all sizes, the approach a community should follow in achieving a successful small venue, and a serious discussion on the appearance of acoustics. This conference will be particularly targeted at many who might not realise the vital effect they have on the planning, design and creation of a performance space and who do need to understand the complexities involved: clients, funders, cost consultants, project managers and both general and specialist contractors. After the success of 2002 we anticipate there will be more press interest and attempts will be made to attract those who, without knowing it, are often the cause of arts building projects going awry.

How can buildings for the performing arts be constructed more rapidly and with the facilities really required by the ultimate users?

Ideas for 2006 include a number of public group discussion meetings controlled by a moderator

In addition to speakers, moderators and delegates there will be a need for sponsors and a range of special deals will be available

If you wish to register your interest in Theatre Engineering and Architecture 2006, to propose topics to be discussed or offer sponsorship, please write, fax or e-mail the Conference Director, Richard Brett.

Topics for discussion and issues on which people might care to speak should be raised early

The Stagehouse, Palace Road,
Kingston upon Thames, KT1 2LG, England.
Tel   +44 (0)20 8549 6535
Fax   +44 (0)20 8549 6545
Email director@theatre-event.com

This index has been prepared carefully but there may be further references in a number of areas which have not been individually identified. Theatre names are generally prefixed by a town or city. Advertisers in this volume are listed at the end of the index.

Advertisers in this volume:

University of Glamorgan / Prifysgol Morgannwg
Learning Resources Centre